CW00537956

# DEVON ROADS

**An illustrated survey of the development and management of Devon's highway network**

1803

# Michael Hawkins

DEVON BOOKS

First published in Great Britain in 1988 by Devon Books

Copyright © Devon County Council, 1988 (except for Chapter 1)

Chapter 1 © D. L. B. Thomas, 1988

Illustrations © Devon County Council (except where indicated otherwise)

ISBN: 0 86114–817–7

All rights reserved. No part of this publication may be reproduced, stored in a retrieval system, or transmitted in any form or by any means, electronic, mechanical, photocopying, recording or otherwise, without the prior permission of the copyright holder.

**British Library Cataloguing-in-Publication Data**

Hawkins, Michael
    Devon Roads: an illustrated survey of the development and management of Devon's highway network.
    1. Devon. Roads, to 1987
    I. Title
    388.1'09423'5

Printed and bound in Great Britain by A. Wheaton & Co. Ltd

**DEVON BOOKS**
**Official Publisher to Devon County Council**
An imprint of Wheaton Publishers Ltd
A member of Maxwell Pergamon Publishing Corporation plc.

Wheaton Publishers Ltd
Hennock Road, Marsh Barton, Exeter, Devon EX2 8RP
Tel: 0392 74121; Telex 42794 (WHEATN G)

**SALES**
Direct sales enquiries to Devon Books at the address above.

Trade sales to: Town & Country Books, P.O. Box 31, Newton Abbot, Devon TQ12 5XH. Tel: 08047 2541.

Photographs are reproduced by kind permission of the following:

Aero Industrial Photos: p. 100; Allhallows Museum, Honiton: p. 48; Baths Photographic: p. 93; BBC Hulton Picture Library: p. 26 (foot); Beaford Archive: pp. 26 (top), 27, 30, 34 (top), 40, 70, 173; J. Bird/Tavistock Times: p. 197; W. J. Chaffe: p. 190 (lower); the late M. J. Chamings: p. 182; Costain Civil Engineering Ltd: p. 150 (top); Devon Commercial Photos: p. 57; Devon Library Services: Torquay Central Library: pp. 152, 154; Devon News Service: p. 124; Exeter City Council: p. 137; Exeter Express & Echo: pp. 23, 33 (top & centre); S. Finch: p. 177; Focus Photography: p. 60; G.E.C.: p. 116; F. M. Griffith: p. 11; Nicholas Horne: p. 136; Images: pp. 16, 17, 21, 32 (top), 34 (lower), 52, 80 (top), 81, 82, 90, 97, 144, 155 (foot), 156, 158, 189, 192, 194, 195, 205, 212, 216; Institution of Highways and Transportation: p. 223; JAS Photographic: p. 145; R. L. Knight: p. 186; P. Lane: p. 59; Mansell Collection: p. 222; K. Northcott: p. 179; Photosource: p. 133; Plymouth City Planning Department: pp. 141, 142, 143, 148, 150 (foot); Roy Stickling: p. 29 (foot); D. L. B. Thomas: pp. 19, 22 (right); Peter Thomas: pp. 28, 131, 138, 139; Torquay Museum (U.S. Army official photograph): p. 155 (top); Nicholas Toyne: p. 157 (foot); L. Wade: p. 180; D. Walton: p. 157 (top); G. Ward: p. 88; Wayside Cafe: information on p. 29; West Air Photography: p. 153; Westcountry Studies Library: title page, pp. 8, 20, 36, 42, 132, 224.

# Foreword

It is a great pleasure and privilege to provide the Foreword to the fascinating story of Devon's roads, as part of the celebrations to recognize the centenary of Devon County Council.

My happiest time in local government was as Chairman for eight years of the Committee responsible for the construction and maintenance of Devon's roads and bridges.

The account presented here provides a great insight into this major method of communication to what was once a distant, difficult and disadvantaged corner of the South West. Devon's roads today vary from the thousands of miles of sometimes narrow, winding country lanes, usually with the traditional banks on either side, to the M5 motorway completed as recently as 1977 – both in their different ways critical communication links. The history records the accelerating pace of road construction in the last fifty years, providing highways and bridges of style and distinction which have occasionally opened up for the visitor to this glorious county vistas of great beauty. It also shows how essential the earlier roads were, after the ports, to Devon's development, and is part of a county history which I hope will stimulate many others to add their part.

Read and enjoy it and spare a thought in passing for all those who have built and maintained Devon's roads and bridges over the centuries.

ARNOLD SAYERS
CHAIRMAN, DEVON COUNTY COUNCIL

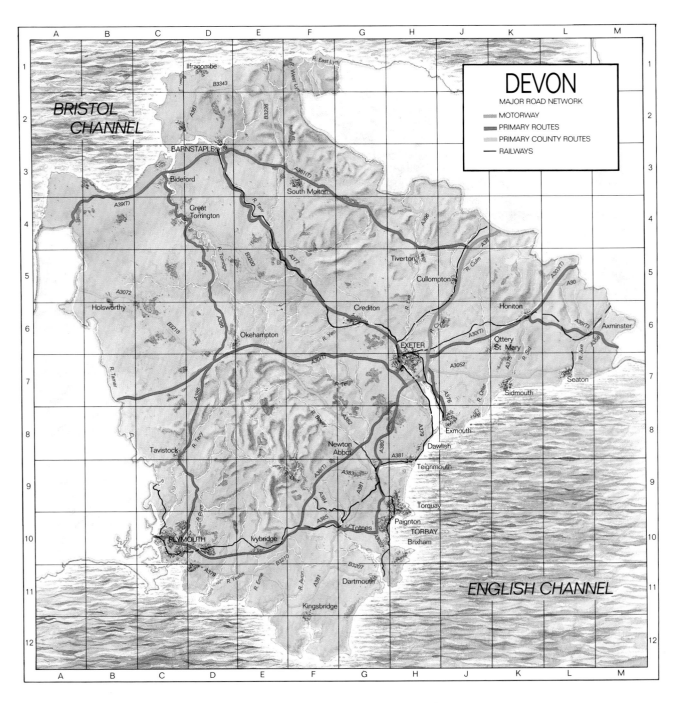

**Principal topographical features of Devon, 1988.**

# Contents

# Acknowledgements

This book has been compiled by the Engineering and Planning Department of Devon County Council, with the assistance of contributors from the civil engineering profession and other fields.

Major contributors:
  Michael Hawkins
  The late Cliff Burgoyne
  Bill Chaffe
  Brian George
  Mike Hatt
  Allan Johns
  Arthur Norman
  Mike Phillips
  Gerald Shapley
  David Thomas
  Noel Waine
  Philip Watts
  Lee Webster

Significant contributions have also been made by:
  Doug Aldridge, Dick Andrews, Roy Ashton, Mike Bailey, Valerie Belsey, Mike Bonning-Snook, Brian Brady, Tony Burrill, Edward Chorlton, Philip Dent, Peter Gimber, Mike Goodge, Bryan Holman, Ian Hunt, Michael Jenkins, Neil Macaulay, Graham Moores (illustrations), Derek Moss, Bruce Peeke, John Pike, June Richardson, Chris Wakefield, Barry Wedlake, Philip Westwell, Peter Wordsworth.

Special thanks are due to:
  Andy Davies (Additional textual advice)
  Derek Moss (Invaluable assistance in compilation of text and photographs)
  Diane Bunn, Sandra Courtney, Renee Forth, Adele Green, Carole Hill, Heather Holland, Jill Ireland, Judith King, Melody Scott, Margery Williams, Julie Wood (Typing and word processing)
  Paula Bright, Sharon Browers, Maria Donnellan, Gill Harvey, Vera Saffin, Therese Seward (Office services)
  Nick Dearsley, Tom Gibson, Bob Jones, Chris Wakefield (Graphics)
  Images, Derek Moss, Mark Norsworthy, Chris Wakefield, Graham Ward, Graham Young (Photography)
  All those who readily made photographs available.

Information, advice and assistance have been provided by:
  Bob Andrew, Automobile Association, Karen Baker, Malcolm Baker, Richard Bayly, Les Brewer, Peter Brewer, Donald Broom, Mike Chanter, Bill Clench, Frank Coneybeer, James Curle, Devon and Cornwall Constabulary, Michael Dickinson, John Doughty, Geoff Downes, Roger Emmett, Bryn Evans, Ray Faircloth, John Forde, David Hook, Roger Howell, David Hughes, Ken Hunt, Paul Hurford, Tony Lawrence, Brian Luff, Bob Mailling, Ian Maxted, Ian Mercer, Don Millgate, Peter Naile, Edward Paynter, Tom Pearce, Doug Reed, Royal Automobile Club, Colin Shears, Colin Shepard, Neville Taylor, Richard Taylor, Keith Thorley, Anne Turner, Philip Virgin, Len Wade, Harry Warner, Frank West, Lester Willmington.

Thanks are also extended to everyone who has been consulted for information or advice during the compilation of this book.

**Note**

As a general rule measurements are given in imperial up to 1970, and in metric from 1971 onwards. Exceptions are made in descriptive passages where for comparative purposes the same units are used.

# Introduction

The development of civilization has always been dependent on mobility, whether by way of the beaten track of primitive man, the sophisticated road network through which the Romans maintained their great empire, the unpopular turnpikes or the modern national multi-lane highway network.

Yet despite this dependence on roads they are commonly taken for granted. The traveller expects only that they carry him to his destination as quickly and as safely as possible, that is until they are for some reason no longer available, when their importance becomes apparent.

On the other hand, the railway network has attracted to itself a form of reverence that persists despite its decline barely more than a century since the first train ran between Stockton and Darlington in 1825. The creation of what was a very comprehensive network of railways across the length and breadth of the country caused, at the time of its construction, as much furore as does the building of the modern road network. Perhaps the secret lies not only with the sheer majesty of the locomotives, which for their time epitomized the achievements of the industrial revolution, but also with the fact that the engineers who laid out the routes had a very good 'eye for country'. This, together with the limitations of gradients and curvature imposed upon them, ensured that many of the routes fitted well into the countryside – a skill still found in today's road engineering.

Whilst roads have never attracted the same attention from the historian, the highways of this country are in many ways far more interesting since roads are frequently the only continuous historical link with the development of towns and cities. It is from a recognition of the importance of the road network of Devon and the part it has played in the development of this great county that this book came about.

Devon is not only one of the largest English counties, but it also has the distinction of containing the greatest length of roads, over 14 000 km in total. There can be few parts of these islands where there is such a comprehensive network of communications, much of which originated in early times and which has since played such an important part in the county's development.

The roadsides abound with features that chronicle the development of the county through the ages. There are roads which were originally laid down by the Romans and roads which were formerly turnpikes, from which the numerous well-preserved tollhouses are distinctive survivors. There are also reminders of the packhorse, the stagecoach and the horse-and-carriage eras through milestones, memorials, markers and even notices threatening transportation for those found tampering with bridges.

The bridge, perhaps more than any other structure, is the symbol of engineering achievement. From early times it has been a dominant feature of the development of civilization; cities grew up around bridges, battles were fought for their possession, even poetry and songs have been written about them. There are over 4000 bridges in Devon, many of them works of beauty. The British have never lost the art of bridge building and many of the modern structures, such as those over the Tamar, Exe, Teign and Torridge, are worthy successors in a distinguished line.

The book not only touches on the highway's contribution to the English landscape, to the extent that its verges and hedges provide a habitat for many varieties of flora and fauna, but also, in contrast, outlines the price of economic development in the growth of traffic and, more grimly, the toll of death and misery which is exacted. Just over one hundred years ago, in 1885, Benz invented the motor car and the century that has followed has seen the total national economy becoming increasingly dependent upon the motor vehicle. It is a far cry from the time when a man with a red flag was obliged by law (from 1865 to 1896) to walk in front of 'every locomotive propelled by steam, or any other than animal power, on any turnpike road or public highway'. Today six out of ten households in this country have access to at least one motor car.

In 1910 a Mrs Rodalph Stawell wrote a book entitled *Motor Tours in the West Country*. Her reference to journeys in Devon begins:

To hurry in Devonshire is absurd. In the first place it is contrary to the spirit of the county; no one does it. In the second place it is impossible. I cannot conscientiously

Engraved for the Univerfal Magazine.

**This map of Devon was drawn in 1748 for a London mapseller.**

recommend Devon as a motoring field for those who find great speed essential to their happiness, for them the alternate use of the gear lever and the brake is apt to be exasperating. But to many of us the reduction of our average mileage is a small matter in comparison with certain important things; such as scarlet poppies in the corn and high banks fringed with ferns and cottages smothered in flowers and wide purple moors, and the rippling emerald seas, and the complete serenity that fills the heart of Devon.

An attractive picture indeed! Yet who will forget the frustration of the congested roads of Devon when, little more than a half a century later, the endurance of waiting on the Exeter bypass or in the Okehampton traffic queues was nationally notorious.

In 1974 the new county councils were created and coincided in Devon with the early years of the greatest road-building era yet seen. Barely a century since the invention of the motor car, the county has a network of new roads completed or under construction which has

revolutionized the economy of Devon and which history may well regard as the twentieth-century equivalent of the great railway era.

None of the modern highway achievements could have been realized without an efficient political organization capable of operating on a countywide basis. It is fitting therefore that the publication of this book coincides with the centenary of the creation in 1888 of the County Councils. It is also an appropriate recognition of those predecessors of mine – be they engineers, technicians or roadmen – all of whom have played a part in the creation and maintenance of the roads of Devon.

This book does not profess to be a complete history of Devon roads, but it gives a broad outline of the development of the road system in the county and describes the maintenance of today's comprehensive road network. It is hoped that it will be of interest in itself and will also whet the appetite of those who wish to study the subject in more detail.

Michael R. Hawkins OBE, C.Eng.
County Engineer & Planning Officer

## Prehistory

**M**an first trod the face of Devon many thousands of years ago when the ice cap, which had covered most of Britain, finally retreated northward. The land was covered with dense forests and thickets, and bears and wolves roamed freely. Prehistoric man would have travelled on the high ground above the forests and around the sources of streams and rivers, reasonably safe from predatory animals. He tended to follow the same path as he went from one place to another and in doing so traced a national network of ridgeways that is probably in use in some form or other today.

Later, around 4500 B.C., settlers sailed to Britain from the northern coast of France, bringing with them sheep and cattle and containers of corn. These settlers, Neolithic man, may have mingled with the natives and with them cleared the upper parts of the forests. They built hill-top settlements such as Hembury, Hazard Hill and Haldon Hill and, with the upper parts of the forests cleared, established fresh trackways further down the slopes. These lower routes, often called 'harrow ways', were more direct than the ridgeways and crossed small streams rather than going around the sources. As agriculture developed it became necessary for farmers to travel further to dispose of their surplus produce and to obtain such necessities as salt, greenstone from Cornwall for axe heads and blue-black flints from Beer and Totnes for scrapers. Trade expanded and the ridgeways and harrow ways were joined to make arterial ways through and across Devon. With the Bronze Age, round barrows, conical mounds of earth, were built as ritual monuments, sometimes with a human body cremated or interred below. These were often built in groups, sometimes close to a trackway, and where they still exist in some cases they are useful indicators that nearby tracks or roads existed before or during the Bronze Age.

The Bronze Age saw the introduction of metal tools, initially of copper and later of bronze. Then, sometime between 900 and 600 B.C., Celtic-speaking invaders introduced the Iron Age into Britain. They used chariots, iron sickles, and lead for glass manufacture and worked in bronze and tin. The tin was exported to Europe and was probably taken overland from Cornwall to the port of dispatch in the Isle of Wight. Various routes across Devon have been suggested. One is from Woolley near Stratton

# 1

# AN HISTORICAL REVIEW

## The Development of Devon's Roads from Early Times

on the border with Cornwall, along Broadbury Down to Okehampton, following the line of the old A30 to Cheriton Cross and across the ridge around Holcombe Burnell to Exeter and on to Honiton. Another enters the county at Saltash and goes through Crownhill, Ivybridge, South Brent, Staverton, Newton Abbot, crossing the Exe at Starcross and following the line of the A30 and A35 to the Dorset boundary.

The lines of prehistoric routes are largely speculative but various physical features do provide useful clues. The presence of barrows has already been mentioned. The boundaries of parishes and counties were laid down between the eighth and tenth centuries A.D. and tracks were often used to mark the boundaries. Thus a contemporary track or road coincident with a parish or county boundary indicates that the track or road existed before these centuries. A kink in an otherwise direct stretch of road points to a diversion made during the twelfth- and thirteenth-century enclosures. Anglo-Saxon charters often refer to tracks as 'boundary ways' or 'highways' and place names can be helpful: 'harepath', for example, means 'highway' or 'army way'; 'anstey' means a track wide enough for only one person; and 'sal' or 'salt' derives from the production of salt. Bronze or Iron Age hill-forts can be expected to have tracks leading to them. Dew ponds – the prehistoric travellers' transport cafés – may provide corroborative evidence. Lastly, a modern track or road running along a ridge is likely to be on a prehistoric line.

A particularly good example of a prehistoric ridgeway exists on Exmoor in the parish of High Bray on the road from Mole's Chamber to Sandyway Cross. This runs along the ridge, is flanked with barrows and dew ponds, coincides with the county boundary and has pronounced kinks where land was enclosed.

What of prehistoric bridges? It is known that Neolithic man built causeways across the Somerset levels and elsewhere and he certainly would have been capable of building timber bridges. Bronze Age man was accomplished at building with large stones and it seems certain that he would have built clapper and clam bridges such as abound on Dartmoor. Some of these Dartmoor bridges are fairly recent – Teignhead Bridge, for example, is known to have been built about two centuries ago – but some others may date from the Bronze Age.

## The Roman Period

The Romans occupied Britain for nearly four centuries and during that time they laid down about 10 000 miles of road, no mean achievement by any standards. As a general rule their roads were 80 ft wide between drainage ditches. During construction, topsoil was first cleared over this width. The carriageway, about 24 ft wide, was built on the sub soil, or sub grade as it is now called. The thickness of carriageway foundation, or 'agger', varied in depth from 18in. to 8ft and was made of locally available materials to suit the ground conditions and type of traffic. Urban roads and roads near the banks of rivers were generally paved with roughly dressed slabs, cobbles or setts, while gravel, as dug, was used for rural roads.

Roman roads are renowned for their straightness but in fact they are straight only between sighting points and then only if it was practicable and economic to make them so. No doubt when surveying the route the Roman engineers would follow a fixed bearing so as to obtain a direct line between places. Individual lengths of road would be set out by lining in poles, or ranging rods, from a pole at the sighting station to a pole or beacon fire at the object station.

Information on Roman roads in Devon is sketchy and has been the subject of much speculation, particularly on the route of the Fosse Way through the county. The Fosse Way enigma – for that is what it remains – could be said to have been sparked off by Geoffrey of Monmouth, a Welsh monk who later became Bishop of Saint Asaph. Geoffrey wrote in the twelfth century that the Romans intended the Fosse Way to serve as a paved road between Cornwall and Caithness in the north-west of Scotland. About two centuries later, a Benedictine monk called Ranulph Higden confirmed Geoffrey's statement and added that the road existed only from Devon to Lincoln. He stated that the starting point of the road was 'Tottenesse', by which he may have meant Totnes or, more probably as the word means 'Totta's promontory', the south-west peninsula.

The Fosse Way is readily identifiable from Lincoln to Dinnington, near Ilminster. The Ordnance Survey marks the A358 on the county boundary as 'Foss Way' and shortly afterwards the road crosses Weycroft Bridge, or Stratford Bridge as it used to be called. The name 'Stratford' derives from the Old English for a paved ford carrying a Roman road. From Axminster to Exeter on the A35 and the A30 there are long straight stretches of road that could well have been built on parts of a Roman road. As Exeter was a fortress town and perhaps a base for the conquest of Devon and Cornwall, it seems possible that the Romans intended to continue this major route as a spine road into Cornwall.

Rowe, in 1848, gave the route of what he referred to as 'The Great Central Trackway' as along Chittaford Down, through Hollowcombe and Postbridge. Worth, in 1885, suggested that this trackway might be part of the Fosse Way and, in 1889, Burnard gave a paper to the Devonshire Association in which he described sections of a paved way he had discovered between Hamel Down and Cox Tor. He put forward the theory that this paved way (now believed to be boundary walls between tribal territories) was part of the Fosse Way that ran from Chudleigh to Hamel Down and to Cox Tor and from there to Tavistock and Cornwall. Baring Gould, in 1899, was quite positive that the Great

**This photograph shows with striking clarity the course of a Roman road across a ridge of high ground at Colebrooke, mid Devon. It was probably an 'agger', made by ramming small stones to form an embankment with a wide, flat top, and is thought to have been part of the main route from Exeter to the west. Well-made roads like this would have remained in use by the local population for some time after the withdrawal of the Romans from the region.**

Central Trackway was part of the Fosse Way but he suggested that the route from Exeter to Hamel Down was via Moretonhampstead. Later Joce, in another paper to the Devonshire Association, poured mild scorn on Burnard's theory, stating that the Romans would never have built a road through the difficult country between Chudleigh and Hamel Down. He conjectured that the Fosse Way entered the county at Dunkeswell and passed near Cullompton, Crediton, Bow, Okehampton and Bridestowe, to leave the county at Lifton.

A further theory is that the Fosse Way went no further into Devon than Axmouth near Seaton. This is based on the assumption that Axmouth was a Roman port and that a projection of the Fosse Way line from Lincoln to Dinnington strikes Axmouth.

In 1815, when the present Teign Bridge at Teigngrace was being built, two older bridges were discovered in the alluvium under the bridge that was being replaced. They were one below the other, the upper probably being medieval, but the lower almost certainly Roman. Modern opinion tended to doubt the Roman origin of the lower bridge until 1954, when Diana and Alexander Woolmer reported that they had found traces of Roman agger between Splatford at the bottom of Telegraph Hill and Teign Bridge. Thus it appears that there was a paved Roman road in Devon from Tytherleigh to Teign Bridge, with the latter a major permanent structure.

Beyond Teign Bridge the destination of the road remains as obscure as ever. Perhaps the engineers of the Exeter garrison were engaged on this major project in A.D. 68 when they were posted to Caerleon to help deal with the troublesome Silurian tribes. Work was stopped, never to be resumed.

Roman engineers built three types of bridge. For military purposes and for crossing marshy ground they used timber decks on timber-trestle piers. Julius Caesar built one of this type to cross the Rhine in 55 B.C., described in some detail in his notebooks on the Gallic Wars. Being of a semi-permanent construction, none of these bridges has survived but the type was probably used to cross the Exe at Exeter, the marshy ground between the Axe and the Yarty at Kilmington, the Otter at Fenny Bridges and the Tale valley at Feniton. In the second type, the trestle piers were replaced by solid masonry about 8 feet wide with pointed ends. The bridge discovered at Teigngrace was of this type, as is the bridge at Oakfordbridge, although this latter is not Roman. The third type of bridge was not, as far as is known, used in Britain. It was masonry arch building at its best and fine examples still stand in Italy and Spain.

## The Dark Ages

When the Roman presence was withdrawn in A.D. 410, Devon had a main road network that might have comprised about 700 miles of unpaved trackway and about 50 miles of paved road. There were perhaps a hundred or so timber-trestle bridges and at least one timber-decked bridge with masonry piers.

By the seventh century the Saxons had reached the south west and the extent of their colonization is indicated by the number of settlements with the characteristic suffixes of -ton, -ham or -bury. So complete was it that the number of settlements with ancient British names surviving is very few indeed. By the ninth century, Devon was recognized as a Saxon shire, later to be divided into thirty-six hundreds. The Roman road network would have been adequate for the needs of the time except that, with the new Saxon villages, new local networks would have been formed from homestead to village and from one village to another. No doubt the Saxons kept the road system in a good state of repair. For example, Harold was able to march most of his army from York to London in 1066 at the very creditable rate of 50 miles a day. An indication of the importance that the Saxons attached to the maintenance of bridges is illustrated by one of their taxation laws – the *trinodas necessitas*. This placed on landholders the triple duty of military service, the building of fortresses and the construction of bridges. The Saxons were good carpenters and they would have had no difficulty in keeping the timber bridges in repair and building new ones. Certain bridges, such as Creedy Bridge, Bickham Bridge and Kingsbridge, are mentioned in Saxon charters and this may be taken as an indication that the bridge so named was reasonably substantial and on a main route.

## The Middle Ages

The middle of the twelfth century saw the start of a period of change that was to have a lasting effect on the landscape of Devon. The Saxon open-field system was abandoned as tracts of land were let off by the lords of the manor to be farmed by peasants. Fields were enclosed and surrounded either by walls made from stone picked from the fields or by hedgebanks and if an existing track interfered with the regularity of a field then the track was diverted. The barons and, increasingly, the Church were quick to realize that investment in a centre of population with its fair and market produced a far greater return than the renting of land for agriculture. New towns sprang up, new industries appeared and Devon became the richest source of tin in Europe. The cloth industry prospered and resulted in the rapid growth of towns such as South Molton, Tiverton and Honiton. Dartmouth and Plymouth became naval bases and seaports.

In addition to these a number of new settlements were established, particularly in the reign of Edward I, as attempts by lords of the manor to supplement their incomes. These settlements generally were not economically successful but remain as interesting vestiges of an early endeavour to establish 'new towns'. Examples include Newton Poppleford, South Zeal (with its still well-defined burgage strips) and Rackenford.

The increase and relocation of population and industrial

The old roads of the West Country were long, narrow ways, many of them enclosed between high banks. In accounts of journeys in the past, the state of the roads was frequently criticized, and Devonshire's lanes in particular. A notable exception is the 'Ballad to a Devonshire Lane', penned by the Reverend John Marriott, sometime vicar of Broadclyst, who, whilst acknowledging the drawbacks, nevertheless found great value in the narrow ways which led him to compare them with the institution of marriage. His final verse runs:

*Then long be the journey and narrow the way,*
*I'll rejoice that I've seldom a turnpike to pay;*
*And whate'er others say, be the last to complain,*
*Though marriage is just like a Devonshire lane.*

Although there can be little doubt that some modern roads overlie Roman precursors, the true extent of the Roman road network in Devon is still the source of considerable debate amongst historians and archaeologists. This diagram shows the network generally agreed upon among experts in the subject.

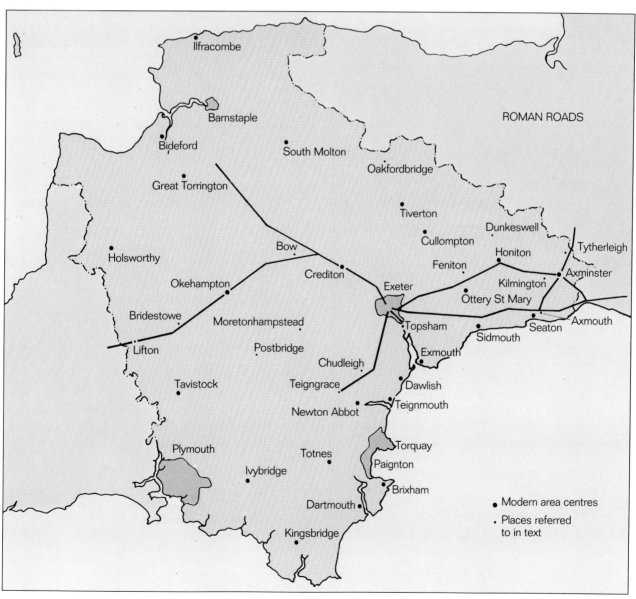

ROMAN ROADS

- Modern area centres
- Places referred to in text

growth did not mean that a massive road-building programme was needed as might be the case today. Over the whole of the Middle Ages individuals continued to travel on foot or, if a horse could be afforded, on horseback. A type of coach called a whirlicote appeared in the fourteenth century but this was rarely seen far from London and, with its complete lack of suspension, must have been very uncomfortable. Most goods were carried by packhorse, usually travelling in trains, although some of the more bulky goods were carried by bullock carts. The mileage of road in Devon must have increased considerably over this period but the new roads, or tracks, would have been formed naturally as the most convenient way to go on foot.

By the sixteenth century the pattern of roads traced over the Devon countryside would not have been very different from today's, except, of course, in density. The system of classification then was very simple. There were the royal roads on which travellers were under the sovereign's protection. They were termed the King's Highway and anyone attacking travellers on these roads could be fined a hundred shillings, a large sum that reflected the importance the State attached to ensuring the safe passage of traders. The road from Exeter via Alphington, Kennford, Haldon, Highweek and Holbeam to Cockington was the King's Highway, although much of it today is a non-principal road. All other roads were termed the Common Highway and the State made no provision for maintaining them nor

did it recognize that any maintenance was necessary. It was an established principle that a traveller had right of way or free passage on the King's or the Common Highway. If the usual way was blocked by some obstruction then the traveller was within his rights to go around it even if this meant entering private land. Thus, for example, places that tended to get muddy became corridors of way rather than tracks with defined edges.

There had grown up the common-law principle, born out of the Saxon *trinodas necessitas*, that a landowner was responsible for the upkeep of roads abutting his land. In those feudal days, the manor, county and later borough courts meted out punishment to those who neglected their duty in this respect. At a court leet of the Manor of Alwington held on 26 September 1459, John Gyfford and John Vyall were required to repair the way between 'Ley Mill and Lewoode' which was 'deep in mud on both sides and overhung by hedges on both sides to the damage of the King's lieges'. Presumably each owned land abutting the road.

Devon's deep lanes were formed as a result of this system of maintenance by owners of adjoining land. As the roads got muddier, the landowner would scrape off the mud and pitch it on the side and, as time went by, the road became lower and the sides higher. Celia Fiennes, describing a journey on horseback in 1695, noted that, as she left Ashburton,

> Thence I went for Plymouth, ... and here the roads contract and the lanes are exceeding narrow and so covered up you can see little about; an army might be marching undiscovered by anybody, for when you are on the heights that show a vast country about, you cannot see one road.

Established in Britain by Augustine in the sixth century, the Church of Rome had, by the twelfth century, become immensely rich and powerful. Religious houses, such as at Buckfast, Tavistock, Plympton and Buckland, owned vast estates and established or re-established roads for the supervision and upkeep of their scattered properties. These roads, or tracks, were often marked by the churchmen with stone crosses, particularly on Dartmoor where many still exist. The best known of these tracks on the moor is Abbot's Way, marked on the Ordnance Survey Map as going from Cross Furzes via the fords at Buckland, Red Lake, Erme Pits and Plym, to a point north of Gutter Tor. Worth suggested that this track was more likely to have been further north, from Horn's Cross to Siward's Cross, as that would be on higher ground with fewer river crossings.

The 1530 Statute of Bridges (see p.16) required magistrates to take responsibility for the maintenance of bridges in their county. Not just the bridge, but 300 ft of road on either side, fell under the provisions of the Act. The point on the road where the magistrates' responsibility ended was marked by a stone carved with the letter 'C', for 'County'. These were known as 'bound stones', and there are a number of fine examples in Devon. The stone in the photograph is near Bellever, on Dartmoor.

Most legislation of the Middle Ages was devoted to the safety, rather than the comfort, of travellers. The Magna Carta provided that merchants should have safe passage through England except in times of war. The Statute of Winchester 1285 enacted, among other things, that highways between towns should be widened so that within 200 feet of the road there was no ditch, tree or bush in which a man might hide to do mischief to travellers.

Apart from tracing much of today's road network with their feet, the most significant contribution of the people of the Middle Ages to the country's road system was the building of bridges. The period from the twelfth century to the Reformation may be safely regarded as Britain's first bridge-building era – rather surprising when one realizes that nearly all bridges were built as private ventures with no financial assistance and precious little encouragement from the State. Nicholas Gervase built Exe Bridge in Exeter, part of which still stands, at the beginning of the thirteenth century, while his son, Walter, collected 10 000 marks (£6 666) needed for the project. A grant of pontage might be made to enable those responsible for the maintenance of a bridge to raise money by charging tolls to bridge users. In 1532, the wardens of Exe Bridge charged a toll of four pence for each wagon passing over the bridge.

The Long Bridge in Barnstaple was built by the generous gift of a citizen of London called Stamford. Money or interest in land was often bequeathed for the building or maintenance of bridges. In 1326, Bishop Stapleton left one mark for the repair of Bovey Bridge and, in 1418, Bishop Stafford left 100 shillings towards the rebuilding of Chudleigh Bridge, provided the piers were built of stone. Lady Kirkham left in her will lands in Feniton to provide money for the maintenance of Fenny Bridges although by 1722 the trustees were neglecting the bridge and pocketing the proceeds.

Most bridge building in the Middle Ages was carried out by the Church which regarded this as a sacred duty complementary to the building of churches and cathedrals. The builders of the churches, the master masons and their subordinate masons, would have built the bridges, as can be seen in the similarity of detail between the bridges and churches of the period. Horse Bridge, Greystone Bridge, New Bridge in Gunnislake, Exe Bridge and Clyst St Mary Bridge all have chamfered voussoirs, multiple-arch orders and arch ribs, characteristic of church architecture. Many bridges had a chapel or chantry on the structure or nearby where the incumbents would accept alms or perhaps say Mass for any benefactors of the bridge. Barnstaple Bridge had a chapel dedicated to St Thomas à Becket, Bideford and Plym Bridges to St Mary, Exe Bridge to St Edmund and St Saviour's Bridge, appropriately enough, to St Saviour.

## Post Reformation

By the early part of the sixteenth century, the Church in Britain owned about a quarter of the land, was immensely rich and powerful and made a very significant contribution

There are numerous stone crosses on Dartmoor, some of which have been restored. Most are medieval in origin, and may have served as waymarkers along the moorland tracks running between settlements on the east and west of the moor. Siward's Cross (above) is mentioned in 1240 as a forest bondmark and was probably erected by Siward, the Earl of Northumberland, who in the eleventh century held lands locally.

to the building and maintenance of roads and bridges. At this time Britain's trade was expanding rapidly and the country was well on the way to becoming a colonial power. The population was increasing and moving about more and, with the growth in population, the amount and movement of livestock grew. There was more demand for wheeled vehicles for human transport and for the movement of goods.

Henry VIII knew that dissolving the monastic houses would dismantle much of the machinery for financing and

During the medieval period, the Church frequently provided finance for the construction of bridges as well as for churches. The medieval Exe Bridge in Exeter provided a safe river crossing for those travelling south and west. The arch ribbing is reminiscent of contemporary church architecture.

administering the road system. He had to find an alternative and this he did effectively, as far as bridges were concerned, by his Statute of Bridges 1530. This was a fairly short Act, well constructed and drafted, that laid down a basis of bridge administration that remained virtually unchanged until 1888 when the county councils were formed. The object of the Act was to ensure that 'decayed bridges' should not, merely because of lack of knowledge as to who should maintain them, 'lie long without amendment to the great annoyance of the King's subjects'. Bridges were to be maintained by the counties, which meant the magistrates in Quarter Sessions, unless it could be proved that some other body or individual had always been responsible for doing so. In practice it meant that a county maintained all the bridges in its geographical area except private bridges, bridges in boroughs and small footbridges. In order that money might be raised for bridge repair, the Act authorized the levying of a rate on the inhabitants of a county or borough. This was the first time an Act had allowed the levying of a rate on all the inhabitants of an administrative area and was the foundation of our present system of rating. The Act required the appointment of two collectors to collect the rate money and two 'surveyors' who would 'see every decayed bridge repaired and amended from time to time'.

The modern road network has its origins in the cultural activities of our distant forebears. The patterns they made as they went about their daily business are preserved to a surprising extent in the modern road and footpath network. Some of these ancient trackways remain largely unchanged. One such is Abbot's Way, a track on Dartmoor believed to connect the ecclesiastical centres of Buckfast in the east and Tavistock and Buckland in the west.

Clapper bridges are primitive in terms of design, which often gives rise to misconceptions about their antiquity. Although a few of them may be prehistoric, most are medieval or even post-medieval – the result usually of efforts by the local population to overcome a difficulty in transportation. The photograph shows the clapper bridge over the River Avon at Huntingdon Warren, Dartmoor.

A forcible reminder of the importance of bridges to local communities is set in the stone parapet of this bridge at Stockland. Although it is now in Devon, the village was formerly in a detached part of Dorset. The text reads: 'Any person wilfully INJURING any part of this COUNTY BRIDGE will be guilty of FELONY and upon conviction liable to be TRANSPORTED FOR LIFE. By the court. T. FOOKS 1728.'

Devon appointed two collectors, designated 'treasurers', but apparently decided it could manage without surveyors until as late as 1703.

With any bridge maintainable under the Act, it was required that the road over the bridge and on the approaches for 300 ft on either side should be similarly maintained. Later, in 1831, the Devon magistrates were to have the limits of their responsibility marked by 'bound stones'. These stones are about a metre high and have the letter 'C' cut into one face. Examples exist at Bellever, Bridford, Ponsworthy, Wrixhall and many other bridges.

Procedures under the Act – the presentment, the viewing and the levying and collection of the rate – were slow and cumbersome and were manipulated by the bureaucracy of

the day to avoid or delay expenditure, particularly in the latter part of the eighteenth century. Another shortcoming of the Act was that it dealt with the maintenance of existing bridges and did not give the magistrates power to build new ones. For all that, it was a good piece of legislation in that it allowed bridges to be kept in a reasonable state of repair for three-and-a-half centuries.

The basis of legislation for road maintenance was quite different because, it seems, the law makers considered roads to be largely self repairing, requiring, at most, occasional harrowing or the filling in of potholes with earth or stones. After the Reformation the first piece of legislation that dealt with roads was the Statute of Highways 1555 which made each parish responsible for all roads passing through its area except, of course, roads over and on the approaches to county bridges. Each year the churchwardens in each parish were required to appoint an overseer of highways from among the parishioners. The post was unpaid and labour for repairs was provided, also on an unpaid basis, by each of the parishioners who were required to work for four, later raised to six, days in a year. This became known as 'statute labour' and, as can be imagined, proved to be highly unpopular and inefficient. In 1613, the justices in Quarter Sessions were given power to indict any parish which failed to maintain its roads. The parish so indicted was given time to do the necessary repairs and, if it failed to do so, was fined and the proceeds used by the overseer. In 1654 the Commonwealth government abolished statute labour and substituted the payment of rates. This did not seem to help matters much for, in 1661, complaint was made to the Devon Court of Quarter Sessions of 'the great decaies of highwaies And of the great neglect of supravisors of highwaies within the Countie'. In 1662 statute labour was revived and the surveyors were empowered to levy a rate to supplement statute labour.

While the country was plodding on with this inefficient form of road administration, wheeled traffic was increasing inexorably in volume and, faced with such growth, Parliament attemped to minimize wear and tear on the roads by restricting the efficiency of road vehicles. In an Act of 1621 the use of four-wheeled wagons or loads exceeding one ton was prohibited. In 1629 no more than five horses per wagon were permitted and in 1662 the permitted number per wagon was increased to seven and the width of wagon wheel specified to be a minimum of four inches. Later the width of wheel was increased to a minimum of nine inches with a penalty for contravention of £5 or one month in prison.

Not all legislation was unhelpful to the road user. A late-seventeenth-century Act required parish surveyors to set up at crossroads a stone or timber post incribed with the name of the next town to which the road led. A stone set in the bank on the Wapsworthy to Tavistock road near the Horndon junction is one of these, while the most interesting in the county is the brick cross at the crossroads on the Newton Poppleford to Budleigh Salterton road near Otterton. A curiosity of these guide stones, in contrast to advance direction signs that indicate what lies ahead, is that they indicate what lies behind.

## The Turnpike Age

By the end of the seventeenth century the roads of Britain were in a very poor condition and, in the face of the State's misguided efforts, it fell to private enterprise to find an answer. The principle of levying tolls on road users and using the revenue to maintain and improve the roads was not new. Tolls were collected for the repair of roads in London as early as the fourteenth century and records of pontage, the right to collect tolls for bridge maintenance, appear from the middle of the thirteenth century.

The first turnpike trust, a private body formed under Act of Parliament, was in 1706 in Buckinghamshire and by 1750 there were 400 trusts throughout the country, rising to about 1000 in 1770 and 1600 in 1790. Devon was slow to adopt the turnpike system, probably because the county remained in the packhorse age for longer and was suffering a decline in the cloth industry. The first Devon trust did not appear until about half a century after the Buckinghamshire trust and Devon never really caught up with the other counties. For example, the mileage of turnpike roads as a proportion of the total road mileage in Devon was 11 per cent, compared with 28 per cent in Hampshire and 31 per cent in Middlesex. Apart from the Stonehouse Trust, which was formed in 1751 and had only 4 miles of road, the first trust in Devon was the Exeter Turnpike Trust. This was formed in 1753 'for amending several roads leading from the City of Exeter'. All the main roads leading out of Exeter were included as turnpikes with, at 150 miles, the highest mileage of roads maintained by any trust in Devon and one of the highest in the country. In 1769 the Trust had its powers enlarged to include the building of a new

A collection of roadside information: two milestones and a stone marking the limit of the Exeter Turnpike. All three are set in a wall in Crockernwell, mid Devon.

bridge to replace the ford at Countess Wear and to widen or rebuild Exe Bridge. Some new roads built by the Trust were most of the present A377 between Exeter and Eggesford Bridge, the B3212 as far as Dunsford, the now superseded A30 between Exeter and Crockernwell and the now partly superseded A38 between Exeter and Chudleigh. The Barnstaple Trust was the next largest in Devon and was formed in 1763 with 104 miles of road. It built the A377 along the Taw valley to meet the Exeter turnpike at Eggesford Bridge, the A39 between Barnstaple and Bideford, and lengths of the present A361, B3226, B3217, B3230 and B3231. The Okehampton Trust was formed in 1760 and, among other schemes, built a South Zeal bypass, itself now bypassed. The last trust to be formed in Devon was the Sidmouth and Cullompton in 1846 with 16 miles of road, which brought the total mileage of turnpikes in Devon to 1070.

The mile as a measure of distance was introduced into Britain by the Romans, the name being derived from the Latin 'milia passuum', a thousand paces, that worked out at 1680 yards. The statute mile of 1760 yards was introduced by Act of Parliament in 1593 but was not really established until the Act for the Establishment of Uniform Weights and Measures 1824. The later turnpike Acts required the trustees to measure their roads and to erect stones or wooden posts giving mileages to towns at 1 mile intervals. This they faithfully did and many such milestones still exist. The trustees often marked the ends of their jurisdiction and

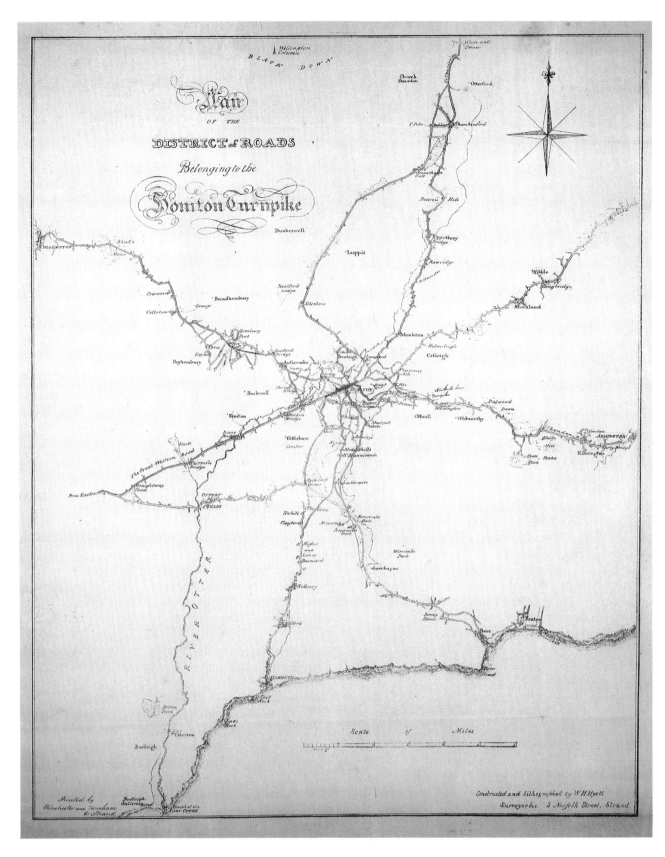

Devon lagged behind the rest of the country where turnpikes were concerned and the mileage never exceeded 11% of the total length of road. The first turnpikes of note in Devon were maintained by the Exeter Turnpike Trust (1753), closely followed by Honiton (1754). The drawing shows the extent of the Honiton turnpike roads in 1825.

The oldest surviving tollhouse in the county, at Newton Poppleford
in east Devon, built in 1758.

only maintenance powers under the 1530 Act, were able to eliminate. To get over this and other problems, Parliament passed the Bridges Act 1803, which gave power to the counties to widen or reconstruct bridges. It also recognized for the first time the need for the counties to have a bridge expert on their staff and vested much of the power under the Act in the expert, or surveyor as he was termed. At this time Devon had five bridge surveyors, none of whom had any connection with the architectural or emerging civil engineering professions. However, Devon continued to employ the five until 1808 when Fenny Bridge, newly erected to the design of one of the five, was destroyed in a flood. This spurred the magistrates into action and they sacked the five, appointing James Green, sometime pupil or junior assistant to John Rennie, as the first professional County Surveyor (see Chapter 9).

With the advent of the railways, revenue from the turnpikes fell off rapidly and by 1890 turnpike trusts had all

An early attempt at road direction signing is seen here at **Brick Cross near East Budleigh**. Legislation passed in the late seventeenth century required parish surveyors to erect a stone or timber post at crossroads to indicate to travellers the town to which each road would lead them.

such boundary stones exist at Barnstaple Guildhall, Crockernwell and elsewhere.

An Act of 1752 permitted the magistrates to relax the law restricting the number of horses drawing wagons on hills. Turnpike trustees obtained special dispensations from the courts and they were usually required to fix markers at the tops of hills where the extra horses had to be unharnessed. One such stone, marked 'Take Off', is still in position on the Okehampton to Tavistock road at Beardon.

The turnpike trustees could designate pretty well any road they chose as a turnpike except those maintained by the magistrates over and on the approaches to bridges. Most of these county bridges were narrow, built alongside fords and intended to provide safe passage for pedestrians, horsemen and packhorse trains in times of flood. Thus the trustees were often faced with bottlenecks in their road system which neither they nor the magistrates, who had

Horses' hooves did considerable damage to unmetalled road surfaces and there were statutory restrictions on the number of horses that could be employed for any particular purpose. If a haulier needed additional horses in order to ascend a hill, he would have to apply to a magistrate for permission to use them. To make certain that he did not exceed his permit the place where he had to remove the extra horses was marked by a 'take off' stone such as this one, which is still in place on the Okehampton to Tavistock road at Beardon.

Milestone, near Exminster.

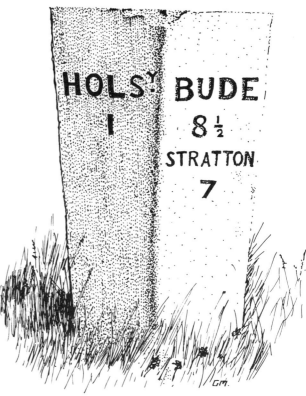

Concrete milestone.

ceased to exist. The turnpikes filled a gap in the highway administrative system but were never popular with the public. Devon had nothing approaching the Rebecca Riots in South Wales, but in 1881 the people of Totnes took down the gates on the town bridge and publicly burnt them.

## The Nineteenth Century

Road-making techniques remained unchanged for most of the nineteenth century but the introduction of new structural materials during this period meant that the appearance of bridges altered. Cast iron was first used in Devon for the delightful little footbridge on the line of the City Wall near Exeter Cathedral. Later Green used the material for reconstructing Axe Bridge and others and Whitaker used it for St Saviour's Bridge. In 1877 a bridge entirely of concrete was built over the River Axe at Axmouth by Philip Brannon, a London civil engineer. Believed to be the earliest surviving concrete bridge in Britain, it was a great advance in its time but with few rivals as the ugliest bridge in the West Country.

The nineteenth century saw the germination of the seed of Henry VIII's 1530 Statute of Bridges and a steady growth towards our present system of highway finance and administration. The Highway Act 1835 regularized the election by the inhabitants of each parish of a highway surveyor. At Epiphany Sessions 1863, the Devon Court of Quarter Sessions, acting under an 1862 enactment, organized the county, excluding the urban areas, into twenty-six districts, each having not more than 300 miles of road and one or two waywardens in each parish. An Act of 1864 permitted parishes to borrow money for the building of roads and bridges and, under the Highways and Locomotives (Amendment) Act 1878, the 1862 districts could apply to the magistrates to have their bridges taken over by the County. By 1881 the number of bridges maintained by the County rose from the 1809 figure of 237 to 618. Under the Local Government Act 1888, responsibility for the police, for weights and measures and for county bridges and their approaches passed from the magistrates to the new county councils and roads designated main roads under the 1878 Act became county roads.

By 1840 James Green was devoting more of his time to

This small bridge in Cathedral Close, Exeter was the first bridge in Devon to be made of cast iron. Built so that the Mayor and Corporation could continue to 'walk the walls', it carries a footway across a breach in the old city wall, formed to provide a new entrance into the city for carriages.

*Sources*
*Transactions of the Devonshire Association* – various papers
Court Rolls of the Hundred of Alwington – Devon Record Office
Quarter Session Order Books – Devon Record Office
Report of James Green, Bridge Contracts, Bridge Drawings, etc. – Devon Record Office
County Treasurers' Accounts, etc. – Devon Record Office
Turnpike Trustees' Order Books, etc. – Devon Record Office
*The Bridges of Devon* D.L.B. Thomas (1980)

private works outside the county than to county work. The magistrates gave him twelve months' notice, voting 'the unanimous Thanks of the Court' for thirty-three years of 'valuable and efficient service'. He was succeeded by Thomas Whitaker who continued the good work of bridge reconstruction and also produced the excellent volumes of bridge drawings now deposited in the County Record Office. When Whitaker retired two County Surveyors were appointed, one for the north-east and the other for the south-west of the county. With the formation of the Devon County Council in 1888, four surveyors were appointed.

## Motorization

At the opening of the twentieth century the railways had clearly taken over from the horse-drawn vehicle, and to some extent from the canals, as the main mover of people and goods over long distances. Local traffic, however, was still heavily dependent on the horse and even in the 1940s milk was being delivered from the churn on the horse-drawn cart into the waiting jug. Nevertheless, the farming community was becoming used to mechanical assistance and many of the early cars appeared on the more prosperous farms, being used for the journey to market once a week. Communication and the transport of produce have always been important to the rural community and even today the ownership of vehicles is higher in the countryside than it is in the towns.

No one, however, predicted the extent to which the car would dominate people's lives, so little allowance was made for future traffic growth and the need to accommodate the half-a-million motor vehicles that are now used in Devon. Between the wars the bus became the natural successor to both the horse-drawn carriage and the tram. The railway network became the focus of much activity and towns flourished where they were well served by it. The lorry was also making an increasingly important contribution to the economy and large firms were in this period establishing transport fleets and distribution depots throughout the country. So it was, for example, that Exeter housed the regional depot for the International Stores serving most of the South West. (This depot was temporarily used for the production of equipment for the army during the Second World War.) This process of distribution has become so important that some large shops are now unlikely to move into an area unless it is well served by the motorway network.

New development proposals are examined closely these days to determine their likely impact on the road network and parking standards are applied to ensure that, whether for dwellings or business, there is adequate space to park off the highway. Estate layouts are carefully checked to ensure that they are as safe as possible for the road user. The ribbon development reminiscent of the 1930s is no longer permitted and accesses on to main roads are very carefully controlled. Even major planning decisions can hinge on the question of access; at a public inquiry in 1987 into the

# 2

# THE MOBILE SOCIETY

The Growth and Social Effects of Road Transport

A clear indication of the local amenity value of roads before motor traffic became common is shown in this photograph of Crediton High Street taken in 1900. Roads were places for discussion, trade, sport and other community activities. The pedestrianization of selected urban roads reflects a growing recognition that these functions may sometimes outweigh the needs of the motorist.

Before the last war Colin Buchanan (*above*) was an engineer in the regional offices of the Ministry of Transport based in Exeter. As urban planning advisor to the Ministry, he was responsible for the report *Traffic in Towns*, published in 1963, which has had a major impact on the way in which roads have been planned in urban areas.

possibility of a major out-of-town shopping centre for Exeter, much of the debate centred on the sheer volume of traffic such a development might impose on the local road network, figures of up to 25 000 additional journeys by vehicle each day being predicted.

The network of roads in Devon developed over the years as a response mainly to very local needs, with the majority of the population regarding only a few miles as a long journey. Although home and work were close, economic pressures created more distant travel patterns, perhaps to the local market or beyond, with agriculture and mining giving rise to their own distinctive patterns of travel and many of the early routes being established between great religious centres. In towns the development of roads was more often dominated by markets and traders than by traffic. Coastal shipping, canals and railways all played their part in the economic development of the county. The growth of tourism was linked strongly with the railway

The concept of 'traffic' has undergone a dramatic change in the last 100 years. This picture, taken at Witheridge at the turn of the century, shows a 'growler' carriage and wagonette, typical of the vehicular traffic of the day and available only to those with substantial means. Private and commercial vehicles together caused little disturbance in rural Devon.

network, but with increasing affluence and personal mobility the car has gradually become the main means of travel by visitors to the county. This mobility is taken for granted, especially by those who have grown up in the last thirty years, and it is hard to realize that before then many people rarely ventured more than a few miles away from home in their lifetime. It is claimed that even until quite recently there were some elderly people in the St Thomas area of Exeter to the west of the River Exe who had never crossed over to the city centre, only a mile or so away but on the east side of the river.

This changing pattern of travel is reflected in the growing importance of different routes into and through the county. The main road pattern was, for example, reinforced by a regional spine road, the M5 motorway and A38 dual-carriageway trunk road from Bristol to Plymouth. This concept was advanced by the South West Economic Planning Council in the document published in 1967 *A Region with a Future*, and was seen to be part of the region's economic strategy not only to assist tourism but also to create opportunities for the growth and development of the area.

## The Increase in Traffic

The gradual build-up of traffic congestion as the number of vehicles on the road increased was emphasized in 1963 by the publication of a report entitled *Traffic in Towns*. It was produced by a Committee chaired by a former road engineer of the Ministry of Transport in Exeter. The document, better known as 'The Buchanan Report', made

Professor (later Sir) Colin Buchanan one of the best-known engineers of his time and paved the way for a surge in highway planning, ironically at the time when another famous name, Dr (later Lord) Richard Beeching, was cutting hard into the railway infrastructure of Devon with a whole series of branch-line closures, thus making the trend towards car ownership even greater.

Buchanan, in accepting predictions for a society increasingly committed to the motor car, recognized that a major programme of road construction was inevitable. The scale of change he considered possible for our towns and cities has never really emerged, especially in Devon, despite the growth in traffic. Increased traffic congestion, continued use of public transport and adjustments to social habits such as late-evening shopping and flexible working hours have all contributed to an acceptance of traffic conditions which would have been unthinkable in Devon in earlier decades. Traffic management, improved vehicle design and driver behaviour have all played their part. Long-distance inter-urban journeys have been catered for by an ever-improving network of motorways and trunk roads, and by the time of the Buchanan Report, the M1 motorway had been constructed. Nevertheless, in Devon tourist traffic was continuing to cause problems and the Exeter bypass was attracting national notoriety. Not

TRACTION ENGINE ACCIDENT, IN FORE ST, EXETER. APRIL 25TH.1

surprisingly, therefore, the early studies that would eventually lead to the construction of the M5 motorway into Devon were begun. The engineering consultants, Freeman, Fox & Partners, started work in 1964 and it was to take a further thirteen years before their work and the M5 were complete.

This planning process was part of a growing recognition of the need to improve the highway network and generate plans for the future that would accommodate the steady growth in vehicle ownership. Traffic predictions have long been with us, but Buchanan brought society face to face with its growing dependence on personal mobility. His Report not only looked at a future with most familiies owning a car but even ventured to suggest what at that time was to many people unthinkable, that a significant level of two-car-owning families would emerge. This has now become commonplace but it is as well to realize just how great this traffic growth has been over the last few decades.

Traffic growth and mobility have been closely related to disposable income and the relative cost of motoring. Similarly the use of public transport has declined as people have opted for the more expensive but more convenient private car. The bus has been an important means of travel over the years, both in the urban and rural parts of the county, and the tram has played its part in the major towns.

Fore Street in Exeter is a steep hill which many early motor vehicles found difficult to climb and accidents were frequent. The load of bricks, seen here spilled over the roadway, could not have weighed much more than 2 tons, but was obviously too much for the heavy goods vehicle of its day. The picture was taken in 1906.

Even now the bus to the local market is a special part of rural life in Devon, although the day out on the bus is no longer quite the social event it used to be. The trend away from bus to car caused a considerable reduction in bus travel over the years as growing affluence encouraged increasing car ownership. This has been reflected in the growing number of cars on the road network. Typical traffic levels on Devon main roads were measured in a census of roads in October 1938 which showed that the A38 between Exeter and Plymouth carried between 3000 and 4000 vehicles a day and the A30 between Exeter and Okehampton carried about 2500 vehicles a day. Comparable figures today are 23 000 and 10 000. On a Saturday in peak summer these now rise to 36 000 and 24 000. Fig. 3 on p. 39 shows the traffic-flow trends on the A380 route from Exeter to Torbay, covering a period of about thirty years. From this it can be seen that there has been a steady upward trend over this recent period, with the doubling of traffic between 1954 and 1964 and again between 1964 and

1984. There have been one or two economic hiccups such as the oil crisis when petrol prices soared in 1975 and traffic flows dipped. However, traffic volume soon recovered as petrol prices stabilized.

Traffic expansion also arises from increased accessibility. Before the nation's motorway network was developed few would have visualized tackling some of the extensive journeys that are now undertaken as a matter of routine. Motorways attract traffic that would otherwise use parallel or alternative less speedy routes and this diverted traffic, coupled with growth in travel, accounts for some spectacular increases in traffic movement. At one time the A38 was the main road from Exeter to Bristol and in 1938 carried some 4000 vehicles daily. By 1954 this had increased to 7500, but by 1984 when the traffic between Exeter and Bristol was now accommodated by the M5 motorway, the daily flow in August was well in excess of 30000 vehicles, and on peak Saturdays more than 60000 vehicles on the busiest section between junctions 29 and 30 at Exeter.

## The Growth of the Network

This traffic growth has been accommodated on a gradually improved highway network. In 1952 expenditure on improvements to trunk and county roads in rural Devon was £50000 (£500000 at 1986 prices), but by 1963 this had risen to £1 million (£7.5 million at 1986 prices). In 1986 total expenditure amounted to over £30 million. Many of the plans laid in the early 1960s did not then recognize the

Between 1920 and 1930 the number of car licences issued each year rose from 200 000 to 1 million and ownership of a car assumed an immense social importance. Engaged couples from the professional classes would announce that they planned to have 'one child and a car', and roadside facilities aimed specifically at the motorist began to appear even in the rural areas. The Wayside Café opened in May 1926 on the A30 east of Exeter to sell farm produce and provide refreshments for the motoring public. It was one of the earliest roadside cafés in the country and is still in operation, looking virtually the same today as it did in 1926.

In 1958, when this picture of Lymington Road Coach Park in Torquay was taken, public transport was still very popular in Britain. About a third of the summer visitors to Torquay arrived by coach, another third by train and the final third by private car. The next ten years saw a dramatic decline in public transport usage, and that decline has continued, less steeply, ever since. By 1986, only about a sixth of U.K. holidaymakers were using buses or coaches to reach their destination, whereas nearly three-quarters were using private cars.

For many people, their first journey in a motor vehicle came with motorized public transport. Motor bus companies were active in many parts of Devon before the Great War. *Left:* The 'Devonia', seen here at Bradworthy in 1910, ran as a regular service between Holsworthy and Bideford. *Above:* The attraction of travelling comparatively long distances on 'outings' by motor bus became irresistible among the non-car-owning community in the 1920s and 1930s. This group of High Bickington villagers are all set for a day's adventure, after first having their photograph taken.

extent to which vehicle and driving standards would improve and the ways in which people change their habits to allow for or to avoid traffic problems. The plan that was once seriously discussed for a dual carriageway through Lynton and Lynmouth has fortunately never materialized and a large proportion of the growth in traffic to that part of the county has more appropriately transferred to the North Devon Link Road. Other proposals, such as a dual-carriageway trunk road around Okehampton, have now come to fruition.

Although many of the traffic predictions made in those times have been largely fulfilled in practice, the scale of road building that was envisaged has not occurred. In the urban areas, especially, society has had to accommodate this by tolerating a level of congestion that was previously considered excessive, whilst at the same time benefiting from a major network of national roads that has created considerable relief to the alternative routes. Towns and villages bypassed by these main routes have had a more civilized way of life restored to them and it soon became difficult to remember the constant stream of traffic that used to thunder through Cullompton, Chudleigh and Ivybridge or to recall the solid queues of traffic along the A380 on a Saturday morning. These queues reached back from Exeter through Newton Abbot to Torbay as the Exeter bypass created a bottleneck in both directions. Travelling patterns were different in those days, with substantial numbers of holidaymakers journeying overnight to get past Exeter by daybreak. A Saturday morning would dawn to see a continuous stream of traffic passing along the Exeter bypass, whilst on the A30 beyond Exeter on the way to Okehampton verges would be littered with parked cars whose drivers had earlier got through Exeter and were catching up on their night's sleep. In the daytime drivers on a summer Saturday could expect to be encouraged by sightseers from Exeter who had come to the bypass just to gaze with awe and wonder at the endurance of the human race. On a sunny day the ice-cream sellers were able to ply a welcome trade amongst the stationary vehicles, while queues stretched for up to 30 miles in length.

The pressure from the public for something to be done about this peak summer problem was echoed by the commercial users of the A38 through to Devon from Bristol and beyond. Cars displayed stickers advertising 'The A38, the longest lane in England' and the press regularly carried stories about problems on the Exeter bypass, with the word 'chaos' frequently occurring in the headlines. The government's commitment in principle, in 1963, to a new road was followed by the completion of the M5, some fourteen years later. Although plans were also being considered in the early 1960s for the A30 bypass of Okehampton, it was many years before they bore fruit. Work is now complete on the improvement of the A38 in Devon, with Plymouth at last having a trunk-road bypass on a route that had been protected from development for about fifty years, a tribute to long-term planning. More recently, plans for the trunk road to north Devon involved establishing an entirely new route, the North Devon Link, leading from the M5 motorway at Sampford Peverell through to Fairy Cross beyond Bideford. Construction started at both ends of the link road some 40 miles apart, the first two stages to open bypassing Tiverton and Bideford. The North Devon Link also bypasses South Molton and Barnstaple.

These major schemes have a marked impact on travel patterns, both into and within the county. They carry a high proportion of the long-distance traffic and drivers will divert substantial distances from less suitable routes to gain the benefit of these high-quality roads not only in terms of savings in journey time but also in improved reliability of

The bypass, as a way to relieve pressure on towns and villages and improve the economic efficiency of the road network, has been widely used in Devon. Cullompton bypass, built in 1969, now forms part of the M5 motorway. Cullompton High Street, seen here, could accommodate only a fraction of the 40 000 or so vehicles which now use the motorway on an average summer day.

Urban pedestrian activities and motor traffic are difficult to reconcile and the resulting conflicts are still a feature of many town centres. The solution to these problems is far from easy, given the variety of demands on the average high street, such as at Totnes, shown here.

The post-war period saw a rapid rise in car ownership, and pressure on the routes used by holiday traffic into the West Country became intense. Queuing on the main routes around Exeter became almost a national pastime at holiday periods, testing the stamina of both vehicles and their occupants. *Top:* The motorists here might well sympathize with the remarks of a writer in the *Gentleman's Magazine* in 1752, who would 'no more think of travelling into the west of England for pleasure than of going to Nubia'. *Left:* An ice-cream salesman provides a welcome service to victims of the queue on Exeter bypass before the M5 was built.

*Below:* The M5 in 1988. The completion of this major arterial route has ended the delays in getting past Exeter, even during the periods of heavy holiday traffic each summer.

Catering for the needs of the motoring public has developed into big business since the 1930s. In those days the Beaford Garage *(above)* repaired the few locally owned cars, and supplied petrol from the hand pumps in the forecourt. The other picture shows the Granada service area on the M5 near Exeter, completed in 1978; it has parking for over 500 vehicles, including coaches and heavy goods vehicles, and offers a comprehensive range of services to motorway travellers.

time-keeping. Traffic relief, therefore, applies not only to the towns and villages bypassed but also to the other roads within the network from which traffic is attracted.

The concentration of traffic on to this major-road network has gradually been taken for granted and should a road be blocked for any reason the temporary return of traffic on to the old routes can create chaos. Special permanent diversion signs for key sections of road are often overlooked by the traveller. They are in fact little geometric symbols to be followed once a diversion is brought into operation. In 1987 these signs were used to great effect when a propane gas tanker overturned on the M5 motorway at Exeter. Despite the signs the traffic chaos had to be seen to be believed as the road was closed off and traffic routed back on to the old bypass. Nor were motorists the only ones affected. A local residential caravan park and some private housing had to be evacuated because of the nature of the load being carried.

The road network has always had an important role for the transport of freight but the growth in the number of goods vehicles has not been as marked as that of private cars. For example, the number of freight vehicles has increased in the last ten years by 15-20 per cent, while the general growth in traffic has been 20-25 per cent. This is largely accounted for by the increasing size and weight of goods vehicles, allowing a greater tonnage of goods to be carried by a similar number of much larger lorries. The maximum gross weight permitted for normal lorries has increased from 24 tonnes in 1955 to 32 tonnes in 1964, rising to 38 tonnes for large articulated lorries in 1983, with the prospect of 40 tonne lorries in the future. During the same period the maximum lorry length increased from 33 ft to nearly 51 ft. These vehicles cause concern owing to their sheer bulk which gives rise to serious environmental impact in city streets, but it is the axle weight of heavy lorries that is the major cause of wear on the road network. Motorways and trunk roads carry the greater burden of these vehicles and the effects are readily seen in the major repair programmes that followed a decade or so after their construction.

## Predictions

Engineers' heightened awareness of the growing impact of traffic on the road network during the mid sixties led to more thorough attempts to predict future traffic levels. In 1943, when the Ministry of War Transport published detailed guidance for designing road improvements, traffic growth was mentioned only in passing by an oblique reference to the effect of new housing development. Growth arising from new developments and increased levels of car ownership were eventually seen to be the key components in the procedure for predicting traffic levels. Car ownership was predicted in 1950 as likely to rise to a level of 0.13 cars per person, i.e. about one car to every eight people. By 1956 this prediction had risen to 0.20, in 1960 to 0.40 and in 1966 the Government Road Research Laboratory described the ultimate saturation of car ownership as 0.45 cars per person. The national census in 1981 revealed that in Devon car ownership was typically 0.38 cars per person in rural areas and in the larger urban areas about 0.26.

It was on this basis that the early Land Use Transportation Surveys in Devon were undertaken. The first was completed for Plymouth in 1966, then for Torbay and Exeter. These were based on an extensive number of home interviews to obtain the daily travel pattern of households irrespective of whether they owned a car or not, supplemented by traffic counts and a range of roadside interviews to intercept people coming into the area. These major surveys were becoming feasible at that time because the computing power needed to handle huge quantities of data and to model complex travel patterns was just becoming available through large computer bureaux.

As an aside, it is appropriate to note here that Devon's highway engineers have been eager users of computers ever since these machines became available, initially for the structural design of bridges and for transportation studies. Before long, however, much of the highway-design process was being tackled using computers not only to speed up the process but also to improve the quality and efficiency of designs. Today complex traffic patterns and predictions are analysed on the computer. The impact of major new developments can be estimated, as can the extent to which congestion might occur on an entire urban road network, recognizing the change in journey speeds on parts of the network and new routes that would be chosen to avoid congestion. The modelling of transportation networks has now reached the stage where such techniques are incorporated in the traffic-light control systems and the most efficient co-ordination of traffic signals is constantly being recalculated and applied throughout the day by computers in County Hall controlling traffic lights in Exeter, Plymouth and Torbay.

In the mid sixties, Land Use Transportation Studies were undertaken in these three urban areas. These first detailed studies of traffic gave rise to the framework of highway proposals incorporated in the planning documents of the day, the Development Plans. Many of these proposals were based on the view that 'the money would be found' and in retrospect could be seen to represent an idealistic and expensive traffic solution. The environmental intrusion of the motor vehicle also began to be resented at this time and attempts were begun to curb it. Just as the motorist on the busy holiday routes in Devon changed his habits to avoid encountering congestion, so in the urban areas habits also changed to avoid wherever possible peak periods. This led to roads taking more traffic throughout the day than was originally visualized. By the mid seventies it was recognized that these Development Plans required review as there was much tighter financial control, so by 1976 Exeter, Plymouth and Torbay had all been studied once more. These studies led eventually to the policies contained in the County Structure Plan and the various Local Plans.

Traffic surveys for smaller towns were also carried out, starting in 1962/63 with Teignmouth and Dawlish, Okehampton and Plympton. A small group of staff was established at that time to provide this highway-planning input to Development Plans and particularly the handling of town redevelopment such as at Plympton, Plymstock, Newton Abbot and Exmouth. The proposals for Exmouth were prepared in 1965, just a hundred years after the plan for the Rolle Estate in Exmouth, one of the early examples of town planning. Another small team was set up by the County Council to look at the potential impact of the extension of the M5 motorway into Devon, assessing, for example, the improved accessibility of the county. An indication of this improvement is that before the M5 was constructed a journey from Exeter to Bristol on the A38 often took up to 3 hours, compared with little over 1 hour today. A small booklet was produced by the team, with the title *The Motorway into Devon – The Challenge*, setting out the possible effects of improving travel opportunities. Among the suggestions it made was that the more popular areas of the north and south coasts should have their different tourist images reinforced, emphasizing north Devon as the 'Golden Coast' and the other coast as the south Devon 'Riviera'. It looked for an increase in indoor recreation facilities, especially in the south, to combat the uncertainties of the climate. Reflections of these thoughts can be seen in the recently developed leisure and conference centre in Torquay, the 'Riviera Centre'. These prognostications were not necessarily popular with everyone, however: one County Councillor described the appointment of this planning unit as 'communist inspired'!

## Road Safety

Justifying the spending of large sums of public money on major highway improvements is an increasingly complex procedure. Not only are the obvious benefits to road users, such as less congestion and reduced journey times, taken into account, but also the benefits to the community relieved of traffic are considered, as well as the impact the new road will have on the environment. A significant aspect of such a justification is the potential reduction in accidents that such improvement can provide.

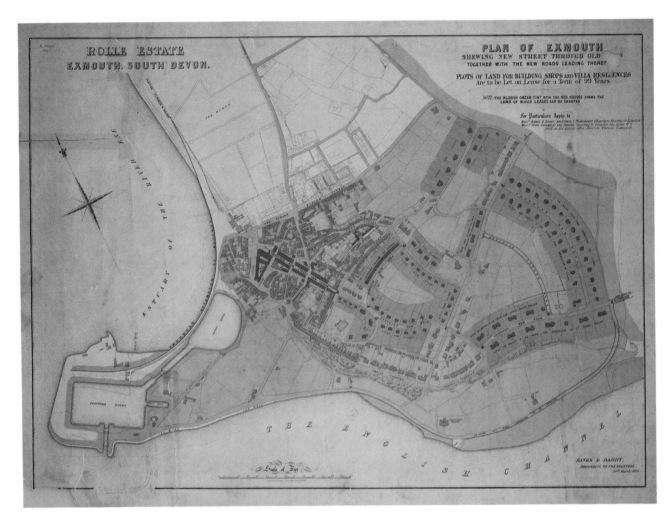

An example of early local planning is demonstrated by this beautifully draughted plan of proposed redevelopment in Exmouth, dated March 1865.

Although society gains greatly from the freedom of movement that the car provides, it has to be accepted that in this process considerable misery is inflicted both to vehicle users and to pedestrians. The Highway Code was first published in 1931 but it is a sobering fact that in 1934, when in the whole of England only 2.4 million vehicles were licensed, over 7000 people were killed in road accidents. Of these about 120 were killed on Devon's roads. In 1934, however, the government introduced a Road Traffic Act whose key provisions were the imposition of a 30 miles-per-hour speed limit in built-up areas; the introduction of tests for new drivers; greater protection by insurance for persons injured by motor vehicles; pedestrian crossings; and special licensing of the drivers of goods vehicles. After this the accident levels declined and, although the total of all injury accidents in a year is now above the 1934 level, the number of fatalities has remained lower, with the exception of the early war years when they soared to over 9000 in 1941 and the mid sixties when the number of fatalities nationally was nearly 8000.

It was at that stage that more attention was given to road-safety education and publicity measures. The 'Tufty Club' was introduced in 1964 by the Royal Society for the Prevention of Accidents (RoSPA). This was aimed at the very young and sought to engender safety habits on the road through the story-book activities of Tufty the Squirrel. In the early 1970s, the 'Green Cross Code' was introduced for slightly older children as an introduction to kerbside discipline.

In 1984, fifty years after the Road Traffic Act of 1934, the number of vehicles licensed had risen to 20.7 million, but fatalities had fallen to 5600. In Devon in 1984, 430 000 vehicles were licensed and 88 fatalities occurred. There have always been more accidents in the urban areas. The current typical urban accident rate is 172 injury accidents per 100 million vehicle kilometres travelled, compared to a typical rural level of 66 and on the motorway of 12. Because of their severity it is the crashes on the fast dual carriageways in Devon that understandably hit the headlines, but despite the very heavy volumes of traffic carried, these roads still rank as the safest roads with only 10 per cent of recorded accidents in the county occurring on these routes, a low percentage compared to the proportion of vehicles using them.

Influencing the road user to behave more safely has long been an important role for the police, but in 1974 County Councils were charged with this responsibility. Through an extensive range of publicity, training and educational initiatives, Devon County Council has sought to keep down accident levels. The growth in popularity of motor cycling, for example, which followed the increase in motoring costs in the late 1970s carried with it a dramatic increase in fatalities and injuries to motor cyclists. Following this the County Council encouraged and supported the setting up of motor-cycle training centres throughout the county. Both off-the-road and on-the-road training is now available for all novice motor cyclists and is offered to them by many dealers when they sell them their first motor cycle. Similarly, the accident statistics clearly show that the teenager and young adult is especially prone to accidents. This has prompted the County Council to increase road-safety education activities in schools through the development and availability of the Road Safety Education Pack. This stimulates an awareness of road safety by providing material across the curriculum to show how these issues can be integrated into, for example, language, geography, history, drama or mathematics. All schools have been given this pack to enable teachers to support safe behaviour and tackle youthful perceptions, traffic skills and road sense. Nevertheless, fatal and serious-injury accidents continue to occur and, although not rising by the same degree as traffic growth (as fig. 1 on p. 38 shows), they represent a great deal of distress. More starkly, this suffering applies particularly to the younger members of the community and especially to young males; this can be seen by studying the accident statistics and their relationship to the age of those involved (fig. 2). The pronounced peak for young men in the age range from 16 to 21 indicates that they are six times more likely to have road accidents than the rest of the population.

## Accident Investigation and Prevention

Safety on the road is an area of particular concern to the County Council and, whilst road improvements can reduce accidents very significantly by making the highway environment safer, these benefits can soon be negated by driver behaviour, particularly speeding which, despite widespread belief to the contrary, is still one of the greatest causes of injury accidents.

A reduction in accidents has been achieved notwithstanding growth in traffic. There are many reasons for this, including improved driver education, better vehicles, stricter legislation on drinking and speed limits, traffic-management measures and seat-belt legislation. One of the most significant reasons has been the development of motorways and modern trunk roads that have drawn traffic away from the less suitable routes and their much higher accident rates.

The design of highways has always incorporated safety measures in terms of minimum visibility distances to enable the road user to emerge from junctions, to overtake, and to stop in safety. The publication of the H.M.S.O. book entitled *Research on Road Safety* stimulated a much greater interest in the whole subject of engineering for safety during the mid 1960s and the Department of Transport pioneered accident-investigation techniques which are now commonly used throughout the country.

In 1974, the 'Kerb Drill', which had become insufficient to meet the road conditions that children were facing, was superseded by the Green Cross Code. David Prowse (who added to his credibility with children when they discovered that he also played the part of Darth Vader in the film *Star Wars*) has been the Green Cross Man since the scheme's inception. The photograph was taken at Ladysmith School, Exeter, in 1978.

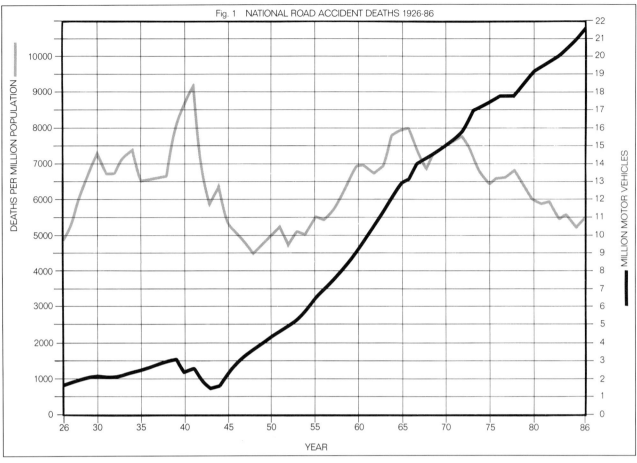

Fig. 1   NATIONAL ROAD ACCIDENT DEATHS 1926-86

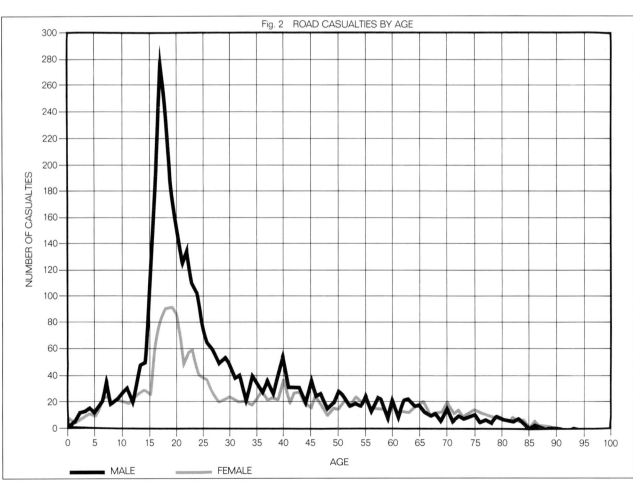

Fig. 2   ROAD CASUALTIES BY AGE

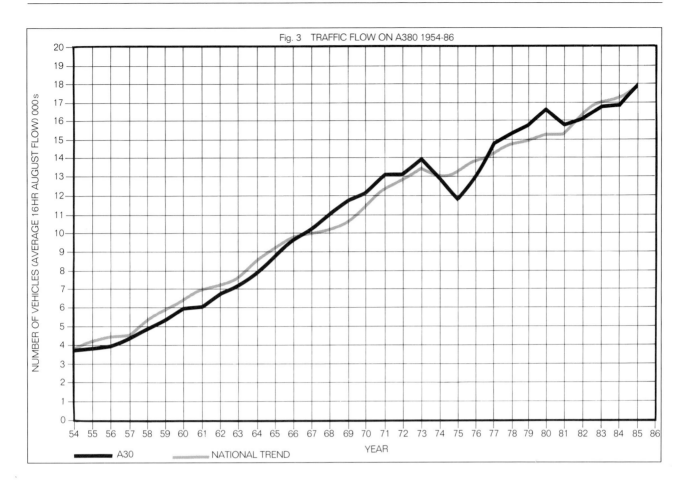

Fig. 3   TRAFFIC FLOW ON A380 1954-86

NUMBER OF VEHICLES (AVERAGE 16HR AUGUST FLOW) 000 s

YEAR

▬▬▬ A30          ▭▭▭ NATIONAL TREND

Road accidents have occurred ever since wheeled vehicles were invented, but the cause is not necessarily directly related to the volume of traffic on the roads. The graphs opposite show a large rise in the volume of traffic accompanied by a consistent fall in the accident rate since the war. The explanation for these statistics lies, to a large degree, in better engineering, better legislation and a travelling public more aware of safety issues than ever before.

In Devon from 1957 accident reports received from the police were plotted on strip maps of all the major roads in the county. Each report was then filed to enable easy retrieval. This system led to the identification of high-risk sites for treatment, particularly those with possible road defects, and in turn investigation and remedial work was undertaken. Computerization of accident records was begun in 1968 as a joint scheme with Cornwall and completely revolutionized the approach to this important subject. This system was developed to provide purely statistical information concerning all reported accidents and to provide regular monthly and cumulative totals of accidents analysed by type and cause.

In the late 1960s considerable national research was undertaken into accident-investigation techniques by the Department of Transport Road Safety Units, one of which was based in Southampton. Some Devon sites were included in this programme of research.

In 1968, Devon County Council's Roads Committee accepted that intensive studies of accidents should take place. Additional staffing was agreed and in the summer of 1970 the Accident Investigation Unit was established. This anticipated a statement by the then Minister of Transport,

John Peyton, in 1971, in which he said that legislation would soon be introduced placing statutory road-safety duties on the new county authorities. These duties were to include accident investigation and the implementation of remedial measures.

The statutory requirements of the Road Traffic Act 1974 were brought into operation on 1 March 1975. The County Council now had a duty to promote road-safety education and to carry out accident studies and implement the consequent engineering measures required. These engineering schemes are designed to reduce the possibility of accidents, both by the careful design and construction of new roads and also the carrying out of minor works such as signing and lining to make the road environment safer.

Devon County Council was now responsible for highways in the whole of the county, including Exeter, Plymouth and Torbay. Accident records for the roads in these areas were added to the system as they became available and the last to be fully computerized were the Plymouth records in 1979. Computerized analysis was improving all the time and priority lists of the worst sites were sent to engineers and road-safety officers throughout the county. Accident investigation by the Unit became more ambitious and more radical solutions were evaluated. Increasing use of the computer made it easier to demonstrate substantial reductions in accidents achieved by these means. Those measures that could be identified by detailed analysis included not only improvements to make the road environment safer but also road-surfacing work to rectify poor skidding resistance.

Many early motor accidents were caused by inferior vehicle design. On a fine August day in 1909, the bus in the photo was carrying a full load of passengers from Holsworthy market when it stopped on the steep hill in Sutcombe. Whilst the driver's assistant was trying to restart the engine, the brakes failed and the bus rolled back down the hill, eventually overturning and crushing a policeman who had leapt from the runaway vehicle and fallen.

The ratio of accident savings to the cost of the remedy for schemes designed by the Accident Unit has continued to improve as better computer techniques have enabled 'treatable' accidents to be identified more easily. A study of the proportion of accidents occurring on wet roads compared to those on dry roads revealed that, at some sites, most accidents occurred in wet conditions, an indication that the road surface had begun to 'polish'. As a result of these studies the first 100 sites treated by improving the condition of the road surface created a reduction of 150 accidents per year.

Advances in computer technology and techniques continue and it is now possible to plot, in map form, accidents throughout the county by type or by time of day or by whatever information is required. The County's computerized Devon Network Information system, known as Devonet, enables this information to be plotted directly on to a map of the road network. This has substantially eased the work of identifying problem areas and greatly enhanced the presentation of the information for both the engineers and the police. Over the past twenty years traffic in Devon has nearly doubled and fatal accidents have halved. As long as resources can be put to accident-remedial measures it is likely that this encouraging trend will continue.

## Improving the Network

To return to the justification of road schemes considered earlier, it should be recognized that, whilst the ratepayer provides a great deal of the money required for the improvement of roads, it is central government that is responsible for expenditure on motorways and trunk roads. On county roads various grant arrangements have existed over the years, related originally to road classification. Just after the last war the grant levels were set to give Class I roads (A roads) a 60 per cent grant from central government, with 40 per cent from the local rate, while Class II roads (B roads) gained a 50 per cent grant and the lesser routes received no grant at all. In the mid sixties these levels were altered so that government grant comprised: Class I 75 per cent; Class II 60 per cent; and Class III, the

more important minor roads, 50 per cent. This had a substantial effect on the way in which the road pattern developed, with County Councils concentrating their efforts on the roads giving higher grant levels and necessarily neglecting all unclassified roads where no grants were received. The great contrast between different standards of roads in the countryside derives from this process which recognizes the importance of the major communications network but leaves much of the long-standing yet minor rural network virtually unchanged. The County Council has developed this policy over the years and has defined a hierarchy of roads to reflect their relative importance throughout the network. This hierarchy of the most important roads in the county is now enshrined in policy within the County Council's Structure Plan and this is shown on p. 54. Today, however, the grant system is very different and central government grant is paid through a mechanism known as Transport Supplementary Grant which in essence results from a bid made each year through the publication of the authority's Transport Policies and Programme (TPP). The TPP is a comprehensive statement of the overall highway policies of the authority and includes its intentions not only for the construction of major schemes but also its road-safety policies, maintenance policies and traffic-management policies. In 1988 this led to an annual expenditure of over £40 million for the overall management, maintenance and improvement of the network.

The high priority given to road safety in Devon stems not just from attempts to reduce the numbers of fatalities, but also from a concern to reduce the real cost to society incurred by accidents. Every fatal road accident costs the community £300 000 (1986 prices).

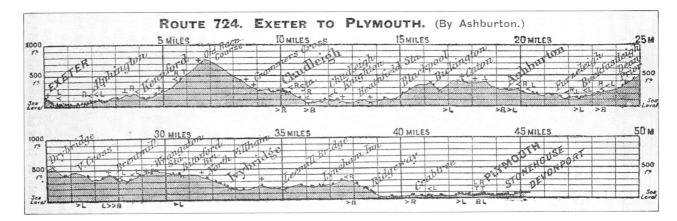

Gradient diagrams, like this one of the road between Exeter and Plymouth, were published in early motoring handbooks. Information of this kind was vital to motorists when planning their routes because a steep hill might very well prove too much for a car to climb. This diagram appeared in *The 'Contour' Road Book of England (Western Division)*, published in 1912–13.

These policies have been administered in different ways over the years but it is worth noting that before 1974 Borough and Urban Districts with a population of 20 000 or more could 'claim' the right to maintain their roads, while many of those with lower populations had that function delegated to them by the County Council. Since 1974 these agency arrangements have by and large been exercised only by the three major urban authorities of Exeter, Plymouth and Torbay and the overall management of the network has been decentralized to four Area Engineers who, as County Council officers, manage the road network from centres in Exeter, Torquay, Plymouth and Barnstaple to cover the east, south, west and north of the county. A committee structure, which has existed since the Second World War, continues in a modified form to accommodate the inclusion of the three major urban areas within the County Council's responsibilities and the Area Engineers between them look after seven area highway sub-committees, in essence covering the four corners of the county and the three major urban areas. Over the years, in addition to the detail of highway maintenance, the work in the Areas has increasingly included greater concern for small improvements designed to reduce accident problems, reduce congestion and allow development to proceed. At the same time there has been a burgeoning growth of traffic-management measures, not only to improve the circulation of traffic on the road network but also to provide the essential controls of car parking on the street, speed limits, traffic signs and so forth. All these policies, however, are a reflection of the basic requirements for the network to be properly managed through a hierarchy of roads from motorway down to country lane, each of which performs its proper function and requires both management and maintenance.

There can be little doubt that the road network of Devon, which had taken thousands of years to develop, underwent its most dramatic change in just twenty-five years from the mid 1960s. In this short period, and in particular after local government reorganization, the road system which had for so long defied the passage of time was transformed into a network of modern highways capable of satisfying many of the traffic needs of the county well into the twenty-first century. It was a period which was to see, amongst many other achievements, the motorway reach Exeter, the building of the A38 dual carriageway from Exeter to the Tamar, a new route providing access to north Devon and the improvement of the A30 west of Exeter, including a bypass which would remove one of the country's most notorious holiday traffic bottlenecks at Okehampton.

The highway network which existed before this era had changed little since roads were classified according to their importance as a result of the Ministry of Transport Act of 1919. Certain roads of national importance, such as the London to Penzance road, became trunk roads and the direct responsibility of the Ministry of Transport by virtue of the Trunk Roads Act 1936.

In the early 1920s the classified roads were 'tarmacked' but the surfaces of many of the unclassified roads remained waterbound until the early 1930s; by the end of that decade most minor roads had at least been surface dressed. A few minor county roads remained in a waterbound condition, a few reverted to green lanes and a few, by lack of use, had been abandoned altogether.

Although a number of small improvement schemes were being carried out, the highlight of the 1930s must have been the unemployment relief schemes, referred to as the '£2 million schemes'. These embraced the construction of the Exeter bypass, the bypasses for Ashburton and Buckfastleigh and the widening of the Dean Prior section of the A38.

The Second World War was a time of standstill as far as the development of the road network was concerned, work being restricted to that necessary for military purposes. Airfield construction at Chivenor, Harrowbeer, Winkleigh, Dunkeswell and Smeatharpe necessitated road diversions and road widening. Later when the county served as a major assembly area for American forces preparing for D Day, approaches to 'hards' were needed, i.e. strengthened hard standings and ramps across the foreshore for tanks brought into the area by the Americans. This affected the

# 3

# THE HIGHWAY NETWORK

## The Development of the Modern Road System

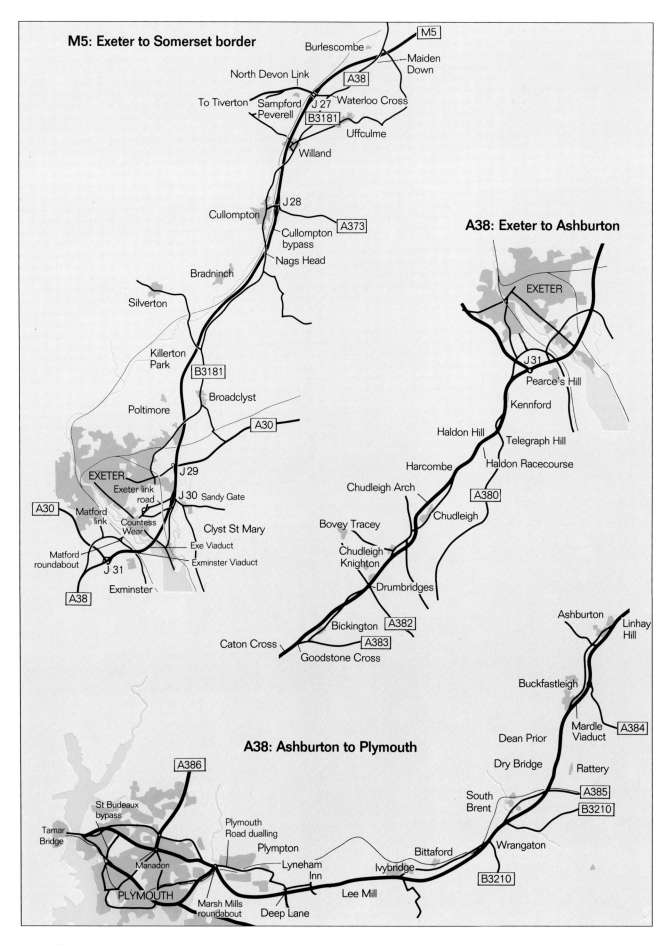

**M5: Exeter to Somerset border**

Burlescombe
M5
Maiden Down
North Devon Link
A38
To Tiverton — Sampford Peverell — J 27 — Waterloo Cross
B3181
Uffculme
Willand
J 28
Cullompton
Cullompton bypass
A373
Nags Head
Bradninch
Silverton
Killerton Park
B3181
Broadclyst
Poltimore
A30
J 29
EXETER
Exeter link road
J 30 — Sandy Gate
A30
Matford link
Countess Wear
Clyst St Mary
Exe Viaduct
Matford roundabout
A38
J 31
Exminster Viaduct
Exminster

**A38: Exeter to Ashburton**

EXETER
J 31
Pearce's Hill
Kennford
Haldon Hill
Telegraph Hill
Harcombe
Haldon Racecourse
Chudleigh Arch
A380
Chudleigh
Bovey Tracey
Chudleigh Knighton
A38
Drumbridges
Bickington
A382
Caton Cross
A383
Goodstone Cross

Ashburton
Linhay Hill
Buckfastleigh
Mardle Viaduct
A384
Dean Prior
Dry Bridge — Rattery
South Brent
A385
B3210
Wrangaton
Bittaford
B3210
Ivybridge

**A38: Ashburton to Plymouth**

A386
St Budeaux bypass
Plymouth Road dualling
Plympton
Tamar Bridge
Manadon
Lyneham Inn
PLYMOUTH
Marsh Mills roundabout
Lee Mill
Deep Lane

Some of the road schemes referred to in the text. (See also map on p. 69.)

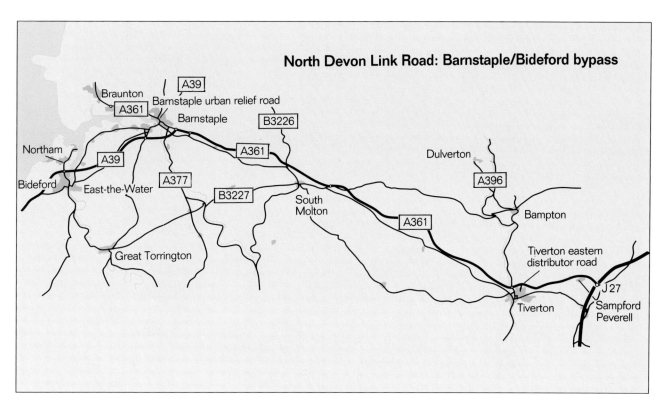

**North Devon Link Road: Barnstaple/Bideford bypass**

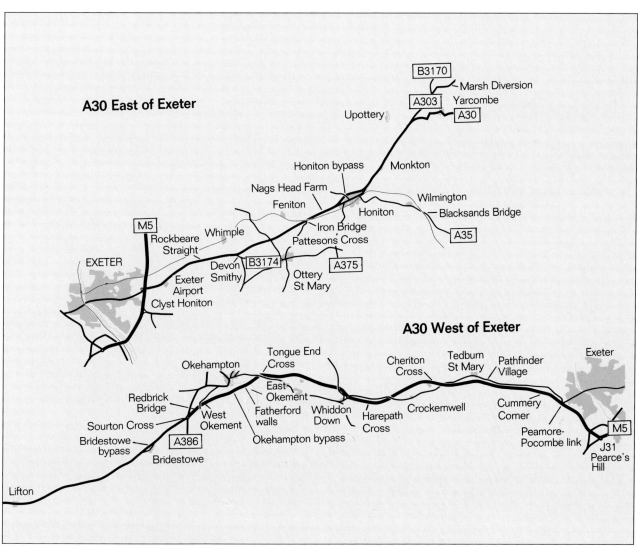

**A30 East of Exeter**

**A30 West of Exeter**

South Hams and Torbay areas with widening of the A379. The A386 between Sourton Cross near Okehampton and Tavistock was also widened and realigned in places.

The strikingly simple provision for traffic control near roadworks shown in this 1933 photograph comprises a man with two flags, one red and one green. The volume and speed of modern traffic now require advance warning signs, lane closures, traffic lights and hundreds of cones to ensure the safety of both workmen and road users.

## The Post-war Period, 1946-64

Immediately after the war, work was concentrated on making good the arrears of maintenance which had accrued during the war, together with a number of small improvement schemes. These minor improvement schemes increased during the 1950s and early 1960s, not only in number but in the scope of each scheme.

### Trunk roads

Between 1946 and 1957 an effort was made to determine the future routes and layout of trunk roads in the county. Based on Ordnance Survey maps dating from 1903, the alignments prepared formed the basis of many improvements and bypasses which followed some twenty years later, including the bypasses of Honiton, Cullompton, Chudleigh and Plympton.

The first trunk-road improvement of any consequence was carried out in 1952 with the reconstruction of Chudleigh Knighton Bridge and its approaches at a cost of £36 201. No further large schemes were approved until 1956 when the Baxworthy Corner diversion at Hartland on

the A39 was carried out to provide a wider carriageway where there had previously been several fatal accidents. After that date the number of schemes prepared and constructed for all trunk roads steadily increased, the exception being the A361/A39 Taunton to Fraddon trunk road, where work was restricted to relatively minor schemes.

On the A30 east of Exeter improvements were made at Lower Northcote Farm, Honiton and at Reddicks Hill, Upottery. Further schemes for widening and realignment of the existing carriageway to form one half of a planned dual carriageway were carried out between Exeter and Honiton. In 1960 an improvement at Nags Head Farm, Honiton provided the first length of dual carriageway on trunk roads in Devon at a cost of £29 566. In 1965 it was extended to Roebuck Farm, so that it could connect with the western end of the proposed Honiton bypass.

In order to provide lengths of road where slow, heavily laden vehicles could be overtaken, the A30 west of Exeter was widened to a 33 ft single carriageway at Redbrick Bridge, Okehampton Hamlets and at Harepath Cross, Drewsteignton. A further improvement scheme was undertaken at Whiddon Down, to eliminate a dangerous junction and to improve visibility.

On the A38 between Plymouth and Exeter a number of improvements were made, including in 1962 the provision of dual carriageways at Lyneham Inn near Plympton, Haldon Racecourse to Harcombe Quarry at Chudleigh and Red Cross Hill at Kennford. The carriageway was also widened to 33 ft at Bittaford, Cross-in-Hand, Heathfield and Benedict's Bridge to facilitate overtaking. The road was further widened and realigned between Marley Bottom at Rattery and Dry Bridge at Dean Prior with two schemes which ultimately formed part of the Plymouth to Exeter dual carriageway. The A38 north of Exeter towards Taunton was improved at Broadclyst, Hele, Willand, Waterloo Cross, Lamb Hill, Maidendown and Red Ball where, as in other parts of the county, the existing carriageway was widened to 33 ft to provide crawler lanes on hills and permit overtaking elsewhere.

In 1963 two roundabouts were constructed on the Exeter bypass at Matford and Peamore. These roundabouts eliminated two dangerous junctions and at the same time helped to ease traffic conditions on the bypass.

## County roads

On county roads at that time practically all improvements which involved the purchase of land, however little, came under the heading of 'major improvements' for which a grant was required from the Ministry of Transport. The amount of the grant varied according to the class of road, the maximum available being for Class I roads, while there was no grant for Unclassified roads.

Schemes costing over £1 million were included in the Ministry of Transport 'rolling programme', introduced to give some help in preparing the advance work and in the acquisition of land. All schemes costing over £25 000 had to be approved by both the Divisional Road Engineer for the South West region and the headquarters office of the Ministry of Transport. Those costing less than £10 000 were dealt with by the Divisional Road Engineer by means of block grants according to the classification of the road.

Immediately after the war there was a flurry of activity and a few improvements were carried out. Prior to 1948 only six schemes were completed and though the number increased to fifteen in 1950, by 1951 the number had dropped back to four and a total of just £18 265 was spent on major improvements during that year.

During 1950 the first attempt was made to set out how the County's road network should be developed in the future in the form of the 'County Road Diagram'. Whilst the plan contained an unattainable shopping list of bypasses it was used as the basis for all proposals on the main traffic routes in the county and schemes given high priority in the Diagram were later incorporated in the County Development Plan. The Plan, which was approved in 1959, accepted the existing road system with the addition of bypasses for twenty towns and villages which, together with five major diversions, were expected to be completed by 1971. Two further schemes (A380 Kingskerswell diversion

and A358 Axminster bypass) were planned to be completed after 1971. In the event, of all these schemes only the A3052 Clyst St Mary bypass was completed before 1971.

From 1956 onwards the number of improvement schemes for county roads increased, with the most important single scheme being the Telegraph Hill–Rushycombe improvement on the A380. The speed with which this was carried out was remarkable for its time in that it was not known until March of 1958 that a grant would be available, yet by July of that year the road was open to traffic. In that period a survey had been made, the scheme designed, land acquired, and construction carried out. At a cost of £66 250 the scheme was at that time the largest to have been carried out in Devon since the war.

In 1958 the first of the supplementary grants was given by the Ministry of Transport to the County Council. These were provided for twenty-four schemes, costing a total of £290 000, for unemployment relief work in the Ilfracombe and Brixham areas.

During 1959 funds were made available for the improvement of certain roads to form alternative holiday routes and about £60 000 was spent on improvements to the A373 Waterloo Cross to Tiverton road, B3214 Bickleigh Bridge to Crediton road and B3215 Copplestone to Okehampton road. (Supplementary Funds and Alternative Holiday Routes are dealt with more fully later in this chapter and in other chapters.)

At the start of the 1960s the county road programme at last began to gain some momentum with the completion of Clyst St Mary bypass, The Rock improvement at Bideford and the Laira Bridge approach at Plymstock.

A traffic census taken in 1961 clearly indicated that the A380 Exeter–Torquay road carried 40 per cent more traffic than any other administered by the County Council. At a national level the necessity of improving the inter-urban routes had now been accepted and was, as a policy, being applied to the trunk roads. In line with this national policy the County embarked upon a programme for the general improvement of the A380 which was to absorb a major proportion of improvement funds for county roads until 1974. Improvements carried out on this route included the Fiddler's Elbow diversion, Station Road to Penn Inn widening at Newton Abbot and the widening of Kingskerswell Arch.

In terms of accidents per million vehicle miles the minor roads were as dangerous as any, and in much need of improvement, so at junctions the practice was adopted of establishing the priority of one road over the other. This, together with modest visibility improvements where necessary, meant that minor road junctions were made safer. Since the main beneficiaries of such improvements were the local farmers, land acquisition seldom proved a problem. It was not uncommon in the 1950s and 1960s for Divisional Surveyors to secure dedication of any land required for an improvement over a 6d. stamp without compensation, apart from the County Council agreeing to carry out the necessary boundary fencing by way of accommodation works which then became the property of the owner, who maintained them thereafter.

# The Network Takes Shape, 1964-74

## Motorways and trunk roads

By the early to mid 1960s most of the proposals which were to effect such a radical change in the highway transport system of the county within the next twenty-five years had been decided in principle and were in the process of development. Significant amongst these was the announcement by the Minister of Transport of the allocation of an additional £2 million in 1963/64 for improving sections of the A38 trunk road between Exeter and Plymouth. Another feature of this period was the proposed extension of the M5 into Devon; it was originally planned to finish at Edithmead near Burnham-on-Sea in Somerset, but pressure, especially by the South West Economic Planning Council, forced the Department of Transport to reconsider this decision. Freeman, Fox & Partners were subsequently appointed to design a new road of motorway standard from Edithmead to the A38 west of Exeter. At this time a number of County Council staff were already designing the Cullompton bypass with a view to its forming part of the motorway.

In the interests of making an early start on improving the

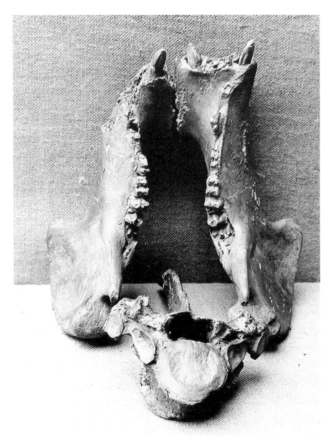

Road construction gangs have been responsible for numerous discoveries of archaeological interest in the course of their excavations. For example, during earth moving for the construction of the Honiton bypass (opened 1966), quantities of bones of prehistoric animals were discovered preserved in silt deposits near the River Otter. The photograph shows the jawbones of a young hippopotamus and the vertebra of an adult animal, now preserved in Honiton Museum.

A38 between Exeter and Plymouth, the County Council was invited to investigate improvements at Lee Mill, Linhay Hill and Caton Cross at Ashburton and sections between Lower Dean and Marley Farm, south of Buckfastleigh. Lengths of road were selected for improvement where dual carriageways could be constructed along the alignment of the existing road. By 1967 contracts for works between Lower Dean and White Oxon had been completed, the schemes having been prepared by a special team set up by the County Council in 1964 and working at a sub-office in Ashburton. It was at this office that much of the feasibility work for the major bypasses along the A38 was to be carried out, work that was subsequently taken over by the South West Road Construction Unit (referred to in Chapter 9).

Whilst attention was at this time concentrated on the A38, a landmark in road construction within Devon was achieved on the A30 in December 1966 when Honiton bypass was opened to traffic. This was somewhat later than expected as construction had been interrupted by the discovery of bones from prehistoric elephants and hippopotami. Nevertheless for the first time in the county a nationally notorious bottleneck had been removed by the completion of a new road to a high standard of design and construction. It was a foretaste of what was to follow. In 1967 a contract for the construction of Cullompton bypass was let at £2 478 727, a sum of money that would have been unthinkable for a single road improvement only a few years earlier.

The Devon Sub-unit of the South West Road Construction Unit was set up in July 1968 with many new staff joining those from the County Council's Ashburton office which was closed to coincide with its formation. The sub-unit was given an initial workload of five major schemes, each about 4 miles long which, with schemes already completed and being designed by the County Council, would bring the A38 between Exeter and Plymouth to a 70 m.p.h. two-lane dual-carriageway standard.

The construction of Plympton bypass, which had been designed by staff of the County Council, was started almost immediately and in rapid succession schemes for Chudleigh bypass, Ivybridge bypass, Ashburton to Buckfastleigh, Drumbridges to Caton Cross and Dry Bridge to Syon Abbey followed between 1971 and 1974. With County Council designed schemes at Haldon Hill, Linhay Hill and Voss Farm to Lee Mill being undertaken, major construction work was in progress at one or more locations along the A38 at almost all times throughout the period 1964 to 1974.

On the A38 to the north of Exeter several smaller schemes designed by County Council staff were carried out between 1967 and 1971. The works generally involved the widening of existing carriageways to 33 ft and providing crawler lanes on steep hills. A similar programme was carried out on the A30 to the east and west of Exeter.

In January 1969 three new schemes were added to the sub-unit's workload, namely bypasses on the A30 at Okehampton and, in Cornwall, at Launceston and

Bodmin. Whilst the routes for the various schemes on the A38 between Exeter and Plymouth were obvious, the bypasses on the A30 required more careful consideration, particularly at Okehampton where the choice of route was so controversial that it remained unresolved for seventeen years. A new length of road to the west of Exeter, joining the end of the M5 motorway at Pearce's Hill to the A30 at Pocombe Bridge was added to the programme as work on Okehampton bypass slowed.

By the early 1970s Freeman, Fox & Partners had reported on the final location of the motorway between Edithmead in Somerset and a point west of Exeter. Following public inquiries in 1971, 1972 and 1973 for the various sections of the scheme, contract documents for the motorway from Cullompton to Exeter were prepared for its construction under four contracts. Construction on the Cullompton, Killerton and Sowton sections began in May 1973.

## County roads

The County Council's aspirations set out in the County Development Plan, drawn up in the 1950s to provide the county with a system of roads to the standards considered necessary by 1971, did not materialize in the timescale proposed.

The major expenditure on roads was not surprisingly concentrated largely on the trunk roads as they carried the heaviest traffic in terms of both weight and volume. The limited funds available to the County Council were concentrated on dealing with the accident 'blackspots' and locations which had high accident potential. There was continued emphasis on the upgrading of the A380 between Exeter and Torquay and plans for the redevelopment of a number of urban areas were coming to fruition. On the A380, 'Rubbish Tip Corner', the site of a number of accidents, was bypassed in one direction with a new length of carriageway at Ideford, and later in 1968 a new length of dual carriageway was completed between Telegraph Hill and Thorns Cross. Shortly after this, in 1969, Dartmouth relief road was completed, as was the first stage of Teignmouth inner relief road.

In north Devon three improvements were completed on the A386 in and around Northam, the most significant being the Northam easterly bypass, completed in 1972. In the same year the A376 Clyst St Mary bypass was extended towards Exmouth, and also in 1972 the dangerous junction at the Bowd Inn on the approach to Sidmouth was improved.

The later part of this period was undoubtedly dominated by the preparation of the Newton Abbot bypass scheme and, with all legal procedures completed and confirmed by the Minister of Transport, work commenced in June 1973.

## Alternative holiday routes

By the mid 1950s Devon was faced with the problem of dealing with massive increases in summer-holiday traffic. In order to ease the situation, a system of 'Alternative Holiday Routes' was established. (The development of this system and how it operated is described in Chapter 5.)

The bulk of the funds made available by the Ministry of Transport for the alternative routes was for the route which ran from the A38 at Waterloo Cross via Tiverton to Crediton and on to Okehampton. Some work was done before 1964, by which time the practice of taking the traffic into Okehampton via Crediton Road was proving unsatisfactory. At the end of the summer of 1965 grants were made available for schemes to enable the Jacobstowe to Sourton Cross route to be used for holiday traffic.

Even after Exeter had been bypassed by the M5 this route had one further role to play. In 1977 it was realized that when the A30 dual carriageway was completed to Whiddon Down, drivers travelling to Cornwall would tend to follow the dual-carriageway system as far as possible, thereby causing serious congestion at Whiddon Down and through Okehampton. The only way of easing the problem was to open up the Class III road from Whiddon Down to de Bathe Cross on the Holiday Route, from where the traffic could proceed to Sourton Cross. A low railway bridge precluded the use of the route by high vehicles, but provided that funds could be made available and the necessary land could be acquired it was thought the widening of the route to permit two-way working for light traffic could be carried out by the following summer. The Council approved the proposals, the Ministry of Transport provided the money, the landowners agreed to give the Council access to the land, and by July 1978 the route was ready.

It had long been recognized that the holiday route between Whiddon Down and de Bathe Cross and on to Winkleigh functioned as an unofficial lorry route. Its full potential in this respect could not however be realized because of the restricted width of the section north of de Bathe Cross and the low headroom at the railway bridge near North Tawton. Investigations quickly revealed the potential of formalizing this lorry route and in 1985 work was carried out to create a central Devon north-to-south corridor, with road widening between Culm Cross and Winkleigh and reconstruction of the railway bridge.

## Supplementary funds

Since 1958, when funds were allocated by the government for unemployment-relief schemes in the Brixham and Ilfracombe areas, additional funds have on several other occasions been made available at short notice. In the early 1960s the County was heavily committed to such schemes which had a total additional value of £223 000 over the normal grant. Before the end of the 1963/64 financial year a further £354 000 was added for works in this category.

In the summer of 1966 the Ministry of Transport invited the County Council to submit schemes to advance the future programme. Work to the total value of £950 000 was proposed, ranging from a £318 000 scheme for a dual carriageway on the A380 from the top of Telegraph Hill to

Thorns Cross, to a £200 scheme for a junction improvement in Burrington village. In total, some seventy schemes were submitted and all were authorized, giving a welcome opportunity to complete some of the Class II and Class III road schemes.

Before the end of the 1966/67 year, the Ministry of Transport was able to allocate 75 per cent grant to four schemes in 'Development Areas', which covered the Barnstaple, Bideford/Torrington, South Molton, and Holsworthy Divisions. Shortly after, a further special grant was offered at 100 per cent for work in these Development Areas, enabling fifty-four schemes on county roads, to a value of £506 200, to be put in hand.

In July 1971 it was announced that funds would become available for an 'Infrastructure Works Programme' in the 'Development' and 'Intermediate' Areas for the following two winters. Funds totalled £277 000 and covered thirty-one schemes and included, in addition to the areas already listed, Tavistock, Okehampton and Plympton (excluding Kingsbridge) Divisions.

## The Direct Labour Construction Section

With the increase in road construction activity that started with the 1958 unemployment relief schemes, it proved expedient to place engineers on site to ease the extra loads that would otherwise have fallen on the Divisional Surveyors if efficient execution of the schemes was to be achieved. This practice continued for two or three years, particularly in respect of some of the trunk-road schemes. By 1961, with the prospect of a sequence of fairly large schemes in the Exeter area and as a result of the success of the Red Cross Hill dual-carriageway scheme, it was decided to establish a Construction Section with a Construction Engineer, office support, foreman and workmen. This proved to be an effective and efficient organization, attracting an enthusiastic workforce capable of carrying out both road and bridge works.

By 1973 the larger schemes were being put out to contract, the major roadworks on the A38 were nearing completion and with the imminent opening of the final section of the M5 motorway there was a need for a unit to co-ordinate the maintenance of the major road system throughout the county. It was therefore decided to disband the Section as a construction unit and to assign to it the supervision and maintenance of the M5, the A38 and other major dual-carriageway roads which would eventually be linked to this system. Hence the Motorway Maintenance Unit came into being with the demise of the Construction Section.

## Railway Closures

The withdrawal of railway services on branch lines under the Beeching cuts in the 1960s made it necessary for coach operators to introduce new services on some routes which were inadequate for this purpose. In instances where the government agreed that these services could not be run safely without carrying out improvement schemes, special grants were issued, with the County's contribution being 50 per cent of the total cost.

Examples of such road improvements were those that followed the closure of the Okehampton–Tavistock–Bere Alston line, the closure of the Okehampton–Bude–Wadebridge line, and the withdrawal of passenger services on the Torrington–Barnstaple line.

## Private Contributions

Private industry and developers and other authorities have contributed at various times to the improvement of particular routes where their needs would not be met by the highway authority in the course of its own programme. A few examples of such schemes are given below:

In 1964 and 1975 improvements to the approaches to Stoneycombe Quarry, Kingskerswell, were carried out at the expense of the quarry operators (E.C.C. Ltd).

In 1966 the C.E.G.B. developed the Abham sub-station near Staverton and bore the cost of improvements to enable 250 tonne loads to be brought on to their site.

In 1974 the South West Water Authority, in anticipation of the abnormal traffic which would be generated during the construction of Wimbleball Reservoir, bore the cost of improvements and strengthening of the B3190 from Bampton to the county boundary and into Somerset.

In 1979, following planning approval for long-term development of china-clay resources in the Wotter area, which included a road closure in the Cadover Bridge vicinity, the industry bore the cost of a new road bypassing Wotter on the south side.

In 1981, for the purpose of developing a new substation site at Alverdiscott, to which a load in excess of 300 tonnes would have to be delivered, the C.E.G.B. bore the cost of widening and strengthening roads along the route between Teignmouth Docks and the site.

Between 1984 and 1987 South West Water funded improvements to over 8 km of minor roads between the A30 and the new Roadford Reservoir. The works also included construction of a 220 metre viaduct and a junction improvement on the A30 trunk road.

## The Years of Major Change: 1974 Onwards

At the time of local government reorganization improvements to the county's trunk and principal roads were being designed and constructed at a quickening pace. Capital investment in the highway infrastructure of the South West was greatly increased, as elsewhere in the country the

Nowadays provisions under the Health and Safety at Work Act
demand close attention to personal safety on construction sites. This
roadman has erected temporary works to support a washed-out
culvert using a plank, three bricks and a single jack. Modern safety
advisors would be horrified. The picture was taken as recently as
1965 on the A38 Harcombe Cross to Holmans Wood improvement
scheme.

improvement of motorways and other strategic routes was well advanced. The upgrading of the A30 and A38 trunk roads through Devon to the west of Exeter to full dual-carriageway standard was well under way and at the same time the A380 between Exeter and Torbay was being progressively improved to the same standard.

## Local government reorganization and the main urban areas

Following local government reorganization, the new County of Devon became the highway authority for road programmes inherited from the old County, the Cities of Exeter and Plymouth and the County Borough of Torbay. Until this time the majority of the County Council's highway schemes had generally been limited to the rural parts of the county, but the three large urban areas brought to the authority the problems associated with heavy traffic flows concentrated within built-up areas.

The Roads Committee, superseded in 1974 by the Planning and Transportation Committee, had followed a policy of dealing with the innumerable locations throughout the county where improvements were required in the interests of safety, before embarking on schemes outlined in the County Development Plan. Furthermore it attemp-

**The building of the Totnes inner relief road which included the construction of Brutus Bridge (above), provided much-needed traffic relief to the Bridgetown area of the town, but it was also a conservation measure, protecting the fine nineteenth-century bridge from the pressures placed on it by modern traffic.**

ted to distribute available funds throughout the county as equitably as possible, the only exception being the desire to see the Exeter to Torquay road improved, although progress on this had been rather limited.

The County Borough of Torbay had by 1974 completed studies aimed at determining its transportation strategies through to 1991. The conclusion had been reached that a strategy based upon the development of a ring road was the most advantageous option for the future of the borough. This option required the construction of several major road-improvement schemes, which after 1974 had to be considered for inclusion in any future programme of the new County Council.

Plymouth City Council had, in conjunction with Devon and Cornwall County Councils and the Department of the Environment, employed consultants Scott, Wilson, Kirk-patrick & Partners to undertake the Plymouth and Environs Transportation Study (PETS). The final report of the study, published in 1976, recommended that a deliberate attempt be made to foster travel by improved

# Devon Road Network 1988

**Devon Road Network 1988.**

public transport and that a limited number of new road schemes be carried out. These had now to be accommodated within the overall County budget and programme.

It was left to the new Council to undertake as part of its immediate programme the Exeter and Area Transportation Study (EATS), also in conjunction with Scott, Wilson, Kirkpatrick & Partners. A strategy evolved which called for improvements to the highway network for private transport, although two of the important major components – the Salmon Pool Link and Pyne's Hill Link – met immediate public opposition and were abandoned.

## Structure Plan and Transport Policies and Programme

The Town and Country Planning Act 1971 had placed upon all county councils a duty of preparing a Structure Plan for their area, the intention being that such plans should include broad policies and proposals for the development of land within a county. Devon County Council became a Structure Plan Authority on 1 August 1974 and began investigative work almost immediately. Critical in the preparation of this plan were the transportation needs of the County through the plan period to 1991 and beyond.

It was through the Structure Plan consultation process that the relative merits of the many road proposals were canvassed with the aim of producing a priority list. This involved both those schemes shown in the outdated County Development Plan and those derived from the transportation strategies of the urban areas. The schemes for the Structure Plan were subsequently ranked by a basic cost-benefit analysis system, and a priority list for road improvements was drawn up, although in the process some schemes were delayed indefinitely or even abandoned.

At this time the preparation of the Transport Policies and Programme (TPP) became an important annual task. This was a new system for transport planning and financial programming applying to all local authorities in the country, covering the whole range of transport expenditure including highway improvement schemes. The County Council's first TPP was published in May 1974 for the 1975/76 financial year. An updated edition is published annually, outlining the highway improvement proposals from the most modest of schemes to major bypasses.

## Establishment of the Devon Road Network

Of similar importance to Structure Plans and TPPs in the post-1974 period has been the establishment of a functional route network, a system of categorizing the vast number of roads within the county according to their function or importance, taking into account the traffic flow and the types of vehicle using the various routes. This complete network, known as the Devon Road Network, forms the cornerstone of many of the policies which relate to the management and maintenance of the roads of the county. It determines the level of expenditure for each road and is used as a basis for policies dealing with signing, lorry routeing and coach routeing, and it also fixes the standards for highway improvements and the provision of roadside facilities.

The first three levels of the functional route network are known as the Major Road Network. This comprises motorway and primary routes (trunk and county) – referred to collectively as national routes – together with the primary and secondary county routes.

The national routes provide for through and long-distance traffic movement and access to centres of population and to industrial and outlying rural areas. The Department of Transport is responsible for the construction and maintenance of the motorway and trunk roads which form the major part of national routes.

The primary county routes connect the national network to the principal settlements which serve wide rural areas. Secondary county routes are the main access routes to towns and larger villages and to principal recreational attractions. These towns and villages either serve a rural hinterland or are satellites of larger towns serving a predominantly suburban catchment area.

The Major Road Network policy was adopted in 1976 and was incorporated in the approved Structure Plan. Surveys have shown that with very few exceptions most traffic movements take place on the routes which form the Major Road Network, even though some of these routes have a number of inadequacies. It is envisaged, however, that these sub-standard stretches of road will attract a high priority for expenditure as policies are aimed at developing the Major Road Network within a realistic period.

Following the proven success of the Major Road Network, the Minor Road Network, which includes all other routes, was established. These routes form a large percentage of the total road mileage within the county, serving communities and industries, particularly agriculture.

Small industries have been encouraged over the years in order to create broad-based communities and this policy has brought its own problems as far as rural roads are concerned. Changes in industrial practice have led to increased use of highways for commercial and private use, with wider and heavier vehicles using roads originally intended for farm traffic. Greater financial emphasis has been placed on the major routes, and thus the reduced investment in the lower category roads has meant that structural improvements and repairs have been limited.

## Development of the Major Road Network
### Motorway and trunk roads

By August 1974 the whole of the A38 between Exeter and Plymouth (Marsh Mills) had been improved to dual carriageway. Two schemes, from Drumbridges to Caton Cross and from Dry Bridge to South Brent, had opened in July, with the final section, joining the eastern end of Plympton bypass with the dual carriageway near Lee Mill Trading Estate, opening one month later.

The M5 motorway had by July 1976 reached Willand from the Somerset boundary, bringing with it an instant public dislike for the noise caused by the surface finish of its rigid concrete pavement; construction of the remaining length to Exeter was completed in the summer of 1977.

Acting on behalf of the Department of Transport, the consulting engineers, Freeman Fox & Partners, had been successively letting contracts for the remaining lengths towards Exeter, the final section making a connection to the A38 and A30 trunk roads at Pearce's Hill. Surplus material from the extensive earthworks (2.3 million cubic metres) was placed on land owned by the County Council at Exminster Marshes for use in the future construction of Exminster bypass.

On 27 May 1977 the Prime Minister, the Rt Hon. James Callaghan, carried out the tape-cutting ceremony (shown on p.71) which marked the completion of an unbroken dual-carriageway link between Plymouth and Scotland. The notorious Exeter bypass was itself, at last, bypassed.

It was to be another eight years, however, before a dual carriageway was completed through to the Cornwall county boundary at Tamar Bridge. As early as 1936, proposals were put forward for the new route to the north of Plymouth, which was protected from development and

*This aerial view shows the M5 motorway sweeping across the Exe estuary at Topsham. The Exe Viaduct is the longest bridge in the county, crossing the river, the canal, and the extensive wetlands to the south of the river, while the shorter Exminster Viaduct crosses the railway and the Exminster bypass.*

eventually the A38 improvement from Marsh Mills to Tamar Bridge entered the programme. The Department of Transport had divided the scheme into two sections, with Plymouth City Council acting as agents for the shorter, more expensive section between Marsh Mills and Manadon, and consultants, Mott, Hay & Anderson developing the section which reached as far as the Tamar Bridge. Responsibility for the section between Marsh Mills and Manadon became the County Council's in 1974.

Although the route corridor had been protected since 1937, a public inquiry was still needed before the published orders for the alignment were confirmed. Construction, as with design, was divided into two sections, each having its own unique problems. Besides having to cope with maintaining heavy traffic flows along the existing trunk road and to and from the city centre, especially during the construction of the three-level interchange at Manadon, achieving suitable foundations for embankment building was a particular problem. At Honicknowle a huge volume of household refuse, dumped after the Second World War, had to be removed without endangering the health of nearby inhabitants by the escape of dangerous gases. In the Forder valley, marshland and a buried river channel meant that embankments were constructed in stages, with each stage proceeding only when monitored subterranean pore water pressures indicated that a stable embankment would be achieved.

The whole of the new route, which enables all through traffic to avoid passing along city roads, was opened on 1 April 1985 by the Secretary of State for Transport, Nicholas Ridley. 'The Parkway', as this new length of dual carriageway was to be known, had, at a cost of £45 million, finally completed the upgrading of the A38 between Exeter and Plymouth, extending the M5/A38 trunk road to the Cornwall county boundary.

With the planning and construction of the motorway extending into the south-west peninsula, pressure had built up for a high-standard road connection to north Devon. As early as 1968 Gifford, Graham & Partners had been appointed by the Department of Transport to investigate the feasibility of a link from the M5 to north Devon, based upon the existing A361 corridor. By 1972 the conclusion had been reached that only by the creation of a completely new route could communications to the area be improved and development encouraged. The concept of this, a totally new road over 30 miles long stretching across half the county, had as many supporters as opponents.

Significant in the support for the North Devon Link Road was the role played by many local Members of Parliament. Joining the County Engineer of Devon and the County Surveyor of Somerset and carrying a letter of support from David Owen, M.P., then Foreign Secretary, an all-party deputation, including Jeremy Thorpe, M.P., Sir Edward Du Cann, M.P. and Robin Maxwell-Hyslop, M.P., was able to impress the Minister of Transport, Bill Rogers, M.P., of the backing which both Devon and Somerset gave to this strategically important route.

The opponents, on the other hand, strenuously contested the idea at a Public Inquiry in 1979, claiming that existing routes could be improved to carry the anticipated traffic loadings. The view of the independent inspector, after considering all the evidence, was that the case for the route was proven but that the length between Tiverton and Barnstaple should be a single carriageway, a decision many regretted.

Construction of the first stage, to dual-carriageway standard, from the motorway at Sampford Peverell to Tiverton, was completed in March 1984. The second stage, to Barnstaple, was divided into two sections and construction was timed to coincide with the completion of the bypass of Barnstaple. This, linking with Bideford bypass which was opened in May 1987, provided the means by which north Devon gained access to the national traffic network.

With the development of the North Devon Link Road, the County Council's priority has been to provide adequate connections to it from the towns it bypasses. At Tiverton a new distributor road was constructed to the east of the town, joining the north Devon link at a junction constructed as part of the contract for the first stage. In Barnstaple a new urban relief road was built to take account of the traffic resulting from the north Devon link and the Barnstaple bypass.

## Roadworks and inflation

In the early 1970s the country experienced a national coal strike and the consequent introduction of a three-day week brought home the stark reality of inflation and its effect on public works. At that time civil engineering contracts timed to take more than two years had a 'Variation-of-Price' (VOP) clause. This meant that if the price of materials rose during the course of the contract compensation would be paid to the contractor. Contracts of two years and under were on a fixed-price basis, the view being that within that relatively short time span a contractor could allow for price increases reasonably accurately. In 1973 the government instituted a pay freeze which was to last ninety days, and made a commitment to hold down inflation. Although the former was achieved, the latter was not.

At this time came the first dramatic increase in the price of oil. This was to have a severe effect on road contracts generally, as bitumen, a by-product of the oil/petroleum industries, had up to then been plentiful and relatively cheap. The economics of the use of this material changed immediately, and in the pursuit of economic road construction, combinations of other materials were used to make up the 'flexible pavement', with concrete 'rigid pavements' becoming a viable alternative. (This was probably a factor in the use of concrete in 1974 on the M5 between Chelston and Willand.)

The government was aware of the difficulties that inflation was causing to the construction industry, particularly with respect to bitumen prices, and instituted 'ex-gratia payments', recognizing that the price of hydrocarbons was totally unpredictable. Additionally, from June 1974 the VOP threshold was lowered from twenty-four months to twelve, and remained so until June 1985 when it reverted to twenty-four. Since virtually all the major contracts placed by the County Council and the sub-unit from the early 1970s were programmed to take at least eighteen months, the VOP contract became a standard feature.

## Okehampton bypass

It would be possible to devote a complete chapter to the saga of the Okehampton bypass, but to do so would be to understate the effort and work which had been involved in developing the other parts of the new road network of Devon. However, the case of Okehampton bypass and the circumstances leading up to its eventual construction are unique and worthy of detailed account.

The southern edge of the town of Okehampton abuts the Dartmoor National Park, and the old Exeter–

The Parkway forms part of the A38 which carries trunk-road traffic through Plymouth. The route had been protected from development since the 1930s.

Plymouth railway (which was opened in 1871) forms the boundary between the two. The need to provide a bypass of Okehampton to relieve the heavy flows of trunk-road and holiday traffic through its midst had been evident for many years. Initially routes to the north of the town were considered to be the most viable because of the engineering and environmental constraints on a route to the south. A northern bypass line first appeared on the County Development Plan in the early 1960s.

In 1968 British Rail, as part of its network review, closed the railway line to all but freight traffic from Meldon Quarry and, following proposals to dispose of the quarry, considered plans to abandon the line completely. This proposal enabled a southern route, utilizing the old railway track, to be considered as an alternative to the northern route and an economic assessment showed that the southern route should be the preferred option.

British Rail's plan to sell the quarry and close the line was subsequently withdrawn but by then route-appraisal work had confirmed that a scheme was feasible which would allow both the railway and a new road to co-exist.

Public consultation on the choice of route for an Okehampton bypass took place in 1975 when the routes considered included two to the north of the town, with local variations, and one to the south. The result of this showed a preference for the southern route but with some modifications. The southern route was consequently chosen by the Department of Transport as its 'preferred route'. Draft proposals for the bypass were published in 1978 and the scheme proceeded to a public inquiry in 1979.

The inquiry was fought on environmental issues, together with other strong arguments relating to agriculture and cost. These arguments, powerful as they were, really could not match the fierceness of debate on whether or not the route should be constructed through (or located on) the fringes of the National Park. The inquiry was unusual in that two of the major opposing parties were government departments. The Department of the Environment, which opposed the published route, argued fervently that the recently published 'Sandford Report' placed the National Park route beyond consideration, whereas the Department of Transport argued the case that, on a comparison-type analysis, the published route was so overwhelmingly advantageous as to make all other routes totally unreasonable. The inquiry was the first test of the 'Sandford Report' recommendation (i.e. that new routes should not be constructed through National Parks unless there is no reasonable alternative) and as such, was found to be a very contentious and hotly contested debate, bearing in mind the fact that the issues were of national importance. Every element brought challenge and counter-challenge and it is unlikely that anyone involved could possibly have prepared themselves for the fierceness of the argument or the bitterness which flowed on all sides from time to time.

The inquiry was concluded at the end of January 1980 and the parties retired to await the Inspector's Report. The usual waiting period was three to six months after the inquiry, though in this case, because of the complexities of the arguments, such a timescale would have been unrealistic. Nevertheless, the Inspector could have been expected to give his findings within twelve months.

The Report was most eagerly awaited; a favourable response would have provided the Department of Transport with the earliest opportunity to build a bypass for Okehampton but, equally important, if the Inspector found against the published route, development of an alternative route would have been necessary to provide relief to the town which was generally accepted to be essential. In the event, fate took a hand. The Inspector became very ill and work on his Report came to a virtual standstill. The potential consequences of his failing to complete the work were immense, with the worst being a complete re-run of the whole inquiry before a newly appointed Inspector. Therefore, whatever the outcome, completion of the Report in February 1983, some two years later than expected, was received with great relief.

The Inquiry Inspector's Report gave qualified acceptance to the Department of Transport's preferred southern route and the Secretaries of State announced their intention to confirm the draft Orders. However, proposals for dealing with the issue of 'public open space' were left undecided by the Inspector and these were made the subject of Special Parliamentary Procedure. A Select Committee consisting of Members of both Houses of Parliament was convened to consider the issues. They decided that as public open space formed an integral part of the land required for the construction of the southern route, it was proper that they also consider whether the bypass should be built to the south of Okehampton at all. Their decision was that it should not, so in effect at a stroke they reversed the previous decision of the Secretaries of State.

The Secretary of State for Transport was convinced that the southern route was the better and decided not to accept the recommendations of the Select Committee. Instead, a Bill was introduced in Parliament to confirm the Compulsory Purchase Order. It received Royal Assent at the end of December 1985, thereby giving authority for the construction of the bypass to the south of Okehampton to go ahead.

Construction was eventually started in November 1986 and was completed by the end of 1988. The opening in July of that year by Peter Bottomley M.P., Minister for Roads and Traffic, of one carriageway in time to receive the summer traffic, marked the conclusion of a very long period of uncertainty and debate during which the democratic processes of route selection were subjected to every conceivable scrutiny.

## Other trunk road schemes

In the meantime the first section of the A30 west of the motorway, the Pearce's Hill to Pocombe Bridge link, had opened in April 1976 and two lengths of dual carriageway between Pocombe and Whiddon Down had been completed during 1978. It is interesting to note that on each of these contracts, let whilst the rates of inflation and the oil

The need for a new road to remove the notorious bottleneck on the A30 at Okehampton was recognized in the 1960s. Public consultation on the choice of route began in 1975, but because of differing views and the sensitivity of environmental issues, it was 1988 before the bypass was completed. The photograph shows construction work on the bypass at Fatherford viaduct over the East Okement River.

crisis were still having a serious effect on the construction industry, a fully rigid pavement alternative was rejected in favour of a composite construction of leanmix concrete and bitumen-coated material.

When the Devon Sub-unit of the Road Construction Unit was disbanded in 1981 many of the staff transferred to the County Council to continue with the design of the Whiddon Down to Tongue End Cross and the Okehampton bypass schemes, the former being completed in 1987.

An interesting and somewhat surprising feature of the Whiddon Down to Tongue End Cross scheme was the submission by the contractors George Wimpey & Co. Ltd of a low price tender for the construction of the carriageway in unreinforced concrete. Because of the widespread public criticism of concrete pavement surfaces, and problems which had occurred in other parts of the country in maintaining quality control in construction, the tender was accepted only after considerable consultation between the staff of the Department of Transport and the Devon County Engineer's Department.

In fact there were very few problems with maintaining quality control, both in the strength of the concrete and in the finished 'riding quality' of the road surface. The pavement was laid in a single operation by means of a concrete paving train comprising seven different items of plant, from a 'bottom spreader' laying three-quarters of the 245 mm total depth of construction to a final element providing the surface texture and spraying a concrete

A rare sight in Devon is this comprehensive road-building machine called a 'concrete train'. In the foreground is the bottom layer spreader, which lays the major part of the pavement, followed by the other elements which undertake a further six operations to complete the road. At the back of the train can be seen the blue tentage protecting the newly laid concrete from the elements. The photograph shows a concrete train in action in 1987 on the Whiddon Down to Tongue End Cross section of the A30 dual carriageway east of Okehampton.

curing membrane. In total the train covered a length of 60 metres and travelled at 30 metres per hour, drawing behind it an additional 60 metres of tentage to give two hours' cover to the newly laid concrete.

It would be misleading to give the impression that after 1974 work on the national route network within the county was limited to the types of project which have so far been described, although the scale of these works has on occasions been awesome and the associated costs no less so. Money from the Department of Transport's Regional Fund has permitted the County Council to complete numerous smaller improvements on the trunk roads throughout Devon.

On the A303 the completion of Marsh Diversion in 1976 saw the removal of the temporary bridge which had been erected in 1968 following the loss of the original structure in the east Devon floods. Bridestowe bypass, completed in 1975, ensured that the A30 traffic no longer thundered through the village. On the A35 the notoriously dangerous

Black Sand Bridge was replaced with a realigned carriageway and a new structure over the railway, and in 1987 at Belvedere Cross on the A38 a new underpass was constructed to provide grade separation between the trunk road and the minor county roads to Dunchideock and Telegraph Hill, while also giving access to Haldon racecourse.

Throughout the period since the reorganization of local government in 1974 funds have been used to upgrade and improve the less heavily trafficked trunk roads of Devon, whilst at the same time maintaining a substantial workload for the smaller local contractors who are unable to compete with the national firms for motorway and major scheme work.

Another aspect of trunk-road work has been the erection of crash barriers in the central reservation of the A38 dual carriageway between Exeter and Plymouth. Faced with a history of 'cross-over' accidents and prompted by pressure from all sides, especially from the County Council, the Department of Transport authorized this work at a cost of £2½ million. The policy of erecting central-reservation crash barriers, where appropriate, is being adopted for other lengths of dual-carriageway trunk road throughout the county and extended to include the county road network.

## Haul routes for major trunk-road improvement schemes

The construction of new trunk roads often entails the haulage of materials along minor country roads that are inadequate for the heavy traffic involved. Where this happens the Department of Transport provides funds for the County Council to strengthen and widen the minor roads to cope with this extra load. In such cases local traffic derives significant long-term benefits from the improvements to the minor-road network, as illustrated by the scale of expenditure on the haul routes for Barnstaple bypass, Bideford bypass and North Devon Link, with sums of £300 000, £150 000 and £1.5 million respectively.

## County roads

As far as improvements to the county road network were concerned, construction of a bypass for Newton Abbot on the A380 tended to dominate the thoughts and efforts of the County Engineer's Department in the eighteen months after reorganization. It was let as a fixed-price contract in 1973, but the contractor was soon feeling the consequences of rampant inflation and the effects of rocketing oil prices on the cost of bitumen products. In addition, the findings of an earlier site investigation proved to be unreliable which meant that extensive and costly changes to bridge foundations and roadwork cuttings were required as the contract progressed.

The job was nevertheless completed and, when opened in May 1976, the bypass belied all the problems which had been faced in its construction. Its completion did, however, mark a turning point in the preparation of future highway-

improvement schemes in the County Engineer's Department.

What had been learnt from the construction of Newton Abbot bypass was that adequate site investigation work is a crucial part of the design of major road and bridge works. It has therefore become the policy of the Department to ensure that exhaustive soil surveys and site investigations are carried out on all major road-improvement schemes in the county and, if necessary, to supplement these with advice from a consultant engineering geologist prior to design work being finalized.

For a period the cost of Newton Abbot bypass, £10.58 million, was a major drain on funds allocated to the County Council through the new TPP system. During that time relatively few new schemes featured in the County road programme, the government's emphasis remaining on the improvement of national routes.

It was not until the late 1970s and early 1980s that the County road-improvement programme really began to accelerate. By that time the Structure Plan had been submitted to the Secretary of State for approval and transportation priorities had been determined for the Plan period up to 1991. Construction work was starting on many of the schemes which had been identified in the urban area transportation strategies, and designs were well in hand on many others.

In Torbay the first stage of the ring road between Kerswell Gardens and Gallows Gate was completed in December 1975, and in Plymouth the first stage of the Embankment Road relief road was opened in 1980. The design of this latter scheme took advantage of a corridor left by an abandoned railway line through a built-up area of the city. This practice has been adopted at several other locations in the county in order to provide road schemes with minimal effect on existing property and land holdings. Exmouth urban relief road, which opened in 1981, followed the abandoned Exmouth to Budleigh Salterton line, whilst at Tiverton the southern relief road will ultimately be constructed on the abandoned Exeter–Tiverton line. At Bovey Tracey virtually half of the bypass travels along the corridor left by the abandoned line to Moretonhampstead.

By 1981 the number of schemes being completed showed a marked increase over previous years. In Plymouth two further schemes identified in the traffic study were completed: both Roborough bypass and the Exeter Street/Sutton Road improvement opened in the 1981/82 financial year. A year later, in Exeter, the Matford link road opened to provide a route into and through the Marsh Barton Trading Estate to support the approved strategy of encouraging traffic away from the city centre roads and to provide an easier connection into this expanding commercial area.

An interesting aspect of this period was the increased public awareness of the effects, good or bad, that improvements might have on individual lives and the environment as a whole. Objections to Statutory Orders were becoming more prevalent and schemes which might have been expected to have enjoyed popular support were

The construction of this cutting on the Newton Abbot bypass in 1974/75 encountered a profusion of unpredicted geological problems. This highlighted the need for a thorough site investigation as an essential part of the design process in major highway works. The photograph shows the unexpected complexity of the geology at Humber Lane. In the foreground attempts are being made to blast out a huge lump of limestone, whilst 50 yards away the cutting slopes of sand and silt are collapsing under their own weight.

taken to the full public inquiry stage. Bovey Tracey bypass, the dualling of Plymouth Road at Plympton and St Budeaux bypass were amongst those schemes where public objections were heard by an independent inspector.

The public inquiry for the Plymouth Road, Plympton scheme may well hold the record for being the briefest inquiry ever held. It opened at 10.30 a.m. on 24 July 1984 with the County Council giving evidence in support of the scheme. The only objector was not in attendance to give counter evidence so the inquiry closed at 12.15 p.m. on the same day! This might be regarded as a waste of public money, but at least democracy had been seen to be done.

In recognition of this growing public awareness, a practice has been made of consulting the general public, amenity groups and conservationists on planned road-improvement schemes. This has taken the form either of issuing questionnaires with details of a proposal, backed up with an exhibition of plans and photographic representations of the proposal, or more simply just a public exhibition and public meeting. Projects where consultation has taken place include the 'northern relief road', Tavistock Road dualling and St Budeaux bypass schemes in Plymouth, Kingskerswell bypass, Torbay ring road stages II and III, Tiverton southern relief road, Exminster bypass, Totnes inner relief road and Hatherleigh, Winkleigh and Crediton bypasses and for the relief of the A376 Clyst St George to Exmouth road.

The case of Crediton bypass is a clear example of public opinion being mobilized to effect changes to a bypass proposal. Three routes were canvassed and a particular option was chosen by popular consent. However, the chosen route was considered by many to be a threat to the parkland of Downes House, a Grade II listed building, so a second consultation took place, the result of which persuaded the Council to modify the adopted route in order to move it further away from the house, at a substantial increase in cost. Many more examples of the value of public consultation could be given and it is a feature of the planning process which has been welcomed and encouraged by the County Council.

By the mid to late 1980s many important bypasses, relief roads and improvements had either been completed or were in the course of construction. Totnes, Barnstaple, Newton Abbot, Newton Poppleford, Exminster, Northam, Tiverton and Kingsbridge had all seen substantial road-improvement schemes completed in this period. Bovey Tracey bypass was completed in 1987 and St Budeaux bypass, Plymouth, linking with the A38 Parkway trunk road, in 1988.

The A380 from Exeter to Torquay has continued to be the most heavily trafficked primary route in the county, apart from the trunk roads. In order to find the necessary finance to improve the route to the standard of road required by the number of vehicles using it, the Council made several submissions to the Department of Transport for it to be adopted as a trunk road. These submissions failed, so the Council has continued to improve the route as and when funds allow. Ideford straight, improved originally in 1965, was upgraded to dual carriageway standard in 1985. This was extended towards Exeter in 1987 and Newton Abbot in 1988, and plans are in hand for the whole section between Haldon Thatch and Penn Inn, Newton Abbot, to be completed to dual-carriageway standard by 1990.

The major county-road improvements described have had a significant impact on improving both the safety of road users and the quality of life for the inhabitants of towns and villages throughout the county, and whilst attention is inevitably focused on such schemes, smaller but no less important improvements have been carried out. Since 1974 there has always been a steady flow of minor improvements which in themselves provide substantial benefits to the highway network of the county.

The majority of these so-called minor improvements have been designed in and supervised from the four Area Engineers' offices. Typical amongst such schemes prepared at these offices have been the improvements at Station Road, Cullompton and at Clyst St George in east Devon, whilst in the south area Newfoundland Way/Highweek Street, Newton Abbot and Marldon Road, Paignton have shown the benefits which can arise from more modest levels of expenditure. In north Devon improvements at Chivenor Cross and Deep Lane Head, Holsworthy have been prepared at the Barnstaple office. At Treverbyn House, Plympton, staff have continued the ongoing improvement of Outland Road, now the A386, from the A38 trunk road into Plymouth city centre.

## Materials and Methods of Construction

By their very nature, road improvements, bypasses and even motorways are constructed piecemeal, often by different contractors at different times, under varying circumstances and using different methods of operation. Since the early 1950s the standards for workmanship, materials and tolerances have been set out in the Department of Transport's 'Specification for Road and Bridge Works'. Since its initial publication in 1951 this document, with its successive updated editions, has been the definitive work for the construction of all major highway projects in this country.

Before the publication of the 'Specification', as it was known, road construction had generally been based upon the hand-pitching or waterbound macadam systems, augmented by local knowledge and experience. After the Second World War, with the increase in labour costs, it became necessary to find a system of construction suitable for machine-laying techniques. The machines that were available included bulldozers and excavators, together with the occasional grader which consisted of an adjustable

During the first ten years after publication of the Beeching Report, 260 miles of railway branch lines in Devon were closed. These abandoned routes left opportunities for subsequent road or footpath development which have been exploited at several locations in the county. Bovey Tracey bypass, for example, follows part of the abandoned Newton Abbot to Moretonhampstead line. The building on the right of the picture is the old Bovey station; the canopy had to be removed to avoid being struck by high vehicles, but has been transferred to one of the halts on the Dart Valley Line.

dozer blade set centrally in a long four-wheeled frame. The grader was either self-propelled or towed by a small bulldozer and was used to spread material from a windrow or to even out a loose uneven surface. The use of these machines meant that foundation materials of broken stone could be spread to a fairly even surface.

With these methods of construction the foundation course was regulated to even out the inconsistencies in level before any coated material was laid. Dependent on the extent of the scheme, the improved section was then made available to traffic for a six to twelve month period, during which time some consolidation of the new road took place. The new surface was then regulated again. This usually entailed relatively minor work using a finely graded tarmacadam before a final surface was laid over the whole improvement, including any sections of the original road that were to be part of the new road structure. This process, however, included many features which were incompatible with the construction of extensive sections of new road needed for the high-speed traffic that was becoming common.

During the late 1950s and early 1960s there was considerable experimentation in the specifications adopted for road foundation material. One method of construction made use of 2 in. clean broken stone into which sand or quarry dust was tightly packed with a vibrating roller. This was successful as a form of construction but was a simple operation only in relatively dry conditions. It was a far more tedious process in Devon than it would be in a drier climate. Another form of construction, referred to as 'wet mix', consisted of graded stone which was spread and compacted at an appropriate moisture content.

A further type of roadbase used at the time, and still used, was 'leanmix concrete'. This is a graded stone

This picture at Merrivale shows that the traditional method of road construction was still in use as late as 1957. Building the foundations by 'hand pitching' or placing of stones (known as 'hogsheads') was labour intensive and extremely slow. This system could never have coped with the scale of road building which has taken place in the county since the mid 1960s.

aggregate mixed with cement, the only water being that existing in the voids and on the surface of the stone. It is then spread and levelled and consolidated with a heavy roller. The material is laid as a continuous length, that is without any construction joints, the theory being that although cracking will undoubtedly occur, it will be erratic and will not reduce unduly the load-spreading requirements of the road construction. Used in the county as early as 1961, 'leanmix' was incorporated in the construction of Plympton bypass and of the A30 Pearce's Hill to Whiddon Down dual carriageway.

The Barber Greene and Blaw Knox paving machines, so familiar on modern road construction sites, were originally brought over by the Americans for airfield construction during the Second World War and were not used for laying road construction materials until after the war.

Publication of the third edition of the Department of Transport's Road Specification in 1963 coincided with a general tightening up of all requirements in relation to road and bridge construction, from drainage facilities and granular bases used in pavement construction to the classification of excavated materials used for embankments.

The fourth edition, published in 1969, besides amending further the specificiation requirements of all facets of road and bridge works, brought about a radical change in methodology for the construction of earthworks. (In the

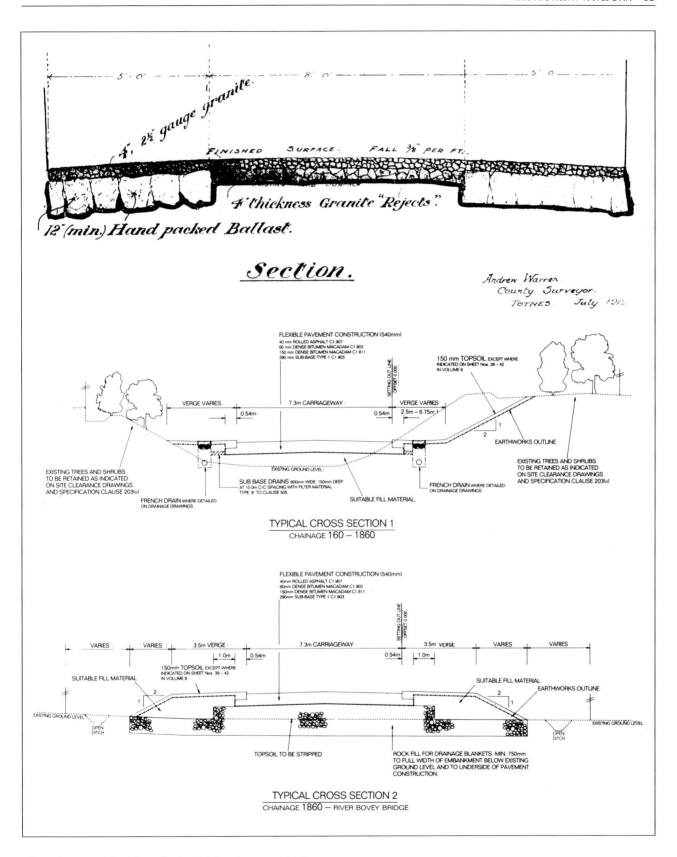

These drawings indicate how the details of road construction have altered between 1919 and the present day. The early drawing was made by hand and was limited in detail. The road surface is unbound macadam, the major proportion of it being hand-packed with no specific details for collection of water other than a fall across the finished surface. The present-day drawing prepared with the aid of a computer gives details of everything from the individual layers of the flexible pavement to the depths of topsoil to be placed on verges.

civil engineering sense, 'earthworks' refers to the shaping of the existing ground prior to the construction of the carriageway or other works.) Previous documents had set down stringent compaction requirements which had to be achieved: in other words, the material had to conform, after compaction, to a certain minimum density. The fourth edition simply said that if a certain material was rolled a certain number of times, it would be acceptable.

As indicated earlier, until 1973 bitumen was plentiful, relatively cheap and, despite inflation, becoming cheaper in relation to other materials. The practice therefore arose of using a bitumen-bound material for at least part of the foundation courses of the road pavement. This was proving to be a very successful form of construction when the oil crisis occurred. The advantages of using this material were immediately reduced and, in the pursuit of economic pavement construction, many more combinations of materials were considered to make up the flexible pavement. For example, on the Ivybridge bypass and Lee Mill diversion schemes, the waste from the English China Clay workings at Lee Moor was used as a sub-base material and the majority of the remaining A38 contracts used 'wet mix' in direct substitution for bitumen-bound materials.

The economics of the time also ensured that concrete became a material warranting serious consideration from both highway-design engineers and contractors. However, the use of concrete in Devon in recent years for rigid-pavement construction was limited to a single section of the M5 and the A30 west of Exeter. The flexible pavement, with its combination of bitumen-bound materials and

**An interesting feature of this improvement in 1933 is the use of reinforced concrete as opposed to hand pitching of the road base. Note also the absence of mechanical excavators and similar plant so prevalent on today's construction sites. The contractor who carried out the work is still involved in the construction of Devon's new roads.**

quarry-crushed clean stone, has continued to be the main method of forming the modern 'blacktop' road seen throughout the county.

Mechanical excavators had been available since the time of the major railway works in the nineteenth century, and by the 1930s they had developed to become very flexible and precise tools. Many were capable of being used as face shovels for mass excavation, as back-acters for trench work, as draglines for dredging or as skimmers when, for example, the base of a road formation could be taken out to a very clean and even surface without disturbance of the ground below. However, they could only excavate and load and were unable to haul the excavated material any distance. Therefore they had to be used in conjunction with dump trucks, lorries or rail-tracked systems with tipping wagons to move the material. This equipment was adequate for the relatively minor improvement schemes that were carried out in the inter-war period and in the first few years after the Second World War.

During the war American earth-moving plant in the form of bulldozers, scrapers and graders were brought in, either by the services themselves or under 'lease lend', primarily for airfield work. Some of this plant remained in the country after the cessation of hostilities and the machines were available to highway authorities, but it was to be several years before they made a significant impact on improvement schemes in Devon.

In the early 1950s traxcavators made their appearance. These machines were capable of loading directly into lorries or transporting excavated material economically in their buckets over relatively short distances, as well as functioning as bulldozers. Such a machine was first used by the County on improvements to the A380 in 1957.

One of the most significant pieces of earthmoving plant in the road-building era has undoubtedly been the motor scraper. These machines scoop up soil in thin layers, about 150mm thick, until they are full, and carry it to a new location where it is spread under the cutting edge and smoothed off as the scraper passes over it. The larger machines, which have a capacity of about 20 cu. metres, besides their own tractive power have to be assisted by a large bulldozer during their loading operation. Nevertheless, it is a very efficient piece of earth-moving equipment, especially when schemes are designed so that the volumes of material excavated and material deposited are in balance over a relatively short distance.

On the majority of the motorway and trunk-road schemes completed in the county, from Cullompton bypass in 1969 through to Okehampton bypass in 1988, the scraper has been a commonplace item of plant. In 1973, on the construction of the A38 Haldon Hill scheme, a fleet of fourteen Caterpillar and Terex motor scrapers moved 900 000 cubic metres of material into embankments and tips, and more recently scrapers were used with dump trucks to move 1.1 million cubic metres of material on the Whiddon Down to Tongue End Cross scheme.

As the scale of earthworks on an improvement decreases so does the need for scrapers, with earthmoving operations more commonly carried out by a combination of high-powered bucket excavators and rear-tipping, pneumatic-tyred, articulated dump trucks, commonly called 'Volvos' after the manufacturer. This plant is capable of covering rough terrain at high speed, making it both versatile and economic in use.

Whenever material is excavated and placed for embankments in road construction, the loose material has to be compacted before the road pavement material can be laid. Steam-rollers, like mechanical excavators, were available from the nineteenth century, and were gradually supplemented by diesel-driven compactors. Both had their place in road construction throughout the county, with steam-rollers being used for earthworks compaction until as late

Mechanical paving machines such as that shown in the photograph were introduced into this country by the Americans on aerodrome construction during the Second World War. Their use in road construction did not evolve until the early 1950s. Today they are an essential piece of equipment in the construction of all large-scale road works, laying the familiar hot-rolled asphalt, or 'blacktop', road.

as 1962 on the A380 improvements. In recent times compactive effort has been enhanced by tractor-towed or self-propelled vibrating rollers, plant which, with a basic dead weight of 10 tonnes, is capable of providing a compactive effort of some three or four times its own weight.

## Highway Design – Standards and Techniques

In considering the relation between the standard of road and the volume of traffic using it, it is interesting to compare the changes in design capacities which have been used during the last twenty-five years, whether for motorway, trunk-road or county-road improvements. The acceptable capacities of rural roads at the time of the County Development Plan were contained in a Ministry of Transport memorandum on 'The Design of Roads in Rural Areas', published in 1961. This recommended that there should be maximum traffic volumes for comfortable free-flow conditions on different standards of carriageway, as illustrated in the table on p. 70 (1961 column).

Based on these capacities and the then-forecasted rates of growth, 38 miles of classified road were required to be improved to dual three-lane standard, 146 miles to dual two-lane standard and 143 miles to a single 33 ft wide carriageway. At 1963 prices the estimated cost of the county road programme was £79 million.

Modern design standards often demand a great many cuttings and embankments on new roads. Work of this nature is not, in itself, a new development. The railway construction companies solved many of the technical and engineering problems during the last century but they were still dependent on mass labour to execute much of the work. Today's engineers use large earth-moving machinery like this Caterpillar D9 bulldozer, with a ripper attachment, seen here push loading a Caterpillar 621 motor scraper. Push-loaded scrapers can carry over 20 m³ of earth.

In 1968 the Ministry of Transport published an advisory manual entitled 'The Layout of Roads in Rural Areas'. While there was no major change in the standards for the geometric design of roads from those previously accepted, the manual increased the acceptable capacity of the various carriageways, as shown in the table (1968 column).

The design speeds on which the geometry of the roads was based were 70 m.p.h. for all dual carriageways and 60 m.p.h. for two- and three-lane roads, and it was 'The Layout of Roads in Rural Areas' that established the criteria for major improvements within the county through the 1970s and early 1980s.

There was one criterion in the manual which was difficult for the design engineers in Devon to achieve, namely the maximum permitted gradient of 4 per cent (i.e. 1 in 25). The hilly nature of the county made this impossible to achieve in many places without resorting to huge cuttings and embankments. On trunk roads special dispensation from the Department of Transport had to be obtained when a gradient of 4 per cent could not be met. Several locations where this was necessary can be seen

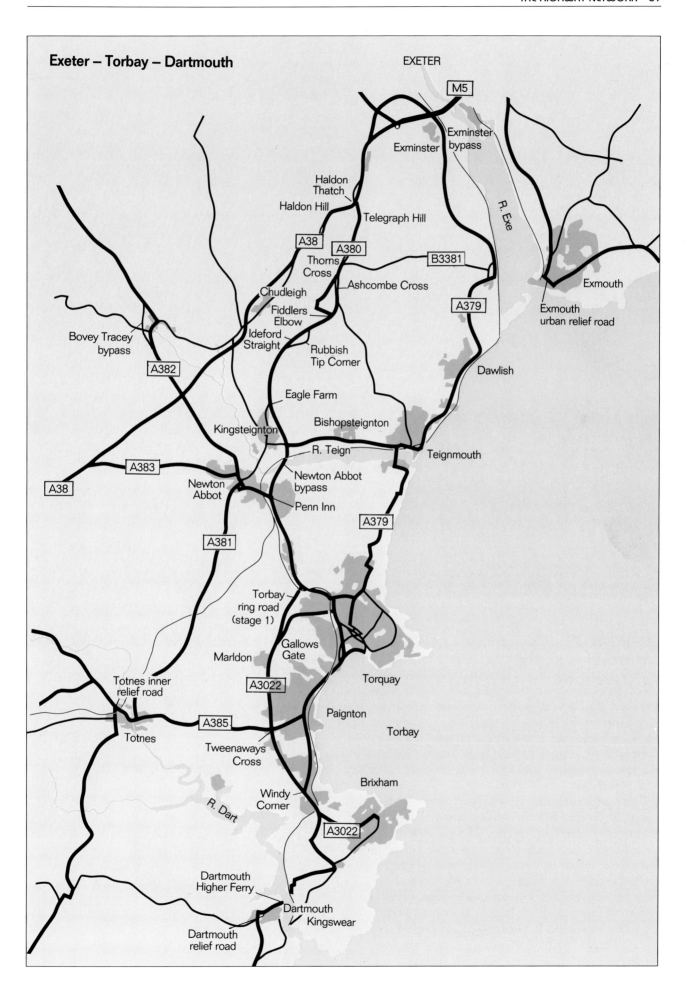

**Exeter – Torbay – Dartmouth**

EXETER

M5

Exminster
bypass

Exminster

Haldon
Thatch

Haldon Hill

Telegraph Hill

R. Exe

A38

A380

Thorns
Cross

B3381

Ashcombe Cross

Exmouth

Chudleigh

A379

Exmouth
urban relief road

Fiddlers
Elbow

Ideford
Straight

Rubbish
Tip Corner

Dawlish

Bovey Tracey
bypass

A382

Eagle Farm

Bishopsteignton

Kingsteignton

R. Teign

Teignmouth

A383

Newton Abbot
bypass

A38

Newton
Abbot

Penn Inn

A381

A379

Torbay
ring road
(stage 1)

Gallows
Gate

Marldon

Torquay

Totnes inner
relief road

A3022

Paignton

A385

Torbay

Totnes

Tweenaways
Cross

Brixham

Windy
Corner

R. Dart

A3022

Dartmouth
Higher Ferry

Dartmouth

Kingswear

Dartmouth
relief road

County Council employees laying the foundation of a road using dry macadam, spread by hand, and compacted by steam-roller. Steam-rollers were in use in the county on road improvements as late as 1958, and six of them still exist, loaned to enthusiasts who keep them in working order.

along the A38, e.g. Haldon Hill diversion 7.5%, and between Dean Prior and South Brent, 5.6% and 7.2%.

In 1981 a new philosophy for the geometric layout of roads was announced by the Department of Transport and issued as 'Highway Link Design'. Besides giving design engineers the scope to produce new and improved road alignments which have less impact on the environment whilst still achieving a safe design, it also provided new standards of maximum acceptable traffic flows. For comparative purposes these flows are given in the table (1981 column).

The numerical basis for the figures shown in the table changed over the 1961–81 period. In 1961 the concept of passenger car units was to give different vehicle types a value to make them comparable to a car. For example, cars were given a factor of 1, heavy goods vehicles a factor of 3 and pedal cycles 0.5. These factors were modified slightly in 1968. In 1981, a new concept of average annual daily traffic flow was introduced. Previously for rural roads 'daily traffic counts' (which in fact covered 16 hours of the day from 6 a.m. to 10 p.m.) had been used for the busiest part of the year; in Devon this was usually August. Now the

### Maximum traffic volumes for varying standards of carriageway

| Standard of carriageway | 1961 (Passenger car units per day) | 1968 (Passenger car units per day) | 1981 (Average annual daily traffic flow) |
|---|---|---|---|
| Two-lane (24 ft) | 6 000 | 9 000 | 13 000 |
| Three-lane (33 ft) | 11 000 | 15 000 | 18 000 |
| Dual two-lane | 25 000 | 33 000 | 46 000 |
| Dual three-lane | More than 25 000 | 50 000 | 50 000 |

*Source: Department of Transport*

annual average daily traffic flow is used with some recognition of the peak hour flows for junction design. Nevertheless the message of the table is clear: greater volumes of traffic than were previously imagined possible are now regarded as acceptable on the road network owing largely to better vehicle design and improved driver capability.

Just as there were changes in highway-design standards from the 1960s, so the use of modern technology has changed the way roads are designed. Highway-design computer programs became available and in the area of surveying the development of Electronic Distance Measuring Instruments (EDMs) enabled distances to be measured with extraordinary speed and accuracy. The most recent development, the 'Total Station' equipment (an electronic theodolite) allows the automatic transfer of angles and distances into 'data loggers' (electronic notebooks), rendering the surveyor's field book and pencil obsolete.

The old method of measuring angles with theodolites and using steel chains or tapes for distances was very labour intensive. All measurements had to be written down on site and drawn up in the office, before a second survey could be undertaken to record level information. EDMs measure

The final length of the M5 Birmingham to Exeter motorway was opened on 27 May 1977. It was a great occasion, not just for the local inhabitants but for all the holidaymakers from near and far who had ever done battle with the traffic queues on the Exeter bypass. James Callaghan, the Prime Minister at the time, considered it important enough to merit his attendance to cut the tape.

length extremely accurately by means of a beam of light emitted from the instrument set up on one point and reflected back to it from a mirror set up on a second point, so distances are read directly with a precision limited only by the accuracy of the instrument itself, typically about 10 mm per kilometre. Increased accuracy allows precise measurement of the vertical differences between points, hence both plan and level information can be recorded at the same time. In the past it had always been possible to measure angles accurately to a precision dependent on the type of theodolite used, but much more difficult to measure distances to the same accuracy. Uneven ground, obstructions such as rivers, stretch of the tape, all caused errors and increased the difficulty.

The analysis of the data recorded during a field survey involved tedious manual calculations, which were speeded up with the advent of desk calculators and then computers, but the latter still entailed typing the data into the machine. This manual step was finally eliminated in 1984 with the purchase of Total Station equipment for the County Engineer's headquarters and area offices, using a highway-design software package developed by Eclipse Associates. The Total Station is an EDM and data-logger combination, enabling the EDM readings and all other survey information to be recorded electronically for subsequent loading directly into a computer which then performs all necessary calculations. The drawing up of survey data to produce a plan kept pace with the development of the surveying equipment. Plotters receiving their instructions

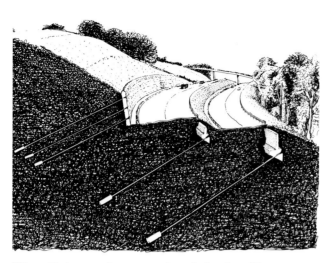

**Where Okehampton bypass cuts through the edge of Dartmoor at East Hill the two carriageways are at different levels. To secure the three cutting slopes, concrete facings were cast against the steeply sloping beds of rock and then fixed by high-tensile steel cables anchored deep in the hillside. The diagram illustrates how the permanently tensioned ground anchors work.**

from sophisticated computer programs produce mechanically drawn plans with contours from the data recorded in the field with the Total Station equipment. The process is not entirely automatic. A certain amount of human expertise is still needed to manipulate and edit the many computer programs involved.

As well as plotting all the survey information automatically, this package enables design engineers to process their designs interactively, which means that the computer responds both graphically and numerically to the data

entered. The engineer can now observe the results in picture form on a separate graphics screen and if necessary make changes to the design as he proceeds.

This equipment has been used extensively in the increased amount of investigation arising from public consultation on such schemes as Crediton bypass, Torbay ring road and Okehampton bypass, particularly during the Special Parliamentary Procedure period. Different routes or variations suggested at the time of consultation can be assessed quickly and plans prepared to show the effects of these suggestions in terms of land required, earthworks, and cost.

The use of the equipment continues to expand rapidly, and already contract drawings for the most recently completed schemes have been produced in part by the computerized plotters. As the schemes for the Structure Plan period, 1991–6, begin to be processed so the amount of design work being carried out and completed by computer-aided design increases and the time is not far off when schemes will be based on drawings produced entirely electronically.

As this book goes to print, so the shape of the strategic road network of Devon and of much of the south-west peninsula is in place, with only a few lengths missing. The last forty years or so have seen road building in the county develop from the faltering steps of the post-war austerity, through the courageous achievements of the sixties with limited funds, to the great surge of work in the seventies and the eighties, with a programme of major road building that truly matches the great railway-building years of the previous century.

## Survivors from Previous Ages

# 4

The development of civilization, even in its most primitive form, has been based on travel and the interchange of ideas. The earliest paths and tracks had to cross natural obstacles, particularly rivers, and to achieve this suitable crossing sites had to be found. The ideal spot had shallow water with a firm river bed, possibly an outcrop of rock. The next stage of development was to provide a crossing which could be used in all weathers regardless of the river level. The obvious site for a bridge would often be adjacent to a ford, as it suited the existing tracks and provided a firm foundation. The earliest bridges were constructed in wood, which was easily worked, readily available and plentiful. Stone gradually replaced wood because the resulting improvement in durability was worth the extra effort involved.

Although the clapper bridge at Postbridge on Dartmoor looks as though it originated in prehistoric times, it is thought to date from some time between the fourteenth and sixteenth centuries A.D. and there are other, much earlier bridges still standing. The oldest to survive in Devon is part of the medieval bridge across the River Exe in Exeter, which was built between 1190 and 1210 by Nicholas Gervase, with money collected by his son, Walter. He did this as the combination of a tidal river and periodic flooding made the existing wooden footbridge and ancient ford dangerous. The masonry bridge which Gervase built had seventeen arches, alternately round and pointed, and it crossed not only the river but also marshy ground on the north bank. The remains of St Edmund's Church are still part of the structure, and the direct line to the foot of the ancient Stepcote Hill is quite clear.

When a new crossing was built, again in stone, on the same spot in 1778, the river was no longer tidal because two weirs had been built downstream and the marsh had been drained. Thus a much shorter bridge was needed, with only three spans on a different alignment to connect with a new road into the city centre. The south-western half of the old bridge was demolished but the north-eastern half was left standing on dry land. This continued in use as a thoroughfare until the late 1960s but is now free of traffic, so the 780-year-old stonework can be examined at leisure.

The 1778 bridge, which was doubled in width from 16½ft to 33 ft in 1833, lasted 126 years. A steel single-span

# THE VITAL LINK

The Story of Devon's Bridges

arch with decorative cast-iron fascias was built in 1905 to accommodate the newly introduced electric trams as well as normal traffic. This, too, proved to be inadequate for both river flows and traffic volumes and was replaced in 1972 by two steel and concrete structures, each of three spans.

The crossing of the River Exe in Exeter has been described in some detail as this site has been vital to road communications in the area for centuries and has undergone all stages of the evolution of bridges. For a brief review of the history of bridges in Devon, the materials used form a convenient framework, although the changes from one to another were gradual.

## The Master Masons

Timber is, by its very nature, short-lived and it is difficult to tell whether it was used on any particular site before being replaced by stone. Stonemasons practise an ancient and skilled craft, and many fine examples of their early work still stand. Clyst St Mary Bridge, dating from the thirteenth century, is no longer used by traffic, but is readily accessible. There is a small structure of similar age under Holloway Street in Exeter which carries a continual flow of heavy traffic, but it is hidden by the surrounding buildings.

Barnstaple's bridge of sixteen arches probably dates from 1280; its repair in stone in 1333 is recorded, when a number of workmen were drowned while carrying out the work. It was first widened in 1796, as trade and traffic increased, by the construction of outer segmental arches springing from the cutwaters – a common procedure as greater width for traffic became necessary.

Staverton Bridge (1413) across the River Dart was followed by Horse Bridge (1437) and Greystone Bridge (1439) both across the River Tamar. Their construction was promoted by the sale of indulgences granted by Bishop Stafford and Bishop Lacey of Exeter. These are excellent examples of early masonry bridges having, typically, semi-circular arches of 20 ft span, carrying a road some 10 to 12 ft wide. They have survived largely in their original form for over 500 years despite the ravages of time and water. Staverton was on the original road from Ashburton to Totnes, while Horse Bridge was the bridge nearest to Plymouth for crossing the River Tamar until New Bridge, Gunnislake was built in 1520.

The spans of most bridges in Devon were less than 20 ft until the end of the eighteenth century when those across the River Exe at Countess Wear and at Exeter were built. The former had six arches, five of approximately 25 ft span and one of 60 ft span, while the latter had two side spans of 37 ft 6 in. and a centre span of 50 ft. When the size of either the seventeen arches of the original Exe Bridge or the six at Countess Wear is compared with that of the three-span 1778 Exe Bridge it is not surprising that the latter proved inadequate to pass major floods.

It was not until James Green became the first Surveyor of Bridges and Buildings for the County of Devon in 1808 that masonry bridges with larger spans were built as a matter of course. He had been a student of John Rennie, the builder of London Bridge and Waterloo Bridge. In seven years, Green was responsible for the construction of six bridges, Creedy River Bridge, Cowley being a fine example, with three arched spans of 50 ft, 55 ft and 50 ft.

---

**Bridges referred to in the text**

| | | |
|---|---|---|
| 1 Axmouth Bridge, Seaton | L7 | |
| 2 Barnstaple Long Bridge | D3 | |
| 3 Bicton Foot Bridge | J7 | |
| 4 Bideford Long Bridge | C3 | |
| 5 Bish Mill, South Molton | F3 | |
| 6 Bolham Road Footbridge, Tiverton | H5 | |
| 7 Bridgemill | A6 | |
| 8 Brutus Bridge, Totnes | G10 | |
| 9 Cadhay | K6 | |
| 10 Cathedral Yard, Exeter | H7 | |
| 11 Chivenor Airfield | D2 | |
| 12 Chudleigh Arches | G8 | |
| 13 Clapper Bridge, Postbridge | E8 | |
| 14 Clawton | B6 | |
| 15 Clyst St Mary | H7 | |
| 16 Codshead, Crediton | G6 | |
| 17 Colleton Mills | E4 | |
| 18 Colyford | L7 | |
| 19 Countess Wear | H7 | |
| 20 Creedy | H6 | |
| 21 Cullompton bypass | J5 | |
| 22 Dartmouth Floating Bridge | G11 | |
| 23 Dunheved Bridge, Launceston | B7 | |
| 24 East Okement Bridge, Okehampton | D6 | |
| 25 Exe Bridges, Exeter | H7 | |
| 26 Exe Cycle Bridge | H7 | |
| 27 Exe Viaduct | H7 | |
| 28 Exminster Bridge | H7 | |
| 29 Fenny Bridges | K6 | |
| 30 Forder Valley Marsh | D10 | |
| 31 Gosford | K6 | |
| 32 Greystone | B8 | |
| 33 Harrowbeer Airfield | D9 | |
| 34 Hatherleigh | D5 | |
| 35 Holloway Street, Exeter | H7 | |
| 36 Honiton Road, Exeter | H7 | |
| 37 Honiton bypass | K6 | |
| 38 Horse Bridge | C8 | |
| 39 Humber Lane Cutting, Newton Abbot | G8 | |
| 40 Iron Bridge, Exeter | H7 | |
| 41 Jacobstowe Arch | D6 | |
| 42 Kenwith Viaduct | C3 | |
| 43 Kersham | E4 | |
| 44 Kilmington | L6 | |
| 45 Kingskerswell Arch | G9 | |
| 46 Laira Bridge | D11 | |
| 47 Landcross | C4 | |
| 48 Landkey | D3 | |
| 49 Little Silver Footbridge | H7 | |
| 50 Little Silver, Shobrooke | G6 | |
| 51 Lynton and Lynmouth | F1 | |
| 52 Manadon Flyover | C10 | |
| 53 Marsh | L5 | |
| 54 Marsh Mills Viaduct | D10 | |
| 55 Matford Lane Arch | H7 | |
| 56 Meldon Quarry | D7 | |
| 57 Merrivale | D8 | |
| 58 Nags Head Cutting | J5 | |
| 59 New Bridge, Gunnislake | C9 | |
| 60 Newton Abbot Railway Bridge | G9 | |
| 61 Newton Poppleford | J7 | |
| 62 Otterton | J7 | |
| 63 Powderham Arch | H7 | |
| 64 Reedy Bridge, Dunsford | G7 | |
| 65 River Mardle Viaduct | F9 | |
| 66 Rolle Bridge, Torrington | C4 | |
| 67 Royal Albert Bridge, Saltash | C10 | |
| 68 St Saviours, Ottery St Mary | K6 | |
| 69 Saltash Ferry | C10 | |
| 70 Shaldon | H9 | |
| 71 Station Road River Bridge, Exeter | H7 | |
| 72 Staverton | G10 | |
| 73 Swimbridge | E3 | |
| 74 Taddiport | D4 | |
| 75 Tamar Suspension Bridge | C10 | |
| 76 Taw | E5 | |
| 77 Teign Viaduct | G9 | |
| 78 Telegraph Hill sign gantry | H7 | |
| 79 Thorverton | H6 | |
| 80 Tipton St John | J7 | |
| 81 Torpoint Ferry | C10 | |
| 82 Torridge | C3 | |
| 83 Totnes Bridge | G10 | |
| 84 Totnes School Footbridge | F10 | |
| 85 Trafalgar Bridge, Weston | K6 | |
| 86 Upottery | L5 | |
| 87 West Bridge, Okehampton | D6 | |
| 88 West Bridge, Tavistock | C9 | |
| 89 West Okement Bridge, Okehampton | D6 | |
| 90 Weycroft | M6 | |
| 91 Whitford Green | L6 | |
| 92 Winkleigh Airfield | E5 | |
| 93 Yeo | F5 | |

# The Age of Iron

Cast iron came into use for bridges towards the end of the eighteenth century, the first being built at Coalbrookdale, Shropshire in 1779 and giving its name to the settlement of Ironbridge. What is thought to be Devon's first cast-iron span was erected near Exeter Cathedral in 1814, though the reason for its construction was unusual. In 1750 a narrow door was inserted in the City Wall, but this would not allow carriages to pass. When the opening was subsequently enlarged, it prevented the Mayor and Corporation from 'Walking the Walls'. This annual ceremony had by that time become a public spectacle, but in previous centuries it had served a serious purpose. There

had been a long-running disagreement between the Corporation and the Cathedral over the ownership of the wall behind the Bishop's Palace, and the annual walk had clearly served to make a point. The Corporation were unwilling to relinquish their claim to the length of wall in question and so built the bridge to maintain continuity of the 'Muraltie Walk'. One way of proving the legality of this action was by the signatures of the Mayor and the Receiver. Thus, as proof, cast into the iron arch rib are the names Burnet Patch Esq., Mayor, 1814; R. Trewman Esq., Receiver.

Subsequent examples of the use of cast iron had a less political and more practical purpose. The superb Laira Bridge across the River Plym in Plymouth was built in

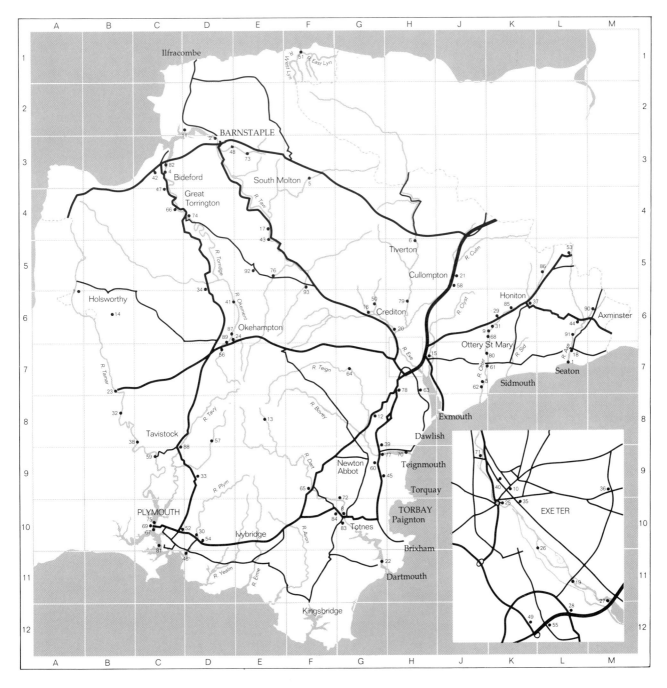

Location map and key to bridges mentioned in this chapter.

1827 for Lord Boringdon, the Earl of Morley, by J. M. Rendel, a former assistant of Thomas Telford; it lasted until the 1960s. Still standing, however, is the fine structure known today as Iron Bridge, erected by the Exeter Improvement Commissioners in North Street. This dates from 1835 and comprises six spans of 40 ft each. Green used cast iron very successfully to widen Barnstaple Bridge by cantilevering footpaths out from the sides of the masonry in 1834, but other bridges he built using the same material were rebuilt in the first half of this century. Another attractive bridge which used the same material is St Saviour's at Ottery St Mary. This was built as late as 1851, although wrought iron was already coming into use elsewhere.

Although first wrought iron and then steel were introduced during the nineteenth century to overcome the shortcomings of cast iron (namely, that it is brittle and weak in tension), they appear to have played little part in the early development of Devon's highway bridges. The railway companies were providing a new communications network in competition with existing highways, and seized on these new materials. One of the most famous examples of this is Isambard Kingdom Brunel's Royal Albert Bridge crossing the Tamar from Plymouth to Saltash. This was completed in 1859 and stands as an impressive monument to that renowned engineer. Many smaller structures were erected as the railways expanded, with Meldon Quarry Viaduct near Okehampton serving as an example of the development from wrought iron to steel. The first track in

1874 used wrought-iron girders, but by 1879 when the second track was added, steel was used, although the trestles were cast iron in both cases.

The first major use of steel for a road bridge in Devon appears to have been the 1905 Exe Bridge referred to above, followed by R. M. Stone's replacement of Green's cast-iron Landcross Bridge in 1926. The road was widened at the same time, but the main reason for the use of prefabricated girders was probably that it avoided temporary supports for a stone arch in the mud of the estuary.

Further advantages were to be gained by using steel because of its strength and apparent durability. The original 1370 ft long toll bridge from Shaldon to Teignmouth across the estuary of the Teign was built in 1827 and was at that time the second-longest timber bridge in Europe. (The record was held by the 1700 ft long Pont

There has been a bridge across the River Exe at Exeter for at least 700 years, probably much longer. The city grew from a settlement which developed round the most seaward point where the River Exe could be forded. At that time the river was tidal, and a large area of marshy ground existed on the north bank. Floods, high tides and a dangerous wooden footbridge were sufficient cause for Nicholas Gervase to build a new stone bridge between 1190–1210 across both river and marsh. It lasted until 1790 when a new entrance was made into the city and a new, much shorter stone bridge was built. This ambitious project involved the construction of a long ramp between retaining walls from the bridge to the top of the cliff to carry New Bridge Street. Floods and pressure of traffic led to the replacement of this bridge in 1905 by a single steel arch designed to carry electric trams. This in turn was replaced by the present two bridges in 1972.

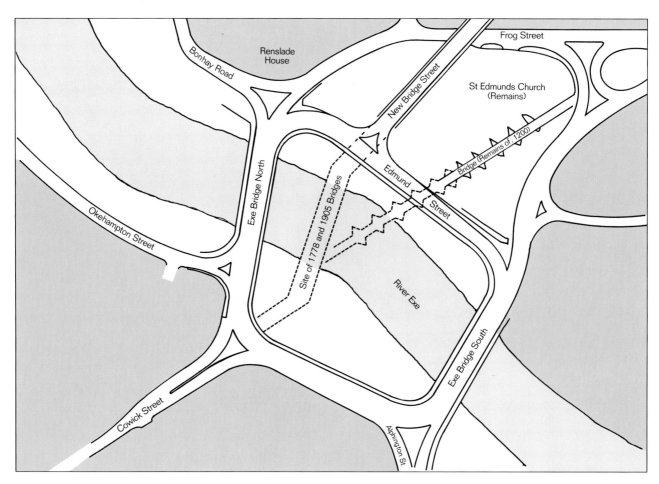

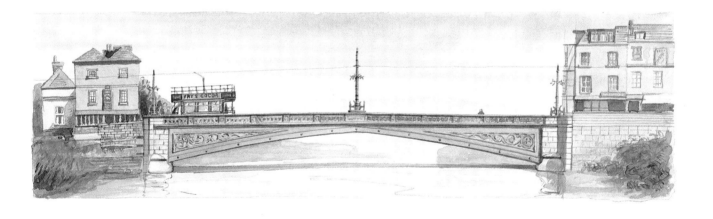

de Lyon in France.) By 1927, it had to be replaced because of decay and attack on the timber by boring worms. Steel appeared to offer many advantages and was used for the piers and main girders, with concrete being used for the deck slab. An opening span was included for shipping in the estuary and, in order to reduce weight on the lifting mechanism, timber instead of concrete was used for the decking. An important date in the history of Shaldon bridge was on 28 October 1948 when the tolls were abolished following a payment by the County Council to the Trustees of £92 020, towards which the Ministry of Transport contributed 75 per cent.

## Floating Bridges

Rendel's construction of Laira Bridge was part of his attempt to improve communications across the estuaries of south Devon in the 1820s. He started surveying for a suspension bridge across the River Dart in 1828, but his proposal was blocked by the landowner. In consequence, Rendel conceived the alternative idea of a floating bridge which used submerged chains to guide a ferry instead of suspension chains to carry a road. He designed the ferry with two pontoons side by side and a steam engine between them that hauled on two chains across the river. At each end of each chain there was a large vertical tube. The chain

**In the medieval period the Church bore a considerable responsibility for major building works and it was not unusual to find Church funding of bridges. Staverton Bridge, shown here, crosses the Dart between Ashburton and Totnes. It was built in 1413 and paid for by the sale of 'indulgences' by the Bishops of Exeter.**

passed over the pulley into the top of the tube, and had a weight hung on the end. The distance across the river between the pullies was 1650 ft.

As the vessel crossed the river it lifted the chains off the bed, and in consequence the weights moved downwards in the tubes. This system kept the chains taut to maintain the direction of the ferry and reduced shock loads on the steam engine.

The Dartmouth Floating Bridges Bill received royal assent on 17 June 1830, construction started in March 1831 and the ferry was opened in August of the same year. The contractors were Isaac Blackburn of Turnchapel for the boat and John Mare of Plymouth for the machinery.

Although one ferry has always been considered sufficient on this Higher Ferry site, the size of the floating bridge has been increased over the years. The present vessel, with a capacity of eighteen motor cars, is guided by two steel ropes and is propelled by paddle wheels driven by a diesel engine. It is now owned and operated by Philip & Sons Ltd of Noss Works, Dartmouth. The demands of modern traffic are such that in addition to the floating bridge there is another crossing for vehicles further downstream, the

Lower Ferry, as well as a passenger ferry. Neither of these uses cables to guide them across the river.

The construction of the floating bridge at Dartmouth was followed by a similar one across the Hamoaze at Saltash in 1832. There had been a ferry at this site for over 600 years and its importance was such that it was served by sailing boats adapted to carry horses as well as rowing boats for foot passengers. The floating bridge did not prosper and three years later the original boats were reintroduced. This continued until 1850, when steam power again took over. The floating bridge remained in use, with various changes of vessel, until it was replaced by the Tamar suspension bridge in 1961.

Further down the Hamoaze at Torpoint there had been a ferry for the half-mile-wide crossing since an Act of Parliament authorized it in 1790. This was worked in the same way as the Saltash Ferry until 1829, when a twin-hulled steam boat was introduced. This proved to be unsuitable, and by April 1834 the lessees had established a floating bridge similar to those at Saltash and Dartmouth.

Rendel designed a large flat-bottomed vessel in three portions side by side, the outer two carrying traffic and the centre portion machinery, like that at Dartmouth, but larger. Once again the bridge was guided by two chains and their ends had weights attached to them in shafts sunk at the head of each landing place. The modern crossing has three ferry boats, each with its own pair of chains. They are

In the seven years from 1808 to 1815, James Green, Devon's first surveyor of bridges and buildings, built a series of fine bridges. This photograph of Cowley Bridge shows one of Green's most impressive, skilfully combining attractive detailing with sound engineering.

Shaldon Bridge, built in 1827, was, at the time, the second-longest timber bridge in Europe, after the Pont de Lyon in France. It lasted 100 years, finally surrendering to the attack of shipworms (*Teredinidae*). It was replaced by the present steel-and-concrete structure which suffered, in its turn, from corrosion caused by salt water.

operated by the Tamar Bridge & Torpoint Ferry Joint Committee of Cornwall County Council and Plymouth City Council and fares are subsidized by the tolls from the Saltash suspension bridge. In 1986 and 1987, each vessel in turn was taken out of service, cut into three pieces, and lengthened by welding in two extra sections. This allowed a fifty per cent increase in the number of cars which each ferry could carry.

## Early Concrete Bridges

When Joseph Aspdin took out his patent for Portland Cement in 1824, he chose the name because when set his material resembled the limestone quarried in Dorset. He did not foresee the far-reaching consequences the material would have on the construction industry. The first bridge in England built entirely of concrete was a railway bridge between Earls Court and Gloucester Road in London which was completed in 1867, but it lasted only eight years. The second one, at Homersfield in Suffolk, consisted of iron frames encased in concrete but this too has since been demolished.

At about the same time the Lord of the Manor of Seaton, Sir William Trevelyan, was confident enough to engage Philip Brannon, a civil engineer from London, to build a concrete bridge across the mouth of the River Axe. This was completed in 1877, and is thought to be the oldest surviving all-concrete bridge in the country. In recognition of the unique place which this bridge now occupies in the history of concrete, it is listed as a Grade 2* building of architectural or historical interest and since 1978 it has been designated an Ancient Monument.

Before the bridge was built there was a ferry crossing on the same site and Sir William bought the rights of passage for £400. Tolls still had to be paid after the bridge was

The eminent engineer J.M. Rendel was employed to improve the road network in south Devon, infamous for its lengthy detours around numerous river estuaries. One of his first proposals was for a suspension bridge across the River Dart, but disputes with a local landowner frustrated this idea. Rendel then devised the floating bridge in which the suspension cables are replaced by two submerged chains used to steer a steam-driven ferry boat. The same principle is still in use, both here at Dartmouth and at Torpoint.

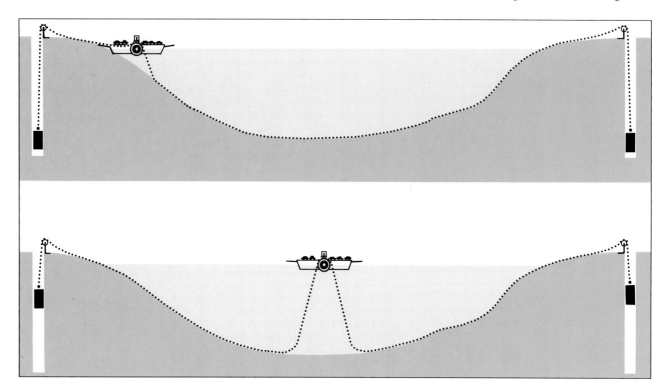

Thomas Whitaker's St Saviour's Bridge, Ottery St Mary, is now designated an Ancient Monument. It was built of cast iron towards the end of the period when that material was in common use, and well after the introduction of wrought iron.

built, so what was more appropriate than a concrete toll-house? This still stands and is a Grade 2 listed building of architectural interest, but it no longer serves its original purpose as tolls were abolished in 1907, long before the County Council bought the bridge in 1930.

Brannon was a prolific inventor, but some of his ideas did not work. At Seaton his theory that specially shaped foundations would avoid the need for piling was wrong; his idea that some of the weight of the structure could be ignored was too good to be true; and he completely misjudged the strength of the ground on which he was building. As a result the western pier settled 2 ft into the underlying silt during construction, a distortion that remains visible. In spite of these errors, the bridge still stands.

It is perhaps fortunate that the Board of Trade rejected Brannon's original proposal which was to cross the river with a single arch. His revised proposal was the three-arch bridge seen today, with spans of 30 ft 7in., 49 ft 1 in. and 30 ft 5 in. The design and detailing show quite clearly that concrete was regarded as a substitute for masonry as the arches are decorated to appear as stone and the pilasters and mouldings are copied from earlier structures.

The Iron Bridge, Exeter, is a fine example of cast-iron bridging from the period when this material was very much in fashion. Although the ironmasters who built these bridges copied the arch form used for so long by master masons, the newer material had serious shortcomings. It was very brittle and weak when resisting forces other than compression. Technological improvements led to the large-scale production of wrought iron and steel, which provided the bridge builder with an adaptable and reliable substitute for cast iron.

The local lord of the manor, Sir W.C. Trevelyan, bought the rights of passage across the River Axe at Seaton and built a toll bridge to replace the ferry. The bridge was designed and built by Philip Brannon, an engineer who was also a prolific inventor. Brannon chose to build his structure in concrete, a relatively new material at the time, in the style of a conventional three-arch masonry bridge. Unfortunately, his innovative designs for the foundations were flawed, and this, together with his lack of awareness of the underlying geology of the site, led to serious settlement of the bridge at its western end, reputedly before it was even open to traffic in 1877.

Axmouth Bridge, Seaton is constructed of mass (i.e. unreinforced) concrete. This is strong in compression but weak in tension so that the three arches behave in the same way as earlier masonry bridges. The weakness of mass concrete in tension limited its use until the idea of using steel 'reinforcement' was perfected. This development enabled the more successful reinforced-concrete arch at Thorverton to be built in 1908 with a span of 84 ft. This remains in good condition, and was once tested to a load of 66 tons. It is a tribute to the ability of the North Devon Surveyor, Samuel Ingram, whose design was prepared in competition with early specialist companies which had pioneered the use of this new construction material.

Between the two world wars reinforced concrete rapidly superseded masonry as the preferred method of building arch bridges and other engineering structures. Economy of materials coupled with advances in methods of design favoured this combination of strong concrete and reliable steel reinforcement. As these developments were taking place, the large, carefully shaped blocks of masonry required for arches became less readily available.

The Surveyor for the north and west of the county in the 1930s, R.M. Stone, developed a capable team to supervise the construction of large arches such as Rolle Bridge at Rothern near Torrington, Hatherleigh Bridge, West Bridge at Tavistock and Codshead Bridge near Crediton. A continuing programme provided new structures over several major rivers including those at Bridgerule and Clawton, the Taw and Yeo bridges on the Morchard Bishop to Winkleigh road, and those at Bish Mill near South Molton, at Landkey and at Swimbridge. These all replaced much older structures and each improved the local road alignment.

By 1936 design techniques had advanced to the stage where Andrew Warren, the Surveyor for South and East Devon, was able to build what was at that time the longest road-over-road reinforced-concrete arch in the country. This required a span of 50 ft to carry the Exeter bypass over the existing Honiton road and, in common with other concrete-arch bridges of the period, had masonry spandrel walls and parapets to retain the fill carrying the road and thus imitated its traditional precursors.

## The Philosophy of Bridge Design

The story of Devon's bridges so far has been one of gradual change in materials and, as a result, in style. For centuries, stone arches provided the only structural form which could be used to cross streams and rivers. Eventually steel and concrete made possible the construction of long, straight beams. Despite this, bridge designers still appreciated the aesthetic quality of the earlier style, so reinforced concrete arches faced with stone were used throughout the county between the two world wars. Economic factors favoured straight beams, so they gradually replaced arches for new work. The Second World War interrupted this process and when bridge building restarted, the change appeared abrupt even though it had been taking place for many years. It is therefore worth pausing to consider the subsequent course of events from the viewpoint of the design engineer as this had, and still has, a critical influence on the way in which bridges are built.

Before any structure can be designed, and a bridge is no exception, it is first necessary to estimate how large it should be. Once the engineer has made a guess – which will be well informed because of experience – calculations must be carried out to demonstrate that it will work.

There are many factors which influence this process. Some may be fixed beforehand, such as the span, the width, the skew angle and, occasionally, even the depth. What is not fixed is the appearance and it is here that the engineer can play a decisive role.

After the Second World War the change from arches to flat slabs continued and was virtually complete by the 1950s. At that time, design methods tended to be both empirical and conservative, while construction materials were only at the start of a period of development and improvement. In consequence the appearance of bridges built on conspicuous sites in the following decade tended to be heavy and subject to a certain amount of criticism.

Various factors combined to remedy this shortcoming in what are very visible structures. The improvements which have taken place owe a great deal both to the computer and to modern construction techniques. Engineers have been at pains to produce appealing designs, and to this end have consulted those trained in aesthetics rather than applied science. At the same time, the speed and power of the computer has made it possible to refine designs and reduce the size of the structural members by a significant amount. Further benefits have accrued from the use of higher strength steel and concrete. The results can be seen in the elegance of such large and very visible structures as the Torridge Bridge and the Exe Viaduct, but they are also present in the smaller bridges which attract far less attention.

An interesting effect of this increasing sophistication has been a realization that although earlier designs were conservative they often catered for forces and effects which were not considered in their own right. For example, the heating effect of the sun shining on the top of a bridge and causing it to expand, while the underside remains cool, may not matter if the design rules err on the generous side. As refinements were made possible by using computers, structures became lighter and some of these reserves of strength were lost. The consequence was that effects such as temperature differences within a bridge had to be considered; design rules grew more complex and calculations grew longer. Fortunately the computer was ideally suited to carrying out the extra work.

The end result is that attractive, elegant structures can be designed which make efficient use of the available materials. 1964 marked the start of this revolution when the first computer was installed in County Hall. This early machine had only the capacity of the present-day home computer, but it had an enormous impact. Programs were developed which made it possible to analyse multi-span, continuous or skew structures, and the slide-rule and mechanical calculator became obsolete in design offices.

Developments have continued apace, with the engineer of today having a whole array of electronic aids at his elbow. At one stage it was necessary to buy time on distant computers, accessed through the telephone network, for the analysis of large structures. The era of the computer bureau has now passed, as machines in County Hall are linked to Visual Display Units (VDUs) in the design offices and much of the process is by way of interaction between engineer and machine.

Further sophistication has been introduced with Computer Aided Drawing. In place of the drawing board is a combination of complex computer programs, an advanced VDU and a plotting machine. Using these instead of set-square, ruler and pencil, the engineer can produce a multiplicity of drawings with unerring accuracy.

## The Lost Thirteen Years: 1939–52

After the outbreak of the Second World War in 1939, the County Surveyor's Department was able to undertake only emergency bridge works. From then until several years after the war there was little money available for public works. The first move away from low-cost care and maintenance towards new construction came early in 1952, but the circumstances were unusual. Public transport was flourishing and provided a valuable service to the tourist industry, but at Powderham on the bus route between Exeter and the resorts of Dawlish and Teignmouth there was a narrow, low arch bridge linking two parts of the estate owned by the Earl of Devon. To enable double-decker buses to use this road, the Devon General Omnibus Company agreed to pay the cost of building a new arch in reinforced concrete.

## First Signs of Expansion

Following the emergency reconstruction of bridges after the 1952 Lynmouth disaster (see p.96), the first substantial new bridge to be built was a replacement for Merrivale Bridge near Tavistock in 1957. To ensure that the appearance was acceptable the 30 ft span reinforced-concrete arch was faced with Dartmoor granite produced from the adjacent Merrivale Quarry. The improvement removed a dangerously narrow and twisting section of road, leaving the original bridge as a picturesque stopping place for tourists.

The first trunk-road bridge of significance to be rebuilt after the war was West Bridge at Okehampton in 1957. Here access to the western end of the town was improved when the existing 20 ft wide bridge was replaced by one 48 ft wide, including two 6 ft wide footpaths where previously there had been none. The demolition of the old arch and reconstruction on the same site was achieved through the use of two temporary Bailey bridges of 50 ft span erected upstream of the existing road.

Although the Second World War appears as a sharp break in the gradual development of the road network in Devon, this is misleading in some instances. As early as 1924, increasing congestion on the ferries crossing the Tamar between Plymouth and Saltash led to agitation for a road bridge. Nothing was done until 1950 when local authorities and other interested bodies met to urge the Minister of Transport to carry out a detailed survey. A technical report produced in 1954 by a panel set up by the Minister stated that the ferries were inadequate and that a bridge was needed.

No national funds were forthcoming, so Cornwall County and Plymouth City Councils decided to go forward with their own scheme. This involved promoting a Bill in Parliament, which received royal assent in 1957. Early in 1959, Government approval was received for the joint committee to invite tenders. The lowest was submitted by Cleveland Bridge & Engineering Co. Ltd and they started work in July 1959.

The Tamar Bridge was a major undertaking by any standards. The centre span is 1100 ft and was the longest in England at that time. To this must be added the two side spans of 374 ft long, while the reinforced-concrete towers which support the suspension cables are 243 ft high. The total cost was £1.8 million. The official opening, performed

in May 1962 by Her Majesty Queen Elizabeth the Queen Mother, took place some months after traffic first used the bridge.

Although far larger than anything which would be built for many years, the Tamar Bridge served to illustrate that bridge improvements could be achieved, even though it often took a long time to obtain the money. The meagre funds available at that time were used on small individual bridges, the largest having been built of steel across the railway at Newton Abbot. A further improvement to the Exeter–Torquay road was effected by the replacement of a narrow tunnel known as Kerswell Arch at Kingskerswell by a much wider bridge and its associated high retaining walls.

During this period, there was a move away from the pre-war arch bridges such as that carrying Exeter bypass across the Honiton road. Improvements in design techniques and construction materials enabled engineers to meet the increasing demand for the large rectangular openings required to provide clearance for high vehicles using dual carriageways. This change in style of bridging signalled the end of masonry or brick parapets, because of the heavy loads which they imposed on long spans. The increase in span of so many structures was facilitated by great

The expansion of the railways in the nineteenth century posed a considerable challenge for the engineers of the day. The most famous of these was Isambard Kingdom Brunel, whose Royal Albert Bridge at Saltash, completed in 1859, is remembered as one of his principal achievements. The massive tubes were built, like the early iron ships, of wrought iron plates rivetted together. The huge chains strung between the ends of the tubes are there to prevent the tubes from flattening themselves out under their own enormous weight.

The Tamar road bridge was the longest in the country until the opening of the Severn Bridge in 1966. It was built directly adjacent to the Saltash bridge simply because the site Brunel had selected a hundred years earlier was the best available.

improvements in the strength of structural steel and reinforcing bars, as well as in the strength of concrete brought about by widespread adoption of scientific concrete mix design and by the improvement of cement.

## The Start of Major Growth

The accelerating pace at which road improvements were carried out led to a corresponding increase in bridge building. Between 1964 and 1968 seven new bridges were built and two were widened as part of the route developed especially for holidaymakers travelling to the north coast of Devon and Cornwall. All nine are underbridges, which carry the road over rivers or streams, and are hardly noticed by the motorist. The only exception to straightforward beam or slab construction is the reinforced-concrete arch which crosses a deep, steep-sided valley at Jacobstowe.

During the same period, in the east of the county four bridges were built as part of a bypass for Honiton, which removed the heavy A30 trunk-road traffic from the town. As all four were designed and constructed together it was possible for the first time to adopt a consistent style for a group of structures. The same approach was possible for the bridges on Cullompton bypass which was opened to traffic in 1969.

It was during the design of Cullompton bypass that the County Council engineers realized that this section of the trunk road would eventually become part of the M5 motorway, and the bridges were built to cater for a subsequent change from dual two-lane to dual three-lane carriageway.

The next major bypass was completed in 1976; it provided an alternative route to the built-up areas of Newton Abbot and Kingsteignton. This included seven bridges, all constructed of concrete, the largest of which is a viaduct across the estuary of the River Teign. There are eleven spans, each 40 m long and 1.5 m deep, supported on pairs of columns 1.5 m in diameter.

From the middle of the 1960s, there was an upsurge in the construction of routes of national importance. In Devon the A38 between Exeter and Plymouth and the M5 motorway started this process, followed by the A30 westwards from Exeter to Cornwall via Okehampton, and later the North Devon Link to Barnstaple. The full story of this development is given in another chapter, but it provides a useful framework here within which to describe the numerous bridges required to enable these roads to cross the many and varied natural barriers on each route. A wide range of different structures is needed when building a major new highway. Two terms that cause confusion, however, are underbridge and overbridge. The former relates to a bridge which enables a road or river to pass under the main road; the latter, which is more visible, passes over the main road.

**Many modern bridges carrying dual carriageways are in reality two identical structures side by side. The steel box girders used for the award-winning River Mardle viaduct, shown here, were fabricated in Middlesbrough from inch-thick steel plates, brought in lengths to the site by road, supported in position and welded together to form continuous beams for the full length between the abutments.**

## Improving the A38

The excitement and challenge presented by a major programme of bridge-building is exemplified by the improvement of the A38 trunk road between Exeter and Plymouth. This involved the design and construction of some seventy-five structures varying in size from small culverts 1.5 m in diameter to two viaducts 400 m long and dispelled any idea that there is such a thing as a standard bridge.

Two overbridges near Chudleigh are arches and one provides a striking frame for a distant view of Hay Tor. However, the appearance of both bridges is marred because they are built at an angle to the main road and this does not show off the arches to the best advantage. What passing travellers do not realize is that the ends of the arches are supported on hinges made out of concrete just 2½ in. thick.

The only way to appreciate the scale of the River Mardle Viaduct is to view it from Buckfastleigh, but this does not reveal the full story behind its construction. The main road had to cross two other roads and the river, so a four-span structure 177 m long was needed. It was decided to use a method of construction, popular at that time, based on two steel girders in the form of hollow boxes. Not long before construction was due to start there were spectacular failures of large box-girder bridges in Australia, Germany and South Wales. These catastrophic collapses, all occurring at

Manadon interchange on the A38 Parkway in Plymouth is the only three-level junction in Devon. The five-span flyover consists of two identical but separate halves. Reinforced-concrete piers up to 17 m high support pre-stressed concrete box girders 189 m long. During construction, successive sections of the concrete boxes were cast and held in place by coupling on further lengths of high-tensile steel pre-stressing cables. After the cables had been tensioned, further sections were cast, eventually forming two continuous beams.

about the same time, could not have been a coincidence, and it was clear that an urgent reappraisal was needed of the design methods.

Research was carried out nationally and new, complex rules were drafted very quickly. The designs for both the River Mardle Viaduct and a similar but smaller bridge near South Brent were checked and altered where necessary to make them safe. This intense period of activity was not to be the end of the story as construction, too, was difficult. Ground conditions at the western end of the viaduct proved to be much worse than anticipated so a vast hole had to be excavated and filled with hundreds of tons of concrete before the foundations could be built.

The River Mardle Viaduct won a national award from the British Constructional Steelwork Association in 1974 for excellence in the use of steel.

On the eastern outskirts of Plymouth there are two identical viaducts which convey the scale and excitement of bridge-building, particularly when seen across the estuary of the River Plym or from below. They cross both the flood plain of the river and the London to Penzance railway line. Massive concrete piers carry eleven spans 115 ft long made out of pre-stressed concrete beams. Each beam was cast in four separate sections at a factory near Norwich. The four parts were assembled to form a single unit by means of steel cables passed through them and subjected to tension. The beams were carried by rail from Norwich to Plymouth before being incorporated in the structure. The bridge deck was formed by casting a concrete slab on top of the beams.

The story did not end there, however. This prestigious structure had been in use for only about ten years when it showed signs of serious deterioration. As a result props had to be inserted under the deck and the load reduced by restricting the width used by traffic. The national ramifications of this problem are described in greater detail in the section on alkali-silica reaction on p.99.

The final length of the A38 to be improved in Devon was the 8.5 km stretch between Marsh Mills roundabout, on the eastern outskirts of Plymouth, and the Tamar Bridge on the boundary with Cornwall. This stretch of dual carriageway, which was completed in 1985, called for the construction of some thirty bridges and other major structures.

The marsh at Marsh Mills posed its own problems and one small culvert was built with a 600 mm hump in the middle so that when the embankment surrounding it settled, it would all be level. This and another culvert 900 m long are unseen successes, but at Manadon there is a group of structures on a much grander scale.

The construction of this three-level interchange, where trunk road and local roads meet, required long high retaining walls, six pedestrian subways, two overbridges and, crossing all of them, a five-span pre-stressed concrete viaduct. This impressive structure, designed by consulting engineers Mott, Hay & Anderson, is really two similar structures side by side. However, the piers and deck of the western half were positioned 7.4 m further south than the eastern half to allow the A38 Parkway to pass underneath at an angle. The tallest piers are 17 m high and the overall length of the deck is 189 m, made up of five spans, two of which are 33 m and three 41 m. The deck is curved to suit the road layout and so both design and construction involved complicated geometry.

Construction of the viaduct was a challenge for the contractors. They succeeded in casting each of the high reinforced-concrete piers, with their distinctive curved shape, in one continuous operation. The concrete for the pre-stressed box-girder deck slabs had to be supported on a temporary structure which allowed traffic to use the roundabout underneath, although this was changing shape as construction proceeded. Starting from the southern end, one span and one quarter of the next span were cast. When the concrete had gained sufficient strength, high-tensile steel cables were threaded through ducts (holes) in the flanges (top and bottom) and webs (sides) of the box girders. The cables were then tensioned (stretched), the force being resisted, through a system of wedges, by

compression in the concrete. When the second span-and-a-quarter was complete, the second set of cables was connected to the first and the tensioning (pre-stressing) procedure was repeated.

To add to the difficulties of construction, a footbridge was required to connect footpaths between subways on both sides of the main road. This has been achieved by suspending a light steel structure from the viaduct. The pedestrians who use it are best able to appreciate the massive scale of this complex interchange.

## The M5 motorway comes to Devon

At the same time as the Devon Sub-unit of the Road Construction Unit was improving the A38 between Exeter and Plymouth, a new motorway was being built between Birmingham and Exeter to replace the A38 trunk road. The final section was opened to traffic in 1977. On the length in Devon, there are some forty-five bridges. In addition to the eleven built earlier by the County Council for the Cullompton bypass, seven were designed by Somerset Sub-unit and the remainder by consulting engineers Freeman, Fox & Partners, including the three most impressive structures on this length of the M5.

The largest of the three, Exe Viaduct, consists of reinforced-concrete piers supporting pre-stressed concrete box girders, which is a common arrangement for such a structure. However, the method of construction is unusual in that the pre-stressing tendons (high-tensile steel cables) do not pass through ducts in the concrete. Instead they are on the inside of the box girders but outside the webs. This arrangement means that the webs are thin as they do not have to accommodate ducts for the cables. The consequent saving in weight was sufficient to allow a reduction in the depth of the box girders and to permit economies in the piers and their piled foundations.

Exe Viaduct, like most bridges carrying a dual carriageway, is in fact two identical structures side by side. Each one is 692 m long and the centre-line of the road is on a horizontal curve of 2150 m radius. They have eleven spans crossing the flood plain of the tidal River Exe as well as the Exeter Canal. Each box girder carries three lanes of traffic, while cantilevers support the hard shoulders. As the M5 passes through a residential area and caravan park on the east bank of the River Exe, the viaduct parapets incorporate noise barriers. These have the unfortunate effect of depriving motorists of attractive views of the Exe estuary.

The sheer size of Exe Viaduct tends to detract from the adjacent Exminster Viaduct which in itself is a considerable achievement. It has the same construction as the much longer viaduct, but is 302 m long on a horizontal curve of 980 m radius with five spans crossing the main Paddington to Penzance railway line and the A379. The magnificent sweep of the two structures can be seen briefly by motorists travelling north on the M5, but the best views are obtained by those using local roads.

Although travellers on the M5 get little chance to

appreciate the impressive scale of the two viaducts, they cannot fail to be struck by the arch bridge crossing the motorway nearby. This bridge, which carries Matford Lane at a high level, uses the firm foundations provided by red Devon sandstone (the Permian Breccia) to spring from half-way up the deep, steep cutting slopes of the motorway itself. It provides an appropriate ending to the motorway and a frame for the two trunk roads to Plymouth and Cornwall.

## The A30 trunk road westwards from Exeter

Although the improvement of the A30 westwards from Exeter was as important as the A38 and the M5, it did not demand spectacular structures. It did, however, produce a range of varied and practical medium-span bridges. Perhaps one of the most striking is to be found just after leaving the motorway near Exeter where Little Silver footbridge crosses at a high level. It is in marked contrast to the nearby Matford Lane Arch as it serves a very different function. The 20 m high Y-shaped pier supports three slender spans in which the pedestrians walk between the beams, thus being sheltered from the wind on an exposed site.

When the road reaches Okehampton the topography changes dramatically, and building a road across two rivers and along a steeply sloping side of Dartmoor called for complex engineering solutions. Siting such conspicuous

**Exe Viaduct.**
**This impressive structure is built of pre-stressed-concrete box girders supported by reinforced-concrete piers. The box-girder decks are unusual in that the pre-stressing cables are still visible from the inside and not, as is more usual, encased in the concrete. Engineers periodically inspect the structure by walking through the middle of the bridge!**

structures in the Dartmoor National Park necessitated great attention to detail to minimize their impact on a very sensitive area.

Two rivers run off the northern edge of Dartmoor and join to form the Okement, from which Okehampton takes its name. To bypass the town, the route of the A30 crosses both tributaries, the East and West Okement. In spite of the similarity in names, the bridging problems were quite different. To the east, the road is 17 m above the river banks before reaching East Hill and is carried on a three-span viaduct on slender concrete piers. To match the nearby masonry railway viaduct the surfaces of the piers were treated by casting vertical ribs on the concrete and then breaking them off, giving them a rough-textured effect. The deck was built in two identical halves, one under each carriageway, of pre-stressed-concrete box girders. Each is curved in plan with three spans 20 m, 40 m and 20 m long. At the other extremity of Okehampton bypass, the West Okement River bridge is at a very low level so that vehicles are not visible above the trees in Bluebell Wood. The road crosses the river at an angle of 45° which resulted in a very wide, awkward-shaped structure, with a skew span of 32 m. The abutments were faced with masonry to blend with the rocky floor of the wood and with the river bed, while the deck was kept as slender as possible by the use of pre-stressed concrete.

Both East and West Okement bridges are in particularly sensitive locations, and great care was taken at the design stage to ensure that their appearance fitted in with the surroundings. Photographs, plans and artist's impressions were submitted to the national body responsible for commenting on prominent public works, the Royal Fine Arts Commission, and the proposed appearance of both bridges was accepted with only one minor change.

Between the two bridges the dual carriageway is cut into the side of a very steep hill. To reduce the amount of excavation into the rock underlying East Hill the two carriageways are built at different levels. However, the massive beds of sandstone are folded in such a way that a steep cutting would be unstable, but a shallower safe one would remove much of the attractive hillside. The problem was solved by having a nearly vertical stone-faced concrete wall up to 7 m high tied to the hillside by high-tensile steel cables anchored and stressed into the underlying rock. A similar approach was adopted on the cutting face between the two carriageways and under the embankment on the low side. These three unusual structures, each up to 200 m long, were another exciting challenge for the County Council bridge designers and for John Mowlem, the contractors.

Bridges needed for improvements to the A30 west of Okehampton, indeed well into Cornwall, were designed by the Devon Sub-unit and provided an unusual opportunity to work in the adjoining county. Bypasses for both Bodmin and Launceston, which were completed in 1976, called for a variety of structures including a cattle underpass and several small culverts all made out of corrugated metal pipes. The largest of the major structures was the 99 m long, three-span, pre-stressed-concrete bridge crossing the River Tamar on the county boundary near Launceston. Every bridge is given a name and the designers used the obvious one but Cornwall County Council pointed out that they had more than enough Tamar Bridges already! They suggested that the old Cornish name for Launceston, subsequently adopted by the Normans, might be appropriate. Thus it was uniquely named Dunheved Bridge, even though the translation is thought to be 'Chief Hill'.

## Linking north Devon to the M5

Gifford, Graham and Partners, the consulting engineers responsible for designing the North Devon Link Road from the M5 at Sampford Peverell to Barnstaple, had four bridge crossings of particular interest out of a total of forty-five structures. Near Tiverton there is a viaduct 232 m long across the flood plain of the River Exe. Like two of the three other major structures it is constructed of reinforced-concrete piers supporting a pre-stressed-concrete deck. Sturcombe Viaduct is 87 m long and crosses a river of the same name at Hare's Down.

Nature obligingly provided conditions for a dramatic end to the M5 motorway from Birmingham to Exeter. The final obstruction, before it was possible to link the motorway and the A38 westwards, was a hill composed entirely of the red Permian breccia more commonly known as Devonian Sandstone. The motorway route cut across a road running along the top of the hill, so setting the scene for this dramatic 21 m high concrete arch, springing from the steep-sided cutting.

The undulating topography of Devon usually leads road engineers to build a series of cuttings and embankments, but at Ash Mill this was unacceptable as an embankment would have obstructed a delightful view along the very pleasant Crooked Oak valley. To protect the landscape a viaduct 145 m long was built in spite of the considerable increase in cost over the more usual earthworks.

The fourth viaduct, too, is unusual, but in a different way. The North Devon Link crosses the Bray Valley on the line of a disused railway, so the piers of a redundant viaduct were pressed into service. They were extended in height, using masonry to match the original. The deck is of pre-stressed concrete, but because the curvature of the road is different from that of the railway, it is built off-centre on the piers.

At the western end of this major cross-country route a bypass has been built around Bideford to remove the A39 trunk-road traffic from the town and, in particular, from the ancient Long Bridge. This is 206 m long with twenty-four arches varying in span from 3.6 m to 7.6 m and with the road at the same level as the Town Quay. Two significant structures were required for the bypass, one across the Kenwith valley and the other across the River Torridge.

Kenwith Viaduct, which was commended by the Concrete Society in their 1987 annual awards, is 270 m long with eight pre-stressed concrete spans, generally of 35.5 m each, supported on tall reinforced-concrete piers. In spite of its length and height, it looks elegant and attractive in its rural setting. In terms of size, however, it is dwarfed

by the Torridge Bridge which is 650 m long with eight spans of up to 90 m each. The headroom for shipping in the navigation channel is 24 m above spring tides. This is a fine example of civil engineering on the grand scale, which gained the premier Concrete Society award in 1988. The river piers are supported on massive cellular reinforced-concrete caissons which were floated into position and then sunk. The deck is constructed of 251 pre-cast-concrete units, weighing up to 100 tonnes each, which are held together by thirty steel cables each stressed to a tension of over 400 tonnes.

These most impressive structures were designed for the Department of Transport by consulting engineers MRM Partnership and built by contractor Edmund Nuttall Ltd.

## More vital strands in the network

Although 'major' can be used to describe schemes which are several kilometres long, equally important improvements are achieved by much shorter routes. As an example, a new relief road for Totnes required a crossing of the River Dart upstream of Fowler's classical arch bridge of 1826. At the time when design of the new bridge started, steel was preferred to concrete for the main beams as it was competitively priced. The Royal Fine Arts Commission

**Footbridges are as great a challenge to the design engineer as road bridges. This one at Little Silver, on the A30 to the south of Exeter, crosses a 62 m wide cutting and is designed in three sections supported by a single central 'Y'-shaped pier instead of piers at each end.**

was asked to comment on the appearance of the structure, and approval was given. There are three spans 20 m, 30 m and 20 m long, the bottom flanges being curved to echo the masonry arches nearby.

To overcome the difficulty of choosing a suitable name, an advertisement was placed in the local newspaper inviting the public to put forward suggestions. The reason for the choice of Brutus Bridge is that it is based on a local legend. This relates how a Trojan warrior landed at Totnes and went on to conquer the whole country. There is already a Brutus Stone set in the pavement of the main street in Totnes to commemorate the event, and the legend goes on to suggest that Britain was named after the same Brutus.

Many other bridges and structures have been built throughout the county as part of small- and medium-sized road improvements to ease the ever-increasing flow of traffic. These may take the form of subways, culverts, retaining walls and footbridges, as well as the more obvious road bridges.

Road safety is a matter of great importance and schemes which separate pedestrians, particularly children, from traffic are often necessary. Footbridges form a group of structures that receive little attention but they have often been instrumental in reducing accidents. Typical of many locations throughout the county where provision has been made for schoolchildren and students are bridges at Tiverton and Totnes, although the latter has been strengthened because of damage from alkali-silica reaction. Routes catering specifically for cyclists are becoming more common and a cycle bridge completed in 1988 across the River Exe in Exeter is of interest. This structure, which forms part of an extensive cycle route along the river bank, is 74 m long with two equal spans of pre-stressed concrete.

The county-wide network of footpaths calls for an altogether different style of bridge. Timber is frequently used as it is more sympathetic to the rural scene and perfectly adequate for crossing streams and small rivers. Modern techniques have extended the range of this versatile material, so that laminated hardwood can be used for quite long spans. One such structure, made by Lamwood of Bideford, with a span of 20.4 m, crosses the River Otter at Bicton in East Devon and was of such merit that it was commended in 1986 by The Civic Trust for 'a contribution to the quality and appearance of the environment'.

## Building on a Firm Foundation

The geology of Devon is very complex and foundations require special care to ensure that no unforeseen problems arise. In recent years, great advances have been made both in the science of soil mechanics and in the technology of site investigations. These, in turn, have influenced the design office, where an increased understanding of the properties and behaviour of different materials has led to considerable benefits. As ground investigation has become normal practice, so another aspect of uncertainty for the designer has been reduced. The County Council's consultant geologist, Dr Frederick Sherrell, has given advice over many years which has been of great value to members of the design teams.

The association between Dr Sherrell and the Surveyor's Department started in 1968 during the construction of Cullompton bypass. A deep cutting was required at a spot known as Nag's Head where the new road was close to the main Paddington to Penzance railway line. When the excavation had been completed, a large section of the hillside started to slide forward, threatening the railway line, and urgent advice was needed in order to find a solution. A detailed investigation showed that water trapped in sloping folds in the rocks forming the steep hillside was exerting upward pressure. Excavating the material to form the cutting allowed this upward pressure to lift the remaining rock and let it slide downwards.

The geotechnical solution developed to halt the forward movement of the hillside depended on drilling deep holes and removing the water by pumping. Permanent pumping was not an ideal solution so, once the hillside had been stabilized, the bottoms of all the boreholes were connected

by a drainage tunnel which now carries the water away by gravity.

Since that time, Dr Sherrell's advice has been sought on numerous occasions, but there is space here to refer to only a few of the major County Council projects with which he has been associated. Not long after the problems at Cullompton had been solved, difficulties of a different kind were experienced during the excavation of Humber Lane Cutting for Newton Abbot bypass. A mixture of many different types of rock was encountered and geological advice was needed to ensure that the cutting and the nearby bridges were safe.

Designers were quite used to designing embankments, cuttings and bridge foundations, but they had learned to recognize when soil and rock conditions were unusual and they needed to ask for help. In these circumstances the consultant recommended both tried and tested methods and also new techniques such as ground anchors to stabilize rock cuttings. This solution was first used on Embankment Road and Tavistock Road, both in Plymouth, and then on a much larger scale on Okehampton bypass.

In marked contrast to finding ways of supporting solid rock was the problem of building a 9 m high embankment on a swamp at Forder valley as part of the A38 Parkway improvement through Plymouth. The embankment was built in carefully controlled stages calculated by Dr Sherrell, with measurements of settlement and pressure changes in the marshy material being used to control the rate of progress. It was predicted before work started that one part of the embankment would settle under its own weight by 2 m and that a culvert in another part would settle 600 mm at its centre while the ends stayed still. These large movements were viewed with both doubt and alarm by the road and bridge designers, but Dr Sherrell's advice once again proved to have been well founded.

## Bridge Maintenance

With a total stock of nearly 4000 bridges under its control, the County Council is responsible for a capital asset valued at hundreds of millions of pounds. Most of the highway bridges are masonry arches and many of these were built about 150 years ago. Thirty-six are scheduled as Ancient Monuments and 135 are listed as buildings of architectural or historical importance.

Maintenance is a constant battle against deterioration caused by the elements, the undermining action of rivers and the weight of modern traffic. It is worth pausing to consider the general causes of bridge failure to appreciate the methods of maintenance that are required. Older bridges fail if their spans are so short and the waterways so constricted that in times of catastrophic flood they are overwhelmed and carried away; if their foundations are so shallow that the soil beneath the piers or abutments is eroded by turbulent flood water; if the construction or materials allow the ingress of rain or river water which is subsequently affected by frost; and, in the case of steel beams, if they become badly rusted.

During the early nineteenth century the responsibility for roads and bridges rested with the Quarter Sessions. In 1820, an advertisement was placed in the *Exeter Flying Post* by Richard Eales, Clerk of the Peace, inviting tenders for the repair of Clyst St Mary Bridge. Eleven years later he published on behalf of the Quarter Sessions a specification for the works which were required to keep in repair the roadway and parapet walls or guard rails of 275 bridges throughout the county. For the administration of this operation, the county was divided into nineteen parts (known as divisions) each one having named magistrates appointed to superintend the work.

Contractors were asked to submit tenders for carrying out the specified work on all the bridges in a division. Those who were appointed, in addition to carrying out repairs, had to keep a watchful eye on all other parts of the bridges for which they were responsible. The Surveyor of Bridges and Buildings at that time, James Green, would carry out inspections with the contractors and his certificate for each structure had to be signed by two magistrates before payment was made.

Although repair work must have continued over the years, there does not appear to have been any repetition of the 1831 initiative for a considerable time. The next period of constructive recording and maintenance appears to have started after the Second World War. By 1957 details of 1500 bridges were recorded and annual reports from all the Divisional Surveyors enabled the most urgent repairs to be identified and included in a continuing programme of work.

During this century tremendous changes have taken place in the nature of the traffic using the national road network. Vehicles have become wider and heavier and the passage of heavy lorries has become much more frequent. Now hundreds of heavy vehicles will pass over a main-road bridge every day and the resulting vibration can be very damaging, particularly to the mortar in old masonry. Most of Devon's bridges were built with a width of 20 ft to allow horsedrawn vehicles to pass easily. There are still many bridges on main roads in the county which are less than the desirable width of 7.3 m for two-way traffic so that inevitably there are accidents when vehicles collide with parapets. The damage caused can on occasion seriously affect the strength of the structure.

The most serious menace that calls for constant watchfulness is the effect of water in causing scour and undermining, which can be detected only with difficulty. When a dry summer occurs and river levels are low, inspection of the foundations and any consequent repair work are awarded high priority as the saving in the cost of construction of temporary dams is considerable. During the 1950s and 1960s, Taddiport Bridge over the River Torridge and Kersham and Colleton Mills Bridges over the River Taw received particular attention as the soft rock on which the piers were founded had been eroded. In these cases a concrete layer was placed over the rock and keyed into the bases of the piers to prevent further erosion.

Several developments took place in the 1950s and 1960s which were to be of lasting benefit to those engineers

The award-winning design of the crossing over the River Torridge near Bideford to carry the new A39 trunk road is in the direct line of bridge-building techniques which have developed over the centuries. Some of the pier foundations were cast on land, floated into position, sunk and finally forced down to rock level in the river bed by a combination of building on top and excavating underneath. The deck is formed of hollow concrete box sections that were fabricated in a factory on site, moved into position by the special gantry crane, and successively pre-stressed to those placed previously.

responsible for the maintenance of bridges. To avoid the costs and risks associated with excavating near bridges, a pump was introduced which was capable of injecting concrete grout (a mixture of cement and sand aggregate) into masonry structures. This meant that cavities could be filled without major disruption to the roadway.

Similar equipment became available for filling masonry joints up to a depth of 6 in. by the injection of mortar under pressure. Another specialized repair technique was used to overcome a particular problem on the fifty-year-old Thorverton Bridge in 1958. The original concrete of the arch had cracked in places, exposing the reinforcement to the elements. All the loose material was hacked off and new protective covering to the steel built up with sand and cement applied as a high-pressure spray. This material, known as gunite or sprayed concrete, has been further developed since and remains a valuable method of repair.

In 1962 a trained diver was appointed to the bridge maintenance staff and, with an assistant, carried out underwater inspections on a regular basis. This replaced the previous arrangement whereby a diver from Exeter Port Authority would be called on, subject to his availability, if the need arose.

The County Council subsequently invested in its own grouting apparatus, and gradually a team of skilled operatives was assembled under the control of a supervisor who was, in fact, also the diving expert. This organization was particularly valuable in the severe east Devon floods of 1968 when ten bridges, including three on trunk roads, were destroyed and had to be replaced (see p.98). In recognition of his service to the community and his leadership in the aftermath of the floods, the team leader, Bryan Wright, was awarded the British Empire Medal.

In 1967, the Department of Transport asked local authorities to assess the strength of all trunk-road bridges as the increasing number and weight of heavy goods vehicles was causing concern. This national programme was called 'Bridgeguard', a name which has been retained by the County Council for the inspection, assessment, repair and replacement of its own highway structures. In 1973, rules were issued for checking arches and other types of construction which previously had created difficulties for engineers carrying out the assessments. Structures built after 1922 were exempt because in that year the Ministry of Transport had published details of loads which newly designed bridges had to carry, and these loading rules have remained largely unchanged since then.

In 1974 a start was made on what proved to be a ten-year task, that of examining in great detail the Ordnance Survey maps of Devon to find previously unidentified watercourses and bridges. When these were located on the ground the result was that the recorded number of bridges with spans in excess of 1.5 m increased from 1500 to nearly 3400, with a further 633 bridges on the network of public rights of way. Included in the total are nearly sixty motorway bridges and over 200 trunk-road bridges, which are maintained by the County Council on behalf of the Department of Transport.

Guided by the inspection and assessment rules, the condition of all bridges included in the records was reviewed in the early 1970s. Details of those which were potentially weak were reported to the County Council in 1974 and a programme of replacement as funds permitted was agreed. Progress was good, as each year six or seven of the smaller bridges and one larger structure were rebuilt.

This had a dramatic effect on the overall condition of the county bridges, with a consequent reduction in the number of replacements carried out. The process of regular inspection and assessment still continues, although there are changes to the rules. Revised criteria were issued in

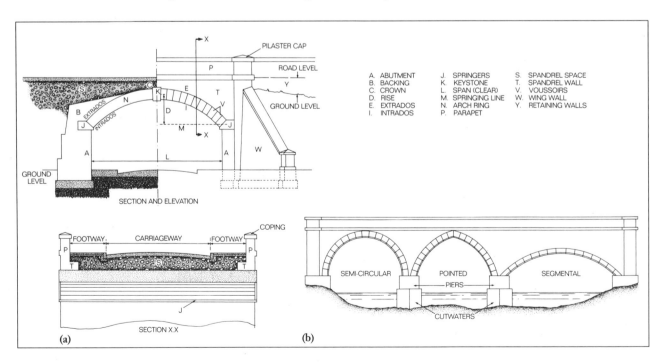

(a) Basic parts of an arch bridge. (b) Types of arch.

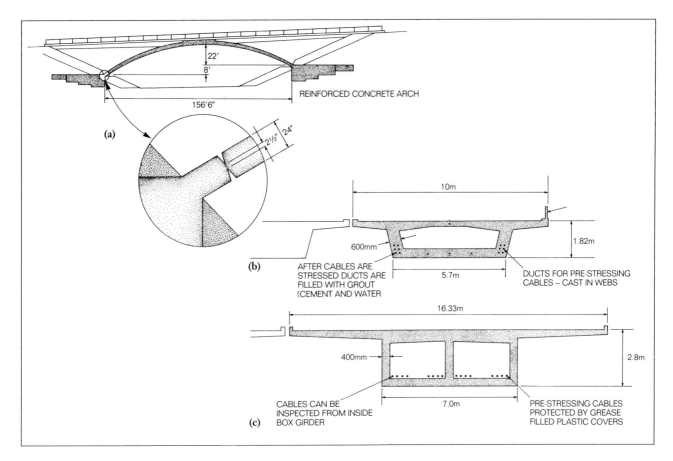

Section through: (a) concrete hinge on Chudleigh arches, A38 south of Exeter (b) Manadon flyover (c) River Exe viaduct.

1984 to take account of the introduction of 38 tonne heavy goods vehicles to conform to European Community standards.

Of all the larger structures needing replacement, those over the River Axe caused most concern. At Weycroft (A358) north of Axminster the arch and spandrel walls were cracked; the girders of the bridge at Whitford Green had rust holes in the webs; at Colyford (A3052) the edges of the deck were seriously weakened by rusting; and the bridge at Seaton needed attention to both the original concrete and the strengthening steel girders added in 1956.

There was insufficient money available to rebuild Weycroft Bridge so a road diversion was arranged while the fill over the arches was removed and all the masonry joints were repointed before concrete replaced the fill. Finally, a steel-sheet-piled apron was used to protect the foundations. In this way it was possible to strengthen an attractive structure without affecting its appearance. Whitford Green Bridge was rebuilt with an adequate width of roadway where previously it had only just been possible for a bus to pass between the parapets. At Colyford, so often the scene of flooding on the highway, a bridge with spans of 20 m, 30 m and 20 m with curved soffits was built and again the opportunity was taken to provide the standard carriageway width and two footpaths. This part of the Axe valley is designated an Area of Outstanding Natural Beauty, and in consequence advice was sought on the appearance of the bridge from the Royal Fine Arts Commission. It was completely satisfied with the design which was submitted.

Age had taken its toll on Axmouth Bridge at Seaton, which has been described in more detail on p. 80. Not only were the original concrete arches badly cracked, but the subsequent steel strengthening beams needed to be replaced. To prevent further damage from settlement and traffic vibration, the foundations needed to be underpinned, the cracks rejoined and the steel beams replaced.

An example of major maintenance operations carried out in recent years is work on Shaldon Bridge which crosses the wide estuary between Teignmouth and Shaldon. When it was freed from toll in 1948 the maintenance responsibility was transferred to the County Council. The paint used when the steelwork was erected in 1927 gave inadequate protection against the ravages of salt-water and sea spray, and the hostile environment affected the concrete as well. In the early 1960s gunite repairs were made to the structure but by 1980 further work was required. Repairs were made to the bottom flanges of all the beams using a mortar based not on cement but on epoxy resin; the lifting section was painted and the mechanism overhauled, and a comprehensive programme of repairing and painting the parapets was carried out. The total cost was £230 000, with the work being spread over two years.

The increasing attention devoted to maintaining the County Council's many bridges is best illustrated by the amount of money spent over the years. After adjusting the figures to allow for inflation, annual expenditure rose from £143 000 in 1950 to £190 000 in 1964 and has remained at just over £1 million since 1974.

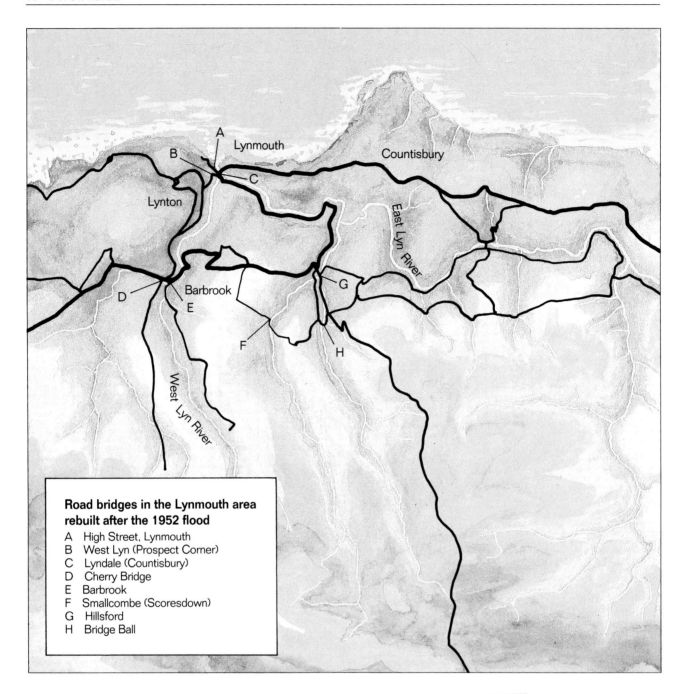

Road bridges in the Lynmouth area rebuilt after the 1952 flood.

**Road bridges in the Lynmouth area rebuilt after the 1952 flood**

A  High Street, Lynmouth
B  West Lyn (Prospect Corner)
C  Lyndale (Countisbury)
D  Cherry Bridge
E  Barbrook
F  Smallcombe (Scoresdown)
G  Hillsford
H  Bridge Ball

The repair and replacement of old weak bridges may not have the glamour of major scheme work, but is, nevertheless, demanding. Such diverse problems as keeping traffic flowing during construction, matching the appearance of an old granite structure on Dartmoor, and maintaining access and amenities for residents, are all part of the designer's job.

## Disasters and Calamities

Although the story of bridge-building in Devon is one of gradual change over hundreds of years, there are from time to time unexpected failures which call for an immediate response. Some of these are the result of unseen forces which gradually erode the fabric; some arise from sudden floods which overwhelm structures; and others may be due to the impact of heavy vehicles. Whatever the cause, the damage has to be repaired as quickly as possible to maintain the life of the community.

## The Lynmouth Flood

Throughout the day and night of 15 August 1952, exceptionally heavy rainfall occurred on Exmoor, the catchment area for the Rivers Lyn and Heddon flowing to the north and the Exe and Barle to the south. In all, some 9 in. of rain fell in 24 hours, so it is not surprising that all four rivers rose to unprecedented flood levels. Trees and floating debris were swept from the banks only to get caught up at bridges, forming dams and increasing flood levels still further. Some of the bridges collapsed under the force of pent-up water to release terrifying surges of water down the valleys. There was loss of life and great destruction in Barbrook and Lynmouth, but the cold statistics cannot convey the full horror. Thirty-four people were killed, ninety-three houses and buildings were destroyed or subsequently demolished, twenty-eight bridges were swept away or badly damaged, 132 vehicles were lost, and river walls were washed completely away. Within Lynmouth only the Lyndale (Countisbury) bridge remained effective.

Following a special meeting of Lynton Urban District Council on Saturday 16 August, an emergency was declared and full aid was promised by both the County Council and the government. The immediate problem, both in Lynmouth itself and in the north Devon flood area, was the restoration of communications. The army erected Bailey bridges at Barbrook and Hillsford, and brought bulldozers to Lynmouth itself to help in restoring the river channel. The village of Lynmouth was evacuated and during the month-long emergency period invaluable work was done by the army, police, fire service, county roadmen and voluntary welfare services.

At the end of the month all communications had been restored, and those who still had homes there were allowed to return to Lynmouth. Others were placed in temporary accommodation which included a caravan site hastily assembled on the Lynton recreation ground.

During this time the West Lyn (Prospect Corner) Bridge, which had been buried by boulders, had been excavated and a temporary bridge for High Street had been built from steel girders with a timber deck. The river was then moved back on to its original course. During the emergency period four replacement bridges for outlying sites, at Smallcombe (Scoresdown), Hunter's Inn, Newtown and Leehamford, had been designed in a temporary office set up in the Royal Castle Hotel and were completed early in 1953.

The problem of the permanent reconstruction of Lynmouth remained. As Robert Carnegie was not only County Surveyor but also Chief Engineer to the Devon River Board, work on roads, bridges, rivers and retaining walls was closely co-ordinated. Clearance of timber from the river was put in hand at a cost of £33 000, and a report by consulting engineers C.H. Dobbie & Partners on the size required for new river channels was accepted by the government ministers concerned. This meant that new bridge spans could be fixed and that money was forthcoming for all the work that needed to be done.

In the new plan the River Lyn was to be 100 ft wide in Lower Lynmouth. This was achieved by excavating in the grounds of the Manor House on the opposite side of the river from Old Lynmouth. At the same time the river was moved to allow a new road between the backs of the shops and houses and the river, thus solving the traffic problem in Lynmouth's narrow main street. The backs of these premises were attractively rebuilt to face the new road.

It was agreed that, above their confluence, the East and West Lyn Rivers should be 80 ft and 60 ft wide respectively. This meant that Lyndale Arch, at only 40 ft

The floods of 1952 destroyed or severely damaged most of the bridges in the Lynton and Lynmouth area. Although they had to be rebuilt very quickly, essential work to widen the rivers and so prevent a recurrence of the disaster was undertaken at the same time. Typical of the replacement structures is Lyndale Bridge, which shows the radial arrangement of local stone used to face the concrete. This imitates another feature of north Devon, the use of vertical stones to face hedgebanks.

span, would have to be reconstructed, and the plan also fixed the spans of the new structures at High Street and West Lyn. By the summer of 1955 the old Lyndale Arch had been demolished and a new one built with twice the span. Although basically it was all concrete, the spandrels were faced with masonry.

In the early 1950s, reinforcing steel was so scarce that it was decided to use, whenever practical, pre-stressed instead of reinforced concrete. This was made possible because bars with a very high tensile strength were beginning to come on to the market. By avoiding delays in material supplies, High Street Bridge was completed at about the same time as Lyndale Arch. The West Lyn Bridge at Prospect Corner was delayed until 1957, but this was as a result of controversy over its appearance, not shortage of steel.

High Street, Hillsford and Barbrook Bridges are of interest because they were among the first large pre-stressed-concrete bridges built, not only in Devon, but in Britain. The last two were not required so urgently as the first because of the presence of Bailey bridges provided by the army. In order to avoid interference with summer visitors to Lynmouth, much of the work was done in the unfavourable winter months, spread over a period of four years.

Other bridges rebuilt after the flood were a reinforced-

Digging the new channel following the Lynmouth flood disaster of 1952 which killed 34 people and damaged or destroyed 28 bridges and 93 buildings. The photograph shows the vast amount of debris that was deposited in the town and which had to be cleared prior to reconstruction work. The new Lyndale (Countisbury) Bridge is here partially constructed.

concrete arch at Cottage Inn, and a pre-stressed-concrete span at Cherry Bridge, respectively downstream and upstream of Barbrook. Bridge Ball, a reinforced-concrete span upstream of Hillsford, and another at Parracombe completed the road bridges, while pre-stressed-concrete footbridges over the West and East Lyn Rivers were built at Barbrook, upstream of the Lyndale Arch and to replace the steel truss at the harbour. The full list of road bridges rebuilt after the flood is shown in Appendix 3.

Time has healed the scars in the flooded and devastated areas of Lynmouth and the valleys of the East Lyn and West Lyn rivers, but the tremendous efforts of all those involved in immediate relief and long-term construction must not be forgotten. For his part in co-ordinating the engineering services, the County Surveyor, Robert Carnegie, was made a Commander of the British Empire.

## Exeter floods: winter 1960

Low-lying parts of Exeter were inundated by floods several times between October and December 1960. The River Exe burst its banks and at the height of the worst flood the army provided amphibious vehicles to rescue people trapped in their houses. One of these vessels sailing up Okehampton Street was swept broadside on to the torrent and became wedged between a lamp-post and a garden wall. The crew of would-be rescuers had to abandon ship!

There were fears at the time that the 1905 Exe Bridge might be swept away but it stood firm. Outside the city four arches collapsed, including Reedy Bridge at Dunsford and

Little Silver Bridge at Shobrooke. All four were replaced with longer spans and, as was usual by this time, with flat reinforced-concrete slabs instead of arches to give increased waterway areas to cope with future floods.

Devon River Authority had embarked on a programme of gauging river flows and the floods in the Exe, Teign and Dart valleys provided invaluable basic data. The prediction and control of maximum river flows were helped by the statistics obtained. Bridge designers, too, benefited as factual information became available to determine the spans and heights required for new crossings of major rivers.

## Bideford Long Bridge: 1968

The Long Bridge at Bideford is steeped in history. It is first mentioned in documents dating from the thirteenth century, though it was of timber construction at that time. Reconstruction in stone started in 1474, encasing the original timbers and, presumably, using the same modest foundations. This bridge was not only repaired but also widened on at least two occasions. The fast-flowing tidal river finally scoured out the foundations and one pier collapsed on 9 January 1968. The Trustees who owned the bridge asked for assistance from the Ministry of Transport (who were responsible for the trunk road), the County Council, and consulting engineers Freeman, Fox & Partners.

By 19 January, a temporary footbridge had been erected by the County Surveyor's Department between the river wall and the remaining masonry structure. In the interim, pedestrians were able to use a ferry provided by Bideford Borough Council. Mains services were made safe, and temporary replacements installed where necessary. Because of the difficulty experienced in demolishing the damaged arches, removing masonry from the river and coping with a large tidal range, it was not until 29 March that a temporary road bridge could be opened to end the detour through Torrington which added 10 miles to the journey to Barnstaple.

The Department of Transport assumed responsibility for the repair and maintenance of the bridge when it became clear that the Trust could no longer afford the ever-rising cost. Complicated underpinning, strengthening and remedial works were called for, so that full traffic flow was not restored until Christmas 1969, nearly two years after the collapse. Subsequently, the County Council was asked by the Department of Transport to take on day-to-day maintenance. This has involved considerable additional work in underpinning, sealing and pointing various parts of the structure, particularly between 1979 and 1982, when £71 000 was spent.

## The east Devon flood

On 10 July 1968, very heavy rainfall over the Blackdown Hills caused a tremendous flood down the River Otter, of a magnitude which is expected to occur only once in 600 years. There was a comparable flood down the River Yarty. In the upper Otter valley 5 in. of rain fell between 4 p.m. and 10 p.m. The floods destroyed or seriously undermined ten bridges of which two were on the A30/A303 Exeter to London trunk road and one on the A35 south coast trunk road. Fortunately, all of James Green's three-span arch bridges over the River Otter survived, at Weston, Fenny, Gosford, Cadhay, Newton Poppleford and Otterton.

A bridge crossing the mill leat at Fenny Bridges was destroyed and a temporary Bailey bridge built by the army was opened on 13 July. The County Council subsequently built a second bridge alongside using steel beams and timber kept in store especially for such an emergency. This was opened one week later so that two-way traffic was restored. The army also erected Bailey bridges to cross the River Yarty at Marsh and Kilmington and the River Otter at Upottery and Tipton St John. Subsequently, new bridges for all the sites were designed in the County bridge office, some being built by the County Council's own workforce and others by contractors.

## Bridge at Exwick

Close to the railway at St David's Station, Exeter, the 1890 bridge over the River Exe that joined Red Cow Village to Exwick was washed away by a flood in September 1974 during the construction of the nearby flood channel. This unfortunate event enabled a narrow bridge of 10 tonne capacity to be replaced by a steel-girder bridge with 225 mm clearance above flood level over a span of 35 m and without a weight restriction. The new bridge provided increased width for both carriageway and footpath so that pedestrians and two-way traffic could use this route.

## Sign gantry on Haldon Hill

At 4 p.m. on Wednesday, nine days before Easter 1979, a lorry carrying a crane with its jib partly raised demolished the sign gantry at the foot of Haldon Hill on the A38 trunk road between Exeter and Plymouth. Serious delays resulted until the steelwork was removed by Council workmen and contractors using steel-cutting equipment. The site was cleared by 7 p.m. (see p.107).

Two days later, the Department of Transport gave authority for a temporary gantry to be erected, and the bridge office arranged for a suitable structure to be obtained. Over the weekend two substantial reinforced concrete foundations were constructed by the County Council's own workforce. The steelwork arrived on Monday to be erected by the same men, and signs which had been manufactured in the County Council's sign factory at Barnstaple were then fixed. The gantry was completed by Wednesday afternoon, a considerable achievement in management and individual effort.

This short-term solution provided a breathing space in which a permanent replacement could be designed. It was not enough to dust off the old drawings, as by this time the rules had changed. The humble sign gantry had the same form as much more grandiose steel-box-girder bridges and therefore had to comply with the same requirements.

## Alkali-silica reaction

The importance of regular bridge inspections was highlighted when in 1979 County Council engineers noticed unexpected cracking in Marsh Mills Viaduct, near Plymouth. The Building Research Establishment and the Cement and Concrete Association diagnosed the cause as a chemical reaction taking place within the concrete. What was discovered involved alkalis in the cement, a particular form of silica in the sand, and water. These three react very slowly to form a gel which absorbs more water and swells, producing sufficient force to crack the concrete.

This problem had not previously been recorded in mainland Britain, although it had occurred widely overseas. Gradually, further cases of what is known technically as alkali-silica reaction (ASR) – and colloquially as concrete cancer – were identified, and work started on finding ways of preventing it. The publication of the causes and effects of ASR on Marsh Mills Viaduct marked the beginning of widespread national interest in the subject. Six more bridges built at the same time, and other notable structures

It is difficult to believe that a gel formed inside concrete can absorb water and expand with sufficient force to cause cracking. However, this is exactly what happens on rare occasions when alkalis in cement react with water and certain forms of silica in the aggregate which makes up the concrete. This example of alkali-silica reaction (ASR, or 'concrete cancer'), on the abutment of Voss Farm bridge on the A38, shows severe cracking.

such as the Royal Devon and Exeter Hospital in Exeter, were found to be affected, and similar cases came to light in other parts of the country.

A national working party of experts was brought together to review all the available information and, after a number of years of research, published Guidance Notes and a Specification for minimizing the risk of ASR in new construction. Practising engineers soon came to know this as the Hawkins Report after the chairman of the working party, Michael Hawkins, County Engineer and Planning Officer of Devon.

The damage caused by ASR led to an extensive programme of repairs and special inspections of affected structures. It was thus drawn to the attention of the public in a spectacular way because of the size and importance of some of the buildings and the high cost of remedial work. At the same time it became clear to engineers and research workers that it was only a small part of a much larger subject, the durability of concrete.

## Bridges Spanning 800 Years

Devon's oldest bridge is a mere youngster compared with others that still stand elsewhere. Nevertheless it is hoped

**There are two popular local theories to explain the irregular spacing of the piers on Bideford's old bridge. The first is that local parishes each paid for part of the bridge, and the size of the spans equates to the depth of the parish purse. The other is that the piers are built wherever rock could be found on the river bed. Behind the old bridge with its twenty-four arches is the new eight-span high-level River Torridge Bridge.**

that this brief review of the last 800 years has shown the importance of the wide range of bridges in the county. Although the largest and most recent examples, such as Torridge Bridge at Bideford, inspire wonder and admiration, the humble clapper bridge at Postbridge was just as important in its day.

Those engaged in the design and construction of bridges have always seen their chosen calling as challenging and yet satisfying. This is as true today as it was for Nicholas Gervase, who bridged the River Exe 800 years ago without the advantage of computers or powerful mechanical equipment, and the famous engineer Isambard Kingdom Brunel whose pioneering achievements in bridge building and many other spheres made him a national hero of the early Victorian era. The successors to such charismatic figures may not attract the same widespread attention but they play an important part in providing vital links in the highway network.

## The Origins of Traffic Management

**5**

There has always been the need to control traffic, and making the best use of the roads in a safe manner became more and more important as the number of vehicles increased. This resulted in many rules that are now taken for granted, such as driving on the left-hand side of the road in the U.K. When the first roundabouts were introduced in Devon in the 1930s, it is claimed that many local residents happily drove round them in the wrong direction. One-way systems have been notoriously confusing and even today when the use of a familiar street is changed by new arrangements drivers tend to be confused initially.

Nevertheless it was not until comparatively recently that the importance of traffic management was fully appreciated and over the years it developed into a science. Safety is often the main objective in the introduction of traffic-management measures, such as speed limits and parking bans, but within the urban areas these measures are also used to increase the capacity of the road network under the continual and increasing pressure of traffic. Management of the road network is, however, for the benefit of all users and the aim is to share the available highway in a safe manner between pedestrians, buses, cars, lorries and bicycles. Thus compromises constantly have to be made, and a whole variety of measures used, mainly traffic regulations, to gain the best use out of available road space.

In the early days traffic-management schemes were often undertaken in the expectation that they would be interim measures before the construction of new roads or of major widening of existing roads. After that it became accepted that in many cases, particularly in urban areas, it was unrealistic and often undesirable to undertake major road construction. Consequently traffic-management measures became the permanent solution and, like Urban Traffic Control (UTC) schemes, became increasingly sophisticated.

The manner in which traffic-management techniques have been applied has changed over the years. Conventional techniques have gradually been augmented wherever possible by more sophisticated systems enabling immediate response to varying traffic demands.

# KEEPING TRAFFIC MOVING

## The Management of the Highway Network

# The Motorist and the Law

## Early developments in restrictions on traffic

The first statute relating to the invention of the internal combustion engine and the pneumatic tyre was the Locomotives on Highways Act 1896, known as the 'Emancipation Act'. This Act repealed the 'Man and Flag Act' of 1865, which set a maximum speed for mechanical vehicles of 4 m.p.h. in the country and 2 m.p.h. in towns and required that a man carrying a red flag or lamp walk in front of each vehicle. The new Act introduced a speed limit of 12 m.p.h.

By 1903 the number of motorists had increased to such an extent that new legislation was necessary. By then the vehicles that had originally been known as light locomotives were called motor cars. The Motor Car Act of 1903 raised the general speed limit to 20 m.p.h. It also compelled drivers of motor cars to take out driving licences, although there was no test of competence to drive at that time.

The need for vehicles to be suitable for the roads on which they travelled has been recognized for a long time. Even throughout the seventeenth and eighteenth centuries efforts were made with this aim in view. The Locomotive Act of 1861 contained provisions to enable bridges to be protected against use by locomotives. The 1903 Motor Car Act gave power to the Local Government Board (later superseded by the Ministry of Transport) to prevent all motor vehicles from using any road less than 16 ft in width if it was considered that such use would be 'specially' dangerous. Notice-boards were erected to indicate the prohibitions. The Roads Act of 1920 contained provisions for the imposition of restrictions on certain roads.

By 1928 traffic had increased to the extent that road conditions were becoming dangerous, both to motorists and to other users, and a Royal Commission on Transport was appointed. The Commission presented two reports, resulting in the 1930 Road Traffic Act which was in essence the start of modern traffic legislation. This Act extended the powers to prohibit or restrict the use of roads by motor vehicles or by certain classes of motor vehicle. It also enabled highway authorities to prevent vehicles of more than a specified maximum weight from using certain bridges. Notices were displayed to this effect. One-way streets were also introduced by this Act.

The Road Traffic Act 1930 abolished the speed limit for private cars, but the Road Traffic Act of 1934 imposed a general speed limit of 30 m.p.h. in all built-up areas. (The 40 m.p.h. speed limit was introduced for use in certain areas as a result of the 1960 Road Traffic Act.) A further provision of the 1934 Act, which came into force in June 1935, required all new drivers from that date to pass a test of competence to drive. The 1934 Act also introduced a special licence for drivers of heavy goods vehicles. Another feature of this Act was the introduction of the pedestrian crossing with its familiar Belisha Beacons, named after the Minister of Transport at the time who later became Baron Hore-Belisha of Devonport.

Provision in the Public Health Act 1935 enabled parts of particular streets to be reserved for parking. However, it was not until the 1956 Road Traffic Act that a charge could be levied for street parking.

## Traffic-regulation orders

In April 1969, when the relevant section of the Transport Act 1968 came into force, it became a duty for authorities outside London, subject to certain provisos, to use the powers available to them 'to secure the expeditious, convenient and safe movement of vehicular and other traffic'. These powers take the form of traffic orders which, in very general terms, can be imposed to prohibit, restrict or regulate the use of a road or any part of a road by vehicular traffic in general or by a specific class of vehicle in order to avoid danger to persons or other traffic and damage to the road or any building; to ease the flow of traffic; or to preserve or improve the amenities of the area.

The most common traffic-regulation order is that prohibiting or restricting the waiting of vehicles. Originally these orders were indicated by the use of signs only and it was not until 1965 that the yellow-line system was generally introduced. In some cases the waiting restriction is accompanied by a restriction on the loading or unloading of vehicles.

Yellow lines are now prevalent in most town and city centres. Their introduction allowed a welcome reduction in the size and number of accompanying signs, although yellow lines themselves represent visual intrusion in many of the more sensitive areas. This problem was soon

COUNTY OF DEVON

TAKE NOTICE THAT THIS BRIDGE(WHICH IS A COUNTY BRIDGE) IS INSUFFICIENT TO CARRY WEIGHTS BEYOND THE ORDINARY TRAFFIC OF THE DISTRICT AND THAT THE OWNERS DRIVERS AND PERSONS IN CHARGE OF LOCOMOTIVES ARE WARNED AGAINST ATTEMPTING THE PASSAGE OF THE BRIDGE WITHOUT THE CONSENT OF THE COUNTY SURVEYOR

BY ORDER OF THE COUNTY COUNCIL

CLERK OF THE COUNCIL

Notices like this were a familiar sight at the beginning of the century. However, in view of the difficulties of making contact with the County Surveyor before crossing any bridge under his supervision, it is questionable to what degree the requirements on the notice were observed.

## Parking on the highway

In the early years of motoring there was nearly always space on the roadside for parking. Problems usually arose only in the town centres where indiscriminate parking caused obstruction to the flow of traffic and this was the reason for prosecutions. The yellow-line system regularizes the situation today and the traffic warden is a familiar part of the urban scene. Parking on the highway is now a problem everywhere, from the residential suburbs of the cities and towns to country lanes, especially those near beaches and moorland sites of interest. This demand for parking reflects both the large number of local vehicles (about a quarter of a million in Devon) and the influx of tourists in the summer.

Various measures have been used to control car parking. The yellow-line system has been complemented by parking meters, as formerly used in Plymouth, and 'pay-and-display' machines which were introduced into the county for street-parking control. In addition, residents' parking schemes were brought into operation in some areas of Exeter and Plymouth.

Parking is also of concern to long-distance motorists particularly on motorways or roads subject to clearway orders. Laybys, service areas and picnic sites have been provided at regular intervals on such roads to cater for motorists' needs. There has been a concerted campaign by the police and the County Council's road safety staff to encourage drivers to 'take a break'; with the opportunities the motorway network offers for hundreds of miles of non-stop high-speed motoring, this is of vital importance.

Within the urban areas the District Councils are largely responsible for the provision of off-street parking and the multi-storey car park has become a significant element in the city-centre environment. However, large car parks are not only expensive to build but also use valuable land and attract considerable volumes of traffic which can overload the urban highway network. 'Park-and-ride' schemes, whereby motorists leave their vehicles in car parks at the edge of town and complete their journeys by bus, have been introduced to ease some of these difficulties, notably at Brixham and Dartmouth in the peak tourist season. A permanent 'park-and-ride' site was opened in Exeter in 1987, with further sites planned.

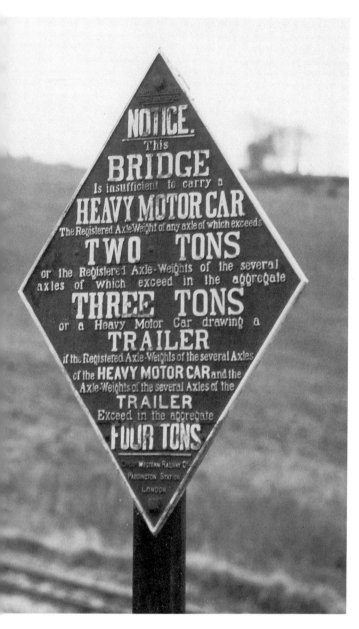

Road vehicles were referred to as 'locomotives' until 1903, when Parliament's growing recognition of the motorist was indicated by the first official reference to 'motor cars' in legislation. The photograph shows one of the diamond-shaped signs erected by the railway companies at the turn of the century. It is doubtful whether many motorists ever stopped to make sense of the instructions on the sign.

recognized and in many such areas it has been possible to use narrower lines and a more acceptable shade of yellow. In Cockington, Torquay, the yellow lines were dispensed with altogether in 1984 as an exception, thus returning to a signs-only system.

In general, traffic orders are introduced for the benefit of most road users, even though there may be inconvenience to some. In all cases the advantages and disadvantages have to be fully considered and an acceptable compromise is usually reached which eases the traffic problem whilst having the least adverse impact on people's lives and interests. Indeed, traffic orders can be effectively enforced only when seen by most people to be necessary.

## The police

The role of the police in the control of traffic and the enforcement of traffic law has resulted in the establishment of a close working relationship between Devon County Council and the police over a range of traffic and road safety matters.

Inevitably the advent of the motor car had a considerable effect on the operation of the police force and it is interesting to note some of the developments.

By 1897 the need for mobility was such that constables were granted an allowance (1d. per mile) when using their own bicycles for police purposes. In 1898, the Chief

As the number and size of freight vehicles gradually increased, so the problems caused by lorries in built-up areas began to develop. Over the years legislation has been introduced to preserve town and village centres as safe places for everyday social activities without hampering the free flow of goods and services to the community. The photograph indicates that the problem still persists in many small towns and villages.

Constable of Devon issued the following order: 'Several motor cars now being in use in the county, I have to draw particular attention to the provisions of the Locomotives on Highways Act 1896 on which officers will thoroughly instruct the men under their command at the next pay parades.' When the 20 m.p.h. speed limit was imposed under the Motor Car Act 1903, the police used stop watches over measured distances to trap speeding motorists.

In 1930 the Police Traffic Department was formed in Devon. Eleven motor cycles and five motor cars not exceeding 12 h.p. were purchased for use in enforcing the Road Traffic Act 1930. Wireless cars were first brought into operation in 1948. Traffic wardens first appeared in Devon in 1965; however, non-police personnel known as 'traffic wardens' were in existence previously to control traffic at junctions. They were first seen in Devon at Teignmouth in 1944.

A Police Traffic Division for Devon and Cornwall was

Before the major involvement of County Councils, the provision of road direction signing was largely undertaken by the motoring organizations. This early AA sign is typical of its kind, including not just local information but also a road-safety message and the distance to the capital. The AA and RAC still sign local temporary events.

established in 1970 when motor patrols, previously operating under territorial divisions, were formed into one department across the whole police force. It has subsequently been renamed the Mobile Policing Division because its officers are involved in the whole range of police duties and not just traffic matters.

Today motor patrols with modern means of communication, computer systems and other sophisticated equipment, as well as the assistance of a helicopter when required, are an essential part of the police force.

## The motoring organizations

The RAC, originally known as the Automobile Club of Great Britain and Ireland, was founded in 1897 as a 'society of encouragement' for the motoring movement and the motor and allied industries in the British Empire, and for 'protecting the interests of the motorist'. In 1907 the title

AA boxes have been built in many different styles since their first appearance in 1912. This early design has survived on the Exeter to Sidmouth road near the Halfway House.

was changed to the Royal Automobile Club as a result of King Edward VII bestowing royal patronage on the club. The famous RAC 'Get You Home' service was initiated in 1912.

As soon as motor cars were capable of a higher speed than that allowed, the police sought to prosecute drivers for speeding. Early types of speed traps (consisting of policemen hiding in hedges) were set for unwary motorists, who predictably sought to protect themselves. It was because of such so-called 'persecution' by the police that the AA came into being, starting as a band of 'scouts' who used to warn motorists of speed traps on the Brighton road. The organization was called the Motorists' Mutual Association but quickly changed its name in 1905 to the Automobile Association. By 1909 it had issued the well-known directive to AA members, 'When a patrol does not salute, stop and ask the reason.'

By 1912 the roadside boxes were in evidence, although patrols were still equipped only with bicycles. The AA and RAC boxes, which were furnished with telephones several years later, became familiar sights in Devon, as did the patrols who did much in those early days to assist motorists. Both organizations also provided signposting at that time when this was not one of the chief priorities of the Highway Authority. As with many services, old equipment was replaced before its historical significance could be appreciated. However, an example of an old-style AA box can still be seen at Halfway House on the A3052.

Nowadays the motoring organizations still provide a service that includes vehicle recovery and repairs at the roadside, as well as route planning, insurance, advice on continental motoring, publication of maps and other material and legal and technical advice.

## Pointing the Way

### Traffic signs

The history of an area is often revealed in the signs along the roadside. Crossroads were important meeting places and in Devon today their names are usually preserved on the direction signs at the junctions, providing fascinating associations with the past. The general Turnpike Act of 1773 required direction posts or milestones to be provided, showing the nearest market town or other places to which the roads led from the crossing point; a determined effort has been made to preserve many of these features. This same Act also required the erection of 'danger' posts to show where and to what depth a road might be flooded.

The Highway Act of 1835 enabled Surveyors to erect signposting with the letters being not less than one inch in height. However, it was the Motor Car Act of 1903 which first authorized local authorities to erect signs warning of crossroads, hills and dangerous corners. These signs were surmounted by the once-familiar red triangle.

The many authorities responsible for roads discharged their obligations in different ways and this led to the 1930 Road Traffic Act which imposed much greater central

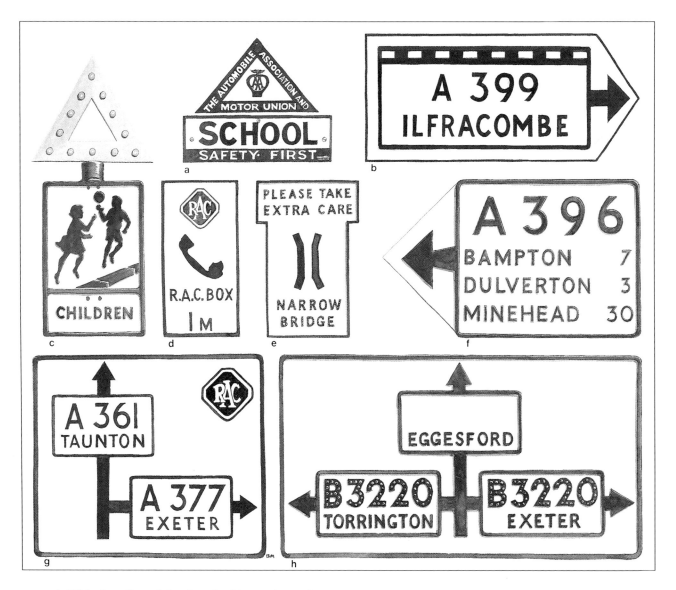

(a) An AA warning sign.
(b) Old style direction signs. An earlier means of indicating routes leading to other roads was to run a black and white chequer along the top of the sign. Today, such routes are indicated in brackets.
(c) Old style school warning sign.
(d) RAC sign indicating call box.
(e) An example of a traffic sign manufactured locally to overcome a particular problem. This wooden sign, which includes reflective glass beads, was located at Stoneshall Bridge near Cullompton and was removed in 1959 when the bridge was widened. It was made by a local craftsman.
(f) Pre-Worboys direction sign.
(g) RAC direction sign.
(h) Early efforts to make road direction signs more visible at night including studding the route numbers with glass beads.

control. This Act allowed local authorities to have signs erected subject to rules issued by the Minister of Transport. The signs had to be of a size, colour and type prescribed by the Minister and no other signs could be erected except by railway, tramway or dock companies.

A Committee was appointed to advise the Minister on the subject of signs and as a result of its report in 1933 the first Statutory Traffic Signs Regulations and Directions were issued. Since then there have been numerous amendments to the Regulations and Directions, including those resulting from another Committee on Traffic Signs in 1944. The 1960 Road Traffic Act consolidated the law relating to traffic signs.

In the past the motoring organizations undertook much of the signposting work and supplied the signs, especially those incorporating route numbers. The direction signs erected by the highway authorities were mostly fingerposts. Many old iron and wooden fingerposts still exist, some bearing the name of the rural district council to which they belonged. One in the village of Lamerton in the former Tavistock Rural District indicates the direction of 'Chipshop'. The name is believed to have originated from the golden days of the Devon Great Consols Mine which in the mid 1800s gave employment to several hundred men. They were paid in chips which they could exchange for goods at the store in the nearby hamlet, hence the name 'Chipshop'.

It is important to understand the framework within which the highway authority has to work, and the need for it to have a highway-signing policy, together with the basic reasons for that policy. For the most part the general signing principles to be followed are covered by instructions and standards laid down on a national basis: indeed the provision of signing on the highway is tightly controlled by regulations.

## Legal considerations

Any traffic sign which is not permitted by the regulations or has not been specially authorized is illegal. Care has to be taken to ensure that signs that can lead to prosecutions, such as speed limits and double white lines are legally correct since court cases have been lost by the police where mistakes in signing have been made. An unauthorized sign on the highway is an obstruction and any highway authority which attempted to use such a sign would be acting beyond its powers.

## Principles of signing

The signing principles adopted in Devon are those which are accepted nationally. To ensure the greatest impact, signs must be kept to a minimum consistent with the need to control and guide traffic and to promote road safety. Properly sited signs of the correct type do much to keep traffic flowing smoothly and reduce accidents by eliminating indecision on the part of drivers.

From a distance a driver should be able to see at a glance the information he requires. The sign should be positioned to ensure that his gaze is not diverted through too great an angle which would distract his attention from the task of driving. In addition, having read the sign, the driver should be left with sufficient time to take any necessary action safely.

To achieve these aims a sign must be legible from the correct distance, not contain too much information, be simple to understand, be sited to give maximum impact and be effectively illuminated or reflectorized. The size of directional signs is determined by the height of the lettering. This is known as the 'x' height because it is based on the height of the letter 'x' of the lower-case alphabet. The 'x' height is varied to suit different road speeds.

Only the most suitable route or routes to a particular location should be signed to ensure that drivers unfamiliar with an area use the road network as intended.

## 'Worboys' signing

Following growing criticism of the inadequate nature of the 1933 British Traffic Signs system for modern traffic conditions, a committee was appointed in 1961, under the chairmanship of Sir Walter Worboys, to review the complete system of road signs. As a result of its studies this committee concluded that the United Kingdom should adopt the main principles of the European signing system. The recommendations of the committee were accepted and in 1964 the United Kingdom fell into line with European practice on traffic signs and what were to become known in the trade as 'Worboys' signs first appeared on British roads.

The introduction of continental-type traffic signs meant

*Top:* **Signing on gantries like this one on the M5 at Sowton, near Exeter, presents clear and precise directions to motorists on high-speed roads.**

**Even at a minimum height above the road of 5.3 m, there are occasions, fortunately rare, when loads which exceed this height attempt passage under gantry signs. The results are predictably spectacular. The photograph was taken on the A38 in 1979.**

a complete change in the style of signs, particularly warning signs and those giving effect to traffic orders, since the Worboys system relies basically on symbols rather than on a worded message. Sign identification and legibility are the main features of these signs. In general, warning signs are triangular, regulatory signs are circular and information signs are rectangular; new styles of lettering were introduced for the wording.

With the introduction of its central-area one-way system in May 1965, Torquay became one of the first places in the country to have a comprehensive system of the Worboys signs. This made it necessary to carry out a publicity campaign to explain their meaning to the motoring public as well as requiring very close co-operation with the Department of Transport and sign manufacturers in sorting out a number of practical problems which were revealed only when the proposals were put into effect.

The introduction of the Worboys signs meant repositioning in many cases because of their increased size. It was also necessary in lighted areas to illuminate a large number of them, although this requirement has subsequently been relaxed owing to the introduction of a highly reflective sign-face material. On high-speed roads, sign sizes became so large that structural engineers had to determine post and foundation sizes!

The changeover from the old 'Halt' and 'Slow' signs at junctions to 'Stop' and 'Give Way' gave rise to considerable misunderstanding since the criteria set by the Department of Transport meant that not all locations which previously had 'Halt' signs were provided with 'Stop' signs. In 1975 a revision to the regulations governing traffic signs led to a completely new shape of 'Stop' sign being installed before the end of 1981.

As part of the Worboys signing, the most important 'A' roads in the country were designated 'primary routes'. On these roads the main direction signs have a green background; these gradually made their appearance during the mid to late 1960s, one of the first routes to be dealt with being the A380 between Exeter and Torquay to link with the signs already in use in Torquay. The places shown on these green signs are normally 'primary destinations', selected as those most useful in assisting drivers to find their way along the primary network.

Directional signs for other 'A' and 'B' roads are normally white with a black border. Local direction signs, which are white with a blue border, can be used on primary and non-primary routes. As the name suggests, these are used locally for smaller communities. (See photograph on p. 112.)

Beyond doubt, when it comes to providing information to the motorist the standard Worboys sign designed to Department of Transport standards is very effective. The whole concept of the sign is that it is clearly seen and read,

but this also means that it can be an intrusion into the landscape. Every effort is made to minimize its adverse effect on the environment.

## Fingerpost signs

In 1975 the Department of Transport indicated that it would be willing to allow the retention of fingerpost signs in rural areas on roads with low traffic flows and low speeds.

Devon has many miles of road of this nature and the Department of Transport's continuing acceptance of this traditional style of sign was welcomed. However, the various fingerposts in use in the county were difficult and costly to maintain, so many of the signs were in a very poor condition. It was therefore decided to develop a new fingerpost which retains the traditional look but is practically maintenance-free and includes the reflective benefits previously associated only with the Worboys signs. A finial is incorporated, on which the County Council's logo is displayed, and the crossroads' name appears vertically on the post.

The need to protect Dartmoor's environment led to the establishment of a unique colour-coded signing system, with the signs (mostly of the fingerpost type) having different coloured edges to indicate the standard of the road ahead. In this way the use of unsuitable roads, especially by large vehicles, is discouraged. The system aims to provide visitors to the National Park with clear and appropriate information, in particular warning them about difficult narrow rural roads.

The standard sign arms are mortised into oak posts. Crossroads' names have been retained and are displayed vertically on the posts; names such as Couples Corner, Cold East Cross, Swallerton Gate, Watching Place, Hospit Cross, Easter Lane, Five Wyches Cross and others give an indication of local history and legend.

Information for the benefit of pedestrians is an important element of the county's signing system. The signs range from the attractive cast metal fingerposts, such as those erected in Exeter in 1987, mainly with tourists in mind, to the less elaborate wooden fingerposts which are used on rural footpaths and bridleways, including the long-distance coast path which has its own distinctive signs and waymarks.

## Tourism signs

The Worboys Committee gave recognition, albeit limited, to the signing needs of tourism and the 1964 Regulations included signs for picnic areas, ancient monuments and scenic routes. Furthermore, the large individual attractions may also, in certain cases, have justified local direction signing. Camping and caravan site signing was also introduced, though it was subject to certain criteria and special authorization. A few years later, signing of recognized historic houses and castles was established, along with signing of National Trust properties, these latter signs including the Trust's 'oak leaves' symbol.

The 1980s saw the next significant change in tourism

**Pre and post Worboys regulatory signs – Halt/Stop, Slow/Give Way.**

signing when the Department of Transport made provision for the inclusion of the English Tourist Board's 'red rose' symbol on local direction signs for individual recognized tourist attractions. This was followed in 1986 by the introduction of tourism signs bearing white letters on a brown background, and came as a result of successful experiments in Kent and Nottinghamshire which unfortunately gave no measure of the heavy demand for these signs in a tourist area such as Devon. In addition to the new colours, descriptive symbols could now be included. In Devon the early signs included an anvil to indicate a craft centre/forge and a shire horse for a shire-horse centre.

The County Council adopted a policy of signing tourist attractions from the nearest 'A' road or recognized tourist route. With the exception of attractions in the main urban areas of Exeter, Plymouth and Torbay, places that attract more than 150 000 visitors each year may also qualify for signing from the nearest motorway or trunk road if they are not more than 20 miles away.

Roadside information boards and signs to various facilities have been provided to serve the needs of all drivers but they are of particular benefit to tourists. The boards were first permitted by the Department of Transport in 1975. Since then Devon has developed an information board which is accepted nationally. It is made up of three panels on which are displayed maps, street plans, information on local places of interest, details of local radio stations, useful addresses and telephone numbers (hospitals, tourist offices, and motoring organizations, for example). Space is made available for advertisements related to tourism (e.g. camp sites, hotels and tourist attractions) for which a modest charge is made. The boards are strategically sited, mainly in lay-bys, throughout the county and each one displays information about the area it serves.

Some of Devon's fingerpost signs. Many of these were made by local craftsmen working to their own designs, hence the wide diversity of types and styles that can still be seen today.
(a) Hand-made wooden sign at Newton St Cyres.
(b) Although manufactured from modern materials, the latest-style fingerposts still retain much of the character of the older versions.
(c) Unique to Devon is this specially developed sign for use originally on Dartmoor. It combines a wooden post with aluminium arms, and incorporates a colour-coded classification system to help motorists find the most suitable route to their destination through the maze of Dartmoor lanes.
(d) Cast-iron sign at Ashill which bears the name of the authority responsible for its erection – the former Tiverton Rural District Council.

Those establishments which do not qualify for tourism signing are encouraged to purchase advertising space on these boards.

Every opportunity is taken to sign facilities such as parking, toilets and picnic areas so that drivers will be persuaded to use them instead of parking indiscriminately, particularly on common land where it is relatively easy to drive off the road on to the grass. Signs are also erected to inform drivers of the services available in bypassed towns and villages and to direct traffic to accommodation which is remote from established communities.

## Boundary signs, river/bridge names and place names

County boundary signs which include the County Council's ship logo have been provided on all the major roads and some of the more important minor roads into the county. Similarly, river names are displayed on all the major road crossings of sizeable rivers, and where the bridge is also of interest then its name appears on the sign.

Place-name signs of a new design were introduced in Devon in 1987. Besides being of a consistent style which will be associated with the county, there is provision for the signs to incorporate local information of interest.

## Variable-message signs

The development of sophisticated electronic communication and control systems has made it possible to respond immediately to the traffic situation as it changes. In some circumstances variable-message signing is the means by which necessary action can be taken. These signs, on which the legend can be changed as required (to direct traffic along one route at certain times of the day and along an alternative route at other times is but one example), represent an important step forward in signing techniques and considerable benefits result from their use.

Variable-message signs are remotely controlled by computers located in Exeter in the Information and Control Centre which was set up by the County Engineer and Planning Officer in 1984.

## Car-park information signing systems

These systems are associated with Urban Traffic Control (UTC) schemes and are worthy of special mention.

**Devon County Council led the way with the development of large information boards with replaceable panels providing a wide variety of local information for tourists and commercial road users. Space is provided for private advertisers connected with the tourist trade as a way of raising revenue to pay for the service.**

In urban areas, particularly holiday resorts, drivers spend a considerable amount of time looking for parking spaces, a problem that adds to general congestion and driver frustration. It can be eased by providing drivers with up-to-date information on parking facilities.

In Torquay the major car parks are equipped with 'occupancy counters' that continuously provide the UTC computer with information on the spaces available in these car parks. The computer in turn can alter the wording on strategically placed car-park information signs. Each of the signs displays the information relevant to the car parks that are easily reached from it. In addition each car park is signed according to the function it serves, e.g. 'sea front', 'harbour', 'central area'.

Under normal circumstances, when parking spaces are available, all signs display ordinary car-park direction information. When the car park occupancy counters show that a particular car park is nearly full the computer alters the wording on the appropriate signs to indicate that the car park in question is 'almost full'. The word 'full' is

Diversion signing
*Top:* In use as normal direction sign.
*Bottom:* With diversion operating.

displayed when no spaces remain and the associated direction arrow is removed.

These variable-message signs have proved to be so successful that the system has been extended to Exeter and is planned for Plymouth.

### Alternative-route signing systems

In the event of delays or congestion on the normal route an alternative route (or diversion route) is brought into operation. The Torbay and Plymouth Urban Traffic Control systems both have a remote control facility to introduce alternative-route signing when congestion is detected. The Torbay system can also be used to activate signing to divert traffic when flooding occurs on Torquay sea front.

In Devon, diversion routes were officially designated for the motorway and trunk roads some years ago, following agreement with the police and the Department of Transport. Such routes are used only on those occasions when the police consider it essential to close a section of road and whenever possible decisions are taken only after discussion with the highway authority.

When a section of the motorway, for example, has to be closed, special signs are brought into use advising of the diversion route. This signing is displayed on the permanent motorway signs, by use of rotating panels or roller blinds which are normally operated from the base of the post, and generally involves the use of a symbol, such as a triangle shape. The diversion route is permanently signed by incorporating the symbol on the normal direction signs along the route. This helps to reduce manpower and hence the time required to bring the diversion into operation.

When an accident occurs the responsibility for deciding

New designs for place-name signs were introduced in the mid 1980s. These provide a distinctive style which complements the county's position as a major tourist centre.

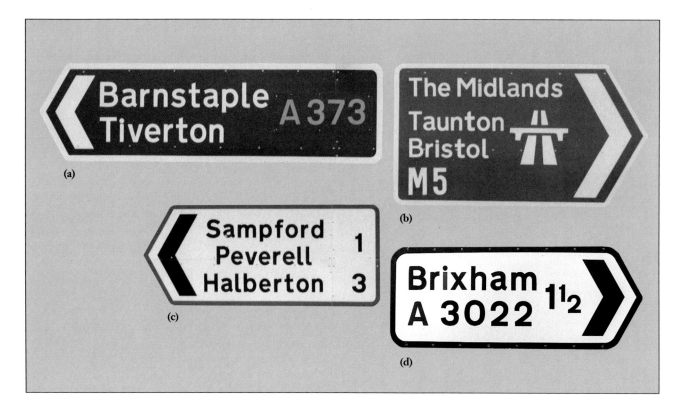

In 1964, following the recommendations of the Worboys Committee Report, a system of signing using symbols was introduced, which brought Britain into line with other European countries. A different colour was also introduced for different types of road in addition to motorways. Those now in use are: (a) Primary routes (b) Motorways (c) Local routes (d) Other routes.

on the action to be taken rests with the police and depends on the circumstances. The first concern is to deal with the incident and to get the emergency services to the site. On the major routes, owing to the large volumes of traffic carried, and consequently the problems which the diversion of such heavy flows can cause, traffic diversions are put into effect only in exceptional circumstances, and certainly not when it is more appropriate to keep traffic waiting. However, access to the scene of the accident for emergency vehicles is a factor which has to be considered and influences the actions taken.

Motorists arriving at the end of the motorway and bound for Cornwall have the choice of using either the A30 via Okehampton or the A38 via Plymouth, and normally no attempt is made to influence this choice. However, there are occasions when it is to the benefit of motorists to be advised to use one route as opposed to the other, and signs have been provided for this purpose.

## Holiday routes

One tends to think of holiday routes as a development of the 1950s, but in fact they were in use in the 1930s, as can be seen from the press notice opposite.

By the mid 1950s the government was pursuing its trunk-road-improvement programme as quickly as financial resources permitted. In Devon it was faced with the complete inadequacy of the A38, the A30/A303 and, to a lesser extent, the A361 trunk roads to cope with the massive increase in summer weekend traffic destined for the holiday resorts of Devon and Cornwall. At the time, moreover, there was no possibility, financially, of these trunk roads being improved to a standard whereby they could cope with the extraordinary volumes of traffic. This weekend congestion, which had developed in the mid 1950s, had reached intolerable levels by the mid 1960s and was to continue each summer until the completion of the M5 to Exeter in the spring of 1977.

Against this background the government, the County Council and the police, together with the RAC and the AA, co-operated to direct traffic on to 'Holiday Routes', whereby a proportion of the weekend traffic was encouraged to make use of county roads.

At the start of each holiday route there were advance direction signs warning of the congestion points ahead and advising use of the alternative route. The route was well indicated at every junction by special yellow signs bearing the legend 'HR' and drivers were advised to follow these signs at the appropriate times to avoid queues and delays. Whilst holiday routes themselves were left permanently signed, the signs which directed motorists off the trunk road on to the holiday routes were of the 'secret sign' design that were brought into operation (by the police) only when the message was relevant and it was to the advantage of the motorist to use them. This procedure gave credence to the signs and reassured the motorist that although the diversion might be longer in terms of distance, he would almost certainly save time and avoid the frustration of stop-start driving.

Publicity was given to the use of these routes and free leaflets distributed at various outlets such as service areas. The leaflets contained a regional plan showing the

Holiday routes were first established in the 1930s at a time when the West Country was becoming a popular holiday destination for the motoring public. As the road network developed, the need for this kind of sign diminished. With the near completion of the major through routes in Devon, its days are numbered.
*Right:* The publication in a local newspaper of a holiday route traffic notice by the Chief Constables of Devon and Exeter.

### NOTICES.

NOTICE TO MOTORISTS: TRAFFIC ARRANGEMENTS FOR SATURDAY, 10th AUGUST, 1935.

In order to relieve traffic congestion in the City of Exeter between 9.30 a.m. and 2 p.m., Saturday, 10th August, the police on duty will advise motorists approaching EXETER from the direction of Plymouth (A.38) and the South Devon coastal route (A.379), who do not desire to stop in the City, to proceed via Countess Wear and the bye-pass to reach the London (A.30) and Taunton (A.38) routes.

Drivers of vehicles proceeding to the South-West from the direction of Honiton (A.30), Lyme Regis (A.35), and Taunton (A.38) will be advised, DURING THE HOURS MEN-TIONED, not to use the Bye-pass, but to proceed direct through Exeter. The con-stable engaged on traffic duty at the Countess Wear roundabout will, except on occasions of emergency, direct motorists not to proceed over Countess Wear Bridge. The Bridge will therefore be a "one-way" road, used only by traffic crossing the Exe from west to east.

Diversion signs indicating the direction to be taken by traffic, as above, will be pro-vided by the R.A.C.

(Signed)

L. H. MORRIS, Major.
Chief Constable of Devon.
F. T. TARRY,
Chief Constable of Exeter.
7th August, 1935.

motorway and trunk-road network and the corresponding holiday routes. Local radio stations and motoring organizations also provided information.

Although the completion of the M5 to Exeter greatly eased the situation, most of the holiday routes remained in operation, particularly in the Okehampton area and in north Devon. However, completion of the Okehampton and Barnstaple bypasses meant that the holiday routes were no longer required.

## Motorway communication systems

The communication system in operation on the M5 in Devon involves the use of signs (officially called signals) sited in the central reservation at about 3 km intervals to give drivers advice on speed and information on lane closures. The signs are remotely controlled by computer and consist of a matrix of cells which are illuminated to form various legends by switching on the appropriate lamps. The sign matrix is surrounded by four flashing amber lanterns which attract drivers' attention to the message.

Gnome Reserve follow signs to Bradworthy 11

Tourism sign, showing English Tourist Board red rose insignia.

## Programmable signs

Another development was the programmable sign. Brief messages typed in by the Control Room staff can be displayed and changed at will. These signs are particularly suitable at places where different messages need to be conveyed at certain times, e.g. diversion because of weather conditions, accidents or severe congestion.

## Queue and count detectors

The Urban Traffic Control systems enable vehicle-count information to be transmitted from site to control centre in order to obtain immediate reaction. There seems little doubt that there will be widespread use of such facilities with the increasing need to manage the highway network directly and in a positive manner. Detectors can be used to introduce warning and route-switching signs, either manually or automatically.

It is possible automatically to record and store not only traffic-flow data but also the characteristics of the individual vehicles involved. Two electro-magnetic loops plus an axle detector in the carriageway are used to record the classification, speed, number of axles and axle spacing of each vehicle passing over these sensors.

## The Sign Factory

At the time that the Worboys system of signing was introduced in 1964 it was decided that Devon should have its own sign-making facility. The Divisional Surveyor of

Most of the signs required by the County Council are made at the Sign Factory in Barnstaple. In order to guarantee consistency and high quality, modern signs use standardized pre-cut letters and symbols fused on to aluminium sheets.

Barnstaple took delivery of a small machine (3M Vacuum Applicator) in 1965 which enabled plastic sheet to be bonded by a heat process to any flat surface to produce traffic signs. Precise design rules allowed overall sizes of designs to be determined before manufacture.

The main materials used were aluminium sheeting, 3M Scotchlite (reflective plastic sheet) and Scotchcal (non-reflective plastic sheet) with a welded aluminium angle frame to support and provide the fixing points. With this arrangement fixed-post centres needed to be known and drilled in the framework before despatch, which was an inflexible method of working.

The factory was located in what had been part of the carpenters' workshop in the Mill Road Depot. It soon became obvious that the premises were inadequate for all the operations required, so it was necessary to spread into a collection of sheds and huts. The production of signs continued in this manner until 1970 by which time it was clear that a review of the sign factory's organization was required.

In 1971 it was decided to employ a manager to organize and run the factory on business principles. New equipment was purchased and changes made to the production methods. The turnover increased rapidly, and by 1975 the factory was operating from purpose-built premises on the Pottington Industrial Estate at Barnstaple.

By 1988 it was possible to undertake computer-aided design at the sign factory as well as to supply complete signing schemes using the latest sign-face materials and including all posts, fixings and light units.

## Traffic signals

The first traffic signals, or traffic lights as they are commonly known, were red and green lights illuminated by gas. Installed in 1868 they were hand-operated by a policeman to help M.P.s cross Bridge Street when they went to and from the Houses of Parliament. These signals had only a short life span before they 'blew up'!

Three-colour light signals were first used in London in 1918, again hand-operated by the police. It was not until 1927 that the first automatic signals were installed and this resulted in the introduction of traffic signals being recommended in the First Report of the Royal Commission on Transport in 1929.

Some of the earliest traffic signals in Devon were those installed in October 1932 at the junction of Lucius Street and Belgrave Road in Torquay, at St Judes, Plymouth in January 1934 and at the Magdalen Road/St Leonard's Road junction in Exeter in November 1936.

Traffic control by the use of signals has become increasingly sophisticated during recent years, although this may not always be immediately apparent. As far as the average road user is concerned the sequence of operation of traffic signals is that which he or she painstakingly learns as part of the driving test, the only obvious change being the flashing amber sequence introduced with pelican crossings in 1969. However, the means of control has changed dramatically.

Traffic signals were previously fixed-time in operation and it was not until the post-war period that they were replaced by the vehicle-activated type: this work was completed in Devon in 1957. These early vehicle-activated signals used rubber pads set in the road surface to detect vehicles on the approaches to the signals. However, the increasing number and weight of goods vehicles caused severe wear-and-tear on this type of detector, so activation by inductive-loop detectors (thin copper wires buried in the road surface), was introduced.

In 1971, the specification for the poles and signal heads was changed: grey poles replaced the black-and-white ones and high-intensity tungsten halogen lamps, which replaced the tungsten-filament lamps, were set in a black head with a white border. The aim of this modification was to improve the visual impact as well as the appearance of the signals and a noticeable reduction in accidents has been achieved.

The control equipment was originally electro-mechanical, but electronic developments resulted in the introduction of solid-state controllers in 1972 and micro-processor controllers in 1983. Each occasion marked a significant technical step forward as it then became possible to implement more sophisticated traffic-engineering techniques and enabled effective signalling of complex junctions, such as Tweenaway Cross in Paignton. The installation of signals can also improve the capacity of large roundabouts; examples can be seen at Cattedown Round-about, Plymouth, where the signals are switched on automatically when detectors in the road surface record the formation of queueing traffic, and at the Exe Bridge gyratory system in Exeter which is one of the most complex in Britain. The success of these schemes depends to a large extent on the ability of motorists to keep in the correct lane!

Equipment that can measure speed of vehicles accurately has enabled signals to be installed on high-speed roads. For instance, the signals at Pottington Industrial Estate on the Barnstaple–Braunton dual carriageway include the most sophisticated speed-measuring detectors available.

Another interesting example of the use of technology in signal control can be found on the narrow A379 Kingsbridge–Plymouth road through Aveton Gifford, where wide vehicles are detected on the approaches to the village; if two such vehicles are detected approaching from opposite directions, the second vehicle has to wait at a red light at the edge of the village. Originally communication between signals was by infra-red lasers but problems caused by the sun led to the decision to use British Telecom lines. Nevertheless, the system was a unique solution to a problem using high-technology techniques.

The value of linking adjacent traffic signals was recognized in 1964 and at that time linking was achieved by cable with a 'master' controller installed to tell the 'slave' controllers when they could turn to green. Such a system was installed in Torquay at that time (see p. 155). However, the cost of cabling is high and since the early 1970s a technique has been available known as cableless linking. Each linked controller has a very accurate clock so that precisely the same event happens at exactly the same time every day. This type of linking has been used in a number of places and is still used as a 'back-up' system in such areas as Exe Bridges, Exeter. Where more sophisticated computer-based systems are now available a centrally controlled minicomputer is used to co-ordinate a network of traffic signals and thus allow vehicles to pass through successive junctions with minimum delays. This system is known as Urban Traffic Control (UTC).

The advent of minicomputers in the 1970s enabled the traffic-signal co-ordination techniques researched in West London and Glasgow to be considered for smaller towns. As a consequence the first 'compact UTC system' in the world was installed in Torbay in 1979 with little popular acclaim. Indeed, surprising as it may seem now, the local resistance to the scheme was such that it was at the time a major political issue. This computer, which has since been updated, controls most of the traffic signals, operates diversions when the sea front floods, advises motorists of space in car parks, detects congestion, monitors traffic flows and gives green signal priorities to the fire brigade in an emergency. The UTC technique has been developed further and another advanced system has been installed in the Mannamead area of Plymouth; this is described in greater detail under 'Bus priorities' on p.127. The

It is unlikely today that the installation of a new set of traffic signals would excite the kind of interest shown here. This was one of the first sets in Exeter, at the junction of High Street and Bedford Street before the Second World War.

computers for these systems are located at County Hall and data is transmitted to the sites by telephone lines on rental from British Telecom, making use of data-concentration techniques to transmit data for a number of sites on one line in order to minimize costs. Many of the concepts used in Devon were innovatory and were subsequently used in other parts of the U.K.

A particularly valuable facility with UTC computers is the instant detection of certain traffic-signal faults. Minor faults at traffic signals can go unnoticed for considerable periods though they cause additional delay to motorists. Even those traffic signals which are not connected to the UTC computers can now be monitored remotely. As soon as a fault occurs the installation can automatically telephone the control centre to report the fact.

A disadvantage with the original UTC systems was that the signals were not very responsive to unanticipated changes in traffic flows which can occur, for example, when it rains in the summer. Accordingly the Torbay system has been modified to introduce a new software package called SCOOT which is an acronym for its very technical description of Split Cycle and Offset Optimization Technique. This adjusts traffic-signal 'green times' and linking times in accordance with changes in traffic flow and congestion within the overall UTC philosophy. SCOOT has also been introduced in Exeter and Plymouth.

## Railway level crossings

The Railway Clauses Consolidation Act of 1845 compelled every railway company whose lines crossed turnpikes or carriage roads to maintain good crossing gates under the control of gate keepers; they were also to keep the gates generally shut against the road unless the Board of Trade authorized the opposite arrangement. However, as a result of the Road and Rail Traffic Act of 1933, the railway companies could ask the Minister to direct that their gates should normally be shut against the rail, either constantly or at certain times of the day, rather than against the road.

In 1987 there were twenty-three railway level crossings over public highways in the county. British Rail systematically replaced the old gated level crossings with a variety of other types – full barrier, automatic half barrier and open.

Full-barrier crossings are the normal type but there are a few half-barrier and open crossings. The open level crossing at Colyford is unusual because it controls a light tramway crossing. Half-barrier and open crossings often result in some public nervousness, but statistically they are very safe, with a low accident record. Of the full-barrier crossings the one at Red Cow immediately north of St David's Station, Exeter has the most adverse effect on traffic. The barriers at this site are over 40 m apart and control an important route linking the large residential area of Exwick with the city centre, where it crosses the multi-track main railway lines. A combination of frequent rail movements and the continual growth in traffic flows has resulted in road traffic being subject to substantial delays at certain times. The planned new bridge is the only satisfactory solution.

British Rail has installed closed-circuit television to monitor some of the crossings and all full-barrier crossings are monitored by railway personnel or closed-circuit television before a green signal is given to trains. Another change was that the audible warning to pedestrians is a warble tone rather than a bell; the sound output is reduced at night.

The locations of level crossings in Devon, together with details of crossing type and method of operation, are listed in Appendix 2.

## Road markings

It was not until after the First World War that white lines began to be used on the roads of Britain, and during the 1920s their use spread rapidly. In 1926 the first Ministry of Transport circular on the subject was issued, and this laid down general principles on the use of white lines. In the 1930s white lines were in use as 'stop' lines at road junctions controlled either by police or by traffic signals; for marking the course to be taken at bends, junctions and corners; and also for indicating the proximity of islands and other obstacles on the carriageway. By 1944, white lines were also being used to indicate traffic lanes and to define the boundary of the main carriageway at the entrances to side roads or lay-bys or in conjunction with 'halt' signs.

The double-white-line system, an important post-war development which regulates overtaking on roads (which should normally be at least 20 ft in width for the system to be used), was introduced in 1959. Continuous white lines are laid in the centre of the road on the approaches to bends or crests of hills where the visibility, determined by

the speed of traffic, is insufficient for overtaking. For a system that has to cater for traffic varying from farm tractors to sports cars it has stood the test of time well and has improved safety. There is little doubt that it is a good indication of the conditions which prevail on the road ahead. Drivers have become accustomed to the system and most realize that the lines are placed on the road for their protection in the interests of road safety.

Over the years there has been a considerable increase in the use of carriageway markings, including edge lines which delineate the limits of the carriageway on rural roads to reduce accidents and to minimize damage to the road edge and verge.

Another interesting development was the use of yellow bar markings which are laid on the approach to those roundabouts which have a history of speed-related accidents. They are set out so that as the roundabout is approached the markings are closer together. This creates the impression to the driver that his vehicle is travelling more quickly than it is and encourages him to reduce speed. These markings can be seen on both approaches to Marsh Mills roundabout, on the approach to Tamar

There are various types of level crossing in use today, including full-barrier, half-barrier and open. Increased traffic flows have meant that many previously gated crossings have been converted to automatic barriers. The photograph shows Crannaford in east Devon where a half-barrier has been installed. The control of the crossing would, at one time, have been the responsibility of a crossing keeper, whose cottage can still be seen.

Bridge, on Newton Abbot bypass (A380) at the approach to Penn Inn roundabout and on the A30 on both approaches to Merrymeet roundabout, Whiddon Down.

As the use of carriageway markings increased, great strides were made in the improvement of road-marking materials and the disadvantages of paint were largely overcome by the introduction of thermoplastic white lines. Later these incorporated fine glass beads (ballotini) and were first laid in Devon in 1961. Their good reflective properties enabled any change in the pattern of the line to be seen at a glance and took some of the strain out of night driving. The spray plastic used today, which sets in 30 seconds or less, provides a durable, instantly reflective material with good colour retention. It is applied at a thickness of 1.5 mm and is guaranteed to last at least two years. Very high-speed sophisticated machinery has been developed for applying the material and electronic equipment gives automatic and accurate application for pre-selected patterns.

## Reflective roadstuds

The familiar 'cat's-eyes', which provide an important safety feature at night, were invented by Percy Shaw, a Yorkshireman, in 1934. There are two versions told of how Shaw, whose main business at the time was tarmacking garden paths, came to invent this famous reflecting roadstud. The first is that when driving home one foggy night he found that the tram tracks which reflected the car headlamps and which he was normally able to follow had been taken up for repair. This was on a stretch of road alongside a sheer drop and he stopped quickly when the headlights of his car picked up two pinpoints of light in the fog. He had been saved from almost certain death by a cat on a fence. The second version tells how he came out of a public house one foggy night and noticed a reflecting road sign which made him think that reflectors at road level would be more effective. He 'acquired' two or three of the reflectors to take home with him and as a result of subsequent experiments he invented the cat's-eye.

Cat's-eyes came into their own during the Second World War. Car headlights had to be masked so that the beam pointed downwards and there was little other light to follow because of the blackouts; the masked car headlights could, however, pick out cat's-eyes.

A clever feature of Shaw's invention is that the rubber-mounted reflectors are self-cleansing. In fact, cat's-eyes must be acknowledged as one of the greatest aids to night driving ever invented, particularly as they have changed little since first introduced other than to be made stronger. It is rare that the basic design of an invention cannot be improved upon.

Other plastic stick-on reflectors have been developed. Motorists will be familiar with the red, green and amber varieties used along the edges of the motorway and some dual carriageways in Devon.

The policy in Devon is to install cat's-eyes on the motorway, on trunk and other main roads, as well as moorland roads and routes particularly susceptible to fog.

## Mini roundabouts

Mini roundabouts, consisting of a flush or slightly raised circular marking as an island, were first introduced in the early 1970s. Their use has always been restricted to urban sites where approach speeds are reasonably low. Sometimes two mini roundabouts have been linked together by a short length of carriageway; the one at the junction of Teignmouth Road and Westhill Road, Torquay was the first of this type in Devon. These junctions have generally performed well and have enabled traffic engineers to achieve maximum capacity whilst maintaining safety at difficult sites where boundaries are confined.

## Roadworks

No chapter entitled 'Keeping Traffic Moving' would be complete without some mention of roadworks as they are part of the everyday scene. Drivers probably regard them as one of the greatest causes of frustration and also, one suspects, as activities which are undertaken with little thought for the consequences. Nothing could be further from the truth.

The temporary traffic-management and safety measures (for both drivers and personnel undertaking the work) employed during the building, renewal or maintenance of highways have of necessity become elaborate over the years and standards have increased to match. A manual giving advice on how to minimize the effects of roadworks of all kinds was published by the Department of Transport in 1974. It is regularly updated in the light of experience, particularly having regard to the main road reconstruction and major maintenance work which is necessary nowadays. Although the manual sets out a code of good practice to cover a wide variety of circumstances it nevertheless has no statutory force. However, the need to adhere at all times to its provisions is strongly stressed.

Whilst a degree of traffic control ranging from signing to traffic-signal-controlled 'shuttle working', coupled with a diversion if necessary, is usually sufficient on ordinary two-way roads, on motorways and heavily trafficked dual carriageways it became necessary to employ more sophisticated traffic-management measures even for some normal maintenance work.

Since 1972 a technique evolved which was to become a common word to the motorist – the contraflow. A number of different layouts have been developed in order to cater for the various types of work and they have been modified with experience. The basic principle remains the same in all cases, however. The layouts have been standardized in published documents which, whilst ensuring a consistent approach throughout the country, also retain a certain flexibility to cater for local circumstances.

It is not always appreciated how much time is required to prepare for and implement a contraflow system. A wide range of matters has to be considered and various procedures initiated. Furthermore, all the problems encountered when maintaining a motorway or dual carriageway under normal traffic conditions still have to be dealt with during contraflow operation. When the reader is next caught in a traffic queue caused by roadworks perhaps the resulting frustration will be tempered with this knowledge and possibly even replaced with some sympathy for those whose task it is to minimize the disruptive effects which inevitably arise from these unwelcome activities.

# Lighting the Highway

## Early street lighting

The first publicly operated oil lamps to be used in Exeter appeared in 1760. Before this date there was no public lighting, but householders were required to provide their own lanterns outside their doors. These were usually fuelled by oil or tallow wax.

In 1817 Exeter became one of the first towns outside London to provide public lighting, with gas lamps in its main streets. Gas lighting reached Plymouth in 1822 and Torquay in 1834, but there was very little public lighting in country areas.

Two of Exeter's former gas street lamps, in Fore Street, Heavitree, which are of particular historical interest, have recently been restored. One of the lamps is dedicated to General Gordon and the other to Mr Nethercott, a member of Heavitree Urban District Council from 1896 to 1913.

Devon's first electric street lamps appeared in Exeter in 1889. They were introduced in Torquay in 1898 and in Plymouth in 1899, but it was several years before the country districts began to benefit from electric street lamps.

As far as legislation was concerned, the Lighting and Watching Act of 1833 enabled rural authorities to light roads and the Public Health Act of 1875 enabled urban authorities to do likewise. The Road Traffic Act of 1934 first gave county councils powers to light county roads, although a county council could not act without informing the local authorities (i.e. district and parish councils) of its plans and it had to be considerate of their wishes.

## Modern street lighting

Highway authorities were given greater responsibility for road lighting under the provisions of the Local Government Act 1966. This act distinguished between 'road-lighting systems' and 'footway-lighting systems' and from 1 April 1967 existing road-lighting systems on county roads, other than those on trunk roads, automatically became the responsibility of the County Council. At that time there were more than 6000 street lights, including those on trunk roads, and in November 1967 the County Council appointed its first street-lighting engineer.

A system was initiated to assess lighting requirements in relation to after-dark personal-injury accidents and the result was the beginning of a programme of street-lighting improvement schemes. In addition, a system of planned routine maintenance, including bulk lamp changes at pre-determined intervals, was introduced and a start made in changing over from time-switch control to photo-electric control for installations operating throughout the hours of darkness. This latter method of control switches the lighting on and off by means of light-sensitive electric cells which measure the daylight level and it provides more accurate operation than electro-mechanical time switches which require periodic readjustments.

By 1972 the number of street lights for which the County Council was responsible had risen to more than 10 000 as a result of improvements to roads and some estate development. However, the whole situation changed quite dramatically in 1974 when, as a consequence of the provisions contained in the Local Government Act 1972,

the County Council became responsible for the operation and maintenance of all road lighting throughout Devon, including that in Exeter, Plymouth and Torbay. The County Council inherited a total of 74 000 lighting units which were formerly the responsibility of the city and county borough councils and the fifteen urban district councils. On 1 April 1975 the County Council accepted responsibility from the parish councils for the maintenance and operation of all footway lighting and this added nearly 3000 more lamps, making a total of 87 000.

The first priority was to formulate a co-ordinated policy to ensure an efficient public-lighting service throughout the county. Early consideration was given to maintenance standards including frequency of night inspections, equipment specification, rationalization of burning hours and Electricity Board tariffs, street-lighting standards for housing developments and industrial roads, energy conservation priorities, and compilation of comprehensive lighting records.

As street-lighting records were inadequate it was necessary to undertake a complete survey of all lighting systems throughout the county. This involved identifying the location of all street lights and recording this information on plans which are regularly updated. Subsequently all the assembled information and data was transferred to the County Council's main-frame computer in the form of a detailed inventory for maintenance purposes. Routine road-lighting maintenance covers such activities as lantern and lamp cleaning, bulk lamp changes, resetting time controls, repairs to underground cables, and scouting for failed lamps and control gear.

## Deteriorated equipment

One of the major problems associated with road-lighting maintenance has always been the advancing age and deterioration of the equipment, particularly in urban areas. Street lighting columns are normally expected to last for about thirty years. Deterioration of both steel and concrete lighting columns can give rise to serious problems relating to public safety. In other cases lanterns can suffer from the ingress of water, internal cables can perish, or control gear and timing devices can reach the end of their useful life.

Funds of the order of £250 000 were made available in 1988 by the County Council to protect its street lighting assets and to continue an annual replacement programme, particularly in the urban areas, in order to reduce its liability and contain the costs of maintenance.

## Energy conservation

One of the chief factors in the road-lighting budget has always been the cost of electricity. The main emphasis in the policy of energy conservation was directed towards the conversion of high-wattage discharge lamps to more energy-efficient light sources without reducing the overall illumination of the highway. By application of this policy,

a

b

c

d

e

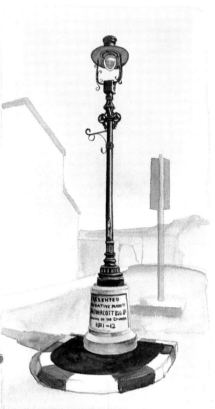

f

energy consumption has been reduced by approximately 40 per cent whilst the existing levels of illumination have been maintained and in some cases improved.

## Colour appearance and rendering

The various types of road lighting differ from one another in colour appearance and colour rendering properties.

Visual comfort in a lighted road is influenced by the colour emitted from the street lamps. Low-pressure sodium lamps, for example, produce a monochromatic yellow light which, although efficient in terms of energy consumption, cannot be used where good colour recognition is required. High-pressure sodium lamps (gold colour) and high-pressure mercury lamps (silver colour), on the other hand, have fairly good colouring-rendering qualities and are largely used in residential roads and areas where appearance is important.

## A rotten problem

It may seem surprising to refer to wood-rot in relation to street lighting maintenance, but such a case has occurred in Devon. The lighting columns along the sea front at Sidmouth are made from an African hardwood known as iroko. These splendid columns were installed in the 1950s and take the full force of the winter gales and salt-water spray, while in the summer they are baked by the long days of sunshine. It is not surprising perhaps that after so long a period of service some timber had deteriorated. In order to replace the rotted woodwork it was necessary to call upon the services of expert craftsmen who are more accustomed to replacing roof timbers in Exeter Cathedral than repairing street-lighting columns. Replacement work was carried out in 1976 and again in 1982.

## The end of an era

The last of the gas-operated street lamps in Devon were removed in 1978. These lamps were located on the Esplanade at Exmouth and were most inefficient by today's standards as well as very costly to maintain.

(a) Lamp column at Colyton, east Devon.
(b) Combined water fountain and lamp column, Axminster, east Devon.
(c) The Esplanade, Sidmouth. These lighting columns were installed in the 1950s and are made of iroko, an African hardwood. They had their first major renovation in 1976.
(d) The Esplanade, Exmouth. These were the last lamps to be lit by gas in Devon. They were removed in 1978 and replaced by craftsman-built reproduction electric lanterns. The cast-iron columns are the original ones, and are in remarkably good condition.
(e) When the 1903 Exe Bridge was removed in 1973, the six cast-iron parapet lamps were put into storage. Two of them have now been restored and re-erected at each end of the ferry crossing in the city's old quay area.
(f) 'Nethercott' lamp in Heavitree, Exeter.

This wall-mounted flood-lighting scheme in High Street, Exeter shows how it is possible to do away with columns in the footpath. The scheme is one of several in Devon to win national awards for good lighting practice and design standards.

The cast-iron columns were interestingly figured and in remarkably good condition. When the lamps were replaced by electrically operated units it was decided to retain the columns and replace the lanterns with a reproduction unit made by local craftsmen, thereby retaining the 'old world' atmosphere along this most attractive seaside promenade.

Many old-style cast-iron ornamental columns can still be seen in private drives and gardens since they were quickly bought up by individuals who recognized their aesthetic as well as their antique qualities.

## Increase in lighting

As a result of the annual capital improvement programme and private estate development in the county, there is an annual growth rate of approximately 0.3 per cent in the number of street lamps. It is of interest to record that in 1987 the number of lights was as follows:

| Exeter | Plymouth | Torbay | Other areas (rural and urban) | Total |
|--------|----------|--------|-------------------------------|-------|
| 8 500  | 24 500   | 12 200 | 44 600                        | 89 800 |

## Road-lighting developments

New techniques are being developed all the time. In the 1960s transparent polycarbonate lamp covers were introduced in Devon and these have reduced maintenance costs arising from vandalism. Another innovation was the illumination from floodlights which are mounted on the walls of adjacent buildings. A good example of this method of lighting can be seen in High Street, Exeter and Fore Street, Okehampton, both of which won awards in national competitions for technical and environmental achievement.

A catenary lighting system (lamps suspended from overhead wires) was installed on the M5 motorway at the Sandy Gate interchange. A further development is high-mast lighting where the floodlights are mounted in clusters on steel masts at a high level above the roadway thus enabling large areas to be illuminated from a single position. This technique was used to good effect for floodlighting the complex multi-level interchange at Manadon, Plymouth, part of the A38 Parkway scheme.

Specially designed lighting systems are important elements of the highway enhancement schemes mentioned in Chapter 8.

Although the efficiency of public lighting has improved considerably over the years, the rapid advance of modern technology is sure to provide even greater benefits to road users of the future.

# Pedestrians and Cyclists

## Zebra and pelican crossings

There have been several variations in the style and layout of pedestrian crossings since they were introduced by the Minister of Transport, Leslie Hore-Belisha, in 1934. These crossings were originally marked with white or yellow 'herring-bone' lines and very soon sported the amber globes which became known as 'Belisha Beacons'. The familiar black-and-white 'zebra' stripes were introduced after experiments in 1947 showed them to be more conspicuous. In 1954 it became compulsory for the beacons to flash. In 1968 the Department of Transport introduced a system which controlled the number of pedestrian crossings in relation to the population density. Criteria were established for the installation of formal pedestrian crossings because it was recognized that unjustified crossings increased rather than reduced the safety risk to pedestrians.

In 1971 it was decided to use zig-zag markings to indicate a zone on both sides of zebra pedestrian crossings called a 'zebra controlled area'. These markings are intended to indicate an area on both sides of the crossing in which vehicles must not wait or park, thus improving visibility of the crossing to approaching drivers. They also define the area in which pedestrians should not cross the road and, on the approach side of the crossing, the area in which overtaking is prohibited.

In 1969 a new type of pedestrian crossing known as the pelican crossing (PEdestrian LIght CONtrol) was introduced. In 1972 the first in Devon were installed at Jury's Corner in Kingskerswell, at Boutport Street in Barnstaple and at Notte Street in Plymouth. Most pelican crossings are equipped with a bleeper to assist visually handicapped pedestrians, though in residential areas the bleeper is turned off in the early hours of the morning to avoid unnecessary disturbance.

Since 1976 the County Council has been installing pelican crossings with vehicle detection so that the equipment can recognize a gap in the traffic and accede to a demand from a pedestrian sooner than it might otherwise have done. Most detectors are the conventional copper loop buried in the road surface, but at a number of sites radar detectors are used. There are over 170 pelican crossings in Devon.

In 1987 new Department of Transport pelican-crossing regulations introduced a number of changes and resulted in zig-zag markings being introduced for the same reasons as those at zebra crossings.

## Subways and footbridges

There has been a trend away from providing footbridges and subways since they are not always liked by pedestrians because of the difficulties and inconvenience of climbing steps and a feeling of insecurity in little-used subways, particularly at night. Nevertheless these facilities still have an important part to play where there are exceptionally busy roads and especially where they can take advantage of the topography. An example is the footbridge across Torbay Road, Torquay which won a Structural Steel Design Award in 1972 and has become a feature of that part of the sea front.

## Pedestrianization and pedestrian-priority schemes

The advantages of pedestrianization and pedestrian-priority schemes in shopping areas have long been recognized and once established these schemes have been successful. The subject is covered in Chapter 8.

## School-crossing patrols

After successful experiments in London, school-crossing patrols were first introduced in Britain in July 1954 following the School Crossing Patrol Act of 1953. The first patrols in Devon were in operation soon after.

Under the 1953 Act the County Council was allowed to appoint part-time patrols to see children safely across the road on the way to and from school. The number of patrols has grown to more than 200, helped by various flexible approaches to their establishment. These have included the acceptance of sponsorship from local businesses to pay for the patrol in return for advertising, the use of volunteers, the use of secondary-school pupils and even the use of teams of people to take it in turns to carry out the duties.

Despite these various approaches the job of 'lollipop person' has always been a difficult one to fill. The job is an invaluable one and can be very satisfying but requires a great deal of personal dedication. Improvements to the

service have included a smarter and brighter uniform developed for Devon patrols, based on designs contributed by art students at North Devon College in Barnstaple.

## Cycling

Cycling has been an important feature in the history of transport, both as a means of travelling to work, especially in industrial areas such as Devonport Dockyard, and for recreation. However, it declined over the years as car travel increased. The hills of Devon have always acted as a deterrent and in recent years it has largely been younger people who have taken up cycling.

As a result of various factors, including the high cost of motor transport and a widespread public desire for greater personal fitness, from the early 1980s there was a renewed interest in the bicycle as a means of transport. This was encouraged by central government which made available grants for the construction of cycleways and authorized a range of highway signs for use with such schemes.

The County Council, being eager to take advantage of this new wave of enthusiasm, joined with Exeter City Council and the Department of Transport to provide a cycleway in Exeter which runs along flat land in the Exe valley with links to the city centre and Marsh Barton

**A new development in the management of certain kinds of traffic is demonstrated by the emergence of 'cycleways', which segregate cyclists from other vehicles to their mutual benefit. The Exe Cycle Route was developed jointly by the County Council, Exeter City Council and the Department of Transport to demonstrate the benefits of cycling facilities in urban areas. It was opened by the Minister of Roads and Traffic, Peter Bottomley MP, in June 1988.**

Trading Estate. A major part of the scheme was the construction of a bridge over the River Exe. The total cost of the cycleway was over £400 000; half of this was paid by the Department of Transport as an indication of its active support; it selected the Exe Cycle Route as one of six national projects to demonstrate facilities that can be provided for cyclists. The City Council met approximately 25 per cent of the cost.

Opportunities have also been taken to provide cycleways along the lines of abandoned railways. One such scheme which received financial assistance from the County Council lies between Saltram Estate, Plympton and Goodameavy on Dartmoor; it was constructed by an organization called Sustrans Ltd (formerly named 'Cycle-bag'). A combined footpath and cycleway of some 14 km in length has also been constructed along the abandoned railway between Barnstaple and Bideford, forming part of the South West Peninsula Coast Path.

## Management of Larger Vehicles

### Lorries

The widely scattered population of Devon and its traditional industries of agriculture, mineral extraction and tourism make the county heavily dependent upon lorries to service its needs. Lorries also provide essential distribution services such as petrol to filling stations and groceries to shops, which penetrate the hearts of towns and villages. While communities benefit from economies in transport, the increase in vehicle size to carry larger and heavier loads has proved to be a mixed blessing. Whether it is the large lorry in the countryside taking feedstuffs to the farm or in the town on its way to the supermarket, the public have seen these vehicles as intrusive in terms of environmental impact.

Regulations have been introduced, notably the Heavy Commercial Vehicles (Controls and Regulations) Act 1973, commonly known as the 'Dykes' Act after its proposer, to enable county councils to designate routes over which lorries of certain sizes may not pass (see p.138). However, in re-routeing it is rare that a satisfactory solution can be achieved without new road building. Furthermore, lorry bans need to be capable of enforcement by the police whose resources for such activities are limited. Voluntary agreements with operators have proved to be successful in a number of instances but restriction orders have sometimes been imposed to ease particular problems.

However, the main thrust of the County Council's efforts to control these vehicles has been the development of the Devon Road Network (described in Chapter 3) which encourages heavy lorries to use the higher standard routes. The reclassification and re-signing of routes is an integral part of this process.

Nevertheless many of the problems that are associated with lorries result from the way in which they reach their destinations after leaving the main traffic routes. The establishment of the Minor Road Network and its associated signing policy was intended to alleviate these difficulties, with preferred routes clearly indicated.

### Coaches

Coaches, together with all other forms of vehicular traffic, are encouraged to use the higher-standard routes of the Devon Road Network (see p.54). However, the special nature of coach traffic often requires access to tourist attractions along routes which are unsuitable, resulting in congestion and frustration to other road users. This inconvenience on the other hand must be weighed against the enjoyment that such excursions give to many visitors and the substantial contribution made to the local economy.

As a result of the problems on Dartmoor an advisory coach route network was established in 1977. The network

Escape roads absorb the colossal momentum of runaway vehicles in beds of specially prepared light gravel. They are surprisingly in frequent use, saving the lives of both drivers and other road users. There are eight escape roads on Devon's notoriously steep hills; the picture shows the one on Telegraph Hill on the A380.

The great width of Plymouth's Royal Parade provided the opportunity to introduce bus lanes. This is a facility in common use by traffic engineers to assist public transport without undue detriment to the general traffic flow. (See p.127.)

was designed to allow operators access to most of the popular tourist destinations but with restrictions on the size of vehicle deemed acceptable on physical, traffic and environmental grounds. In general, the largest coaches were restricted to the main-road system outside Dartmoor, with shorter and narrower vehicles being used on the moor. All the routes within the network were already used by coaches, but over certain sections it became a requirement for coaches to travel in one direction only.

Coach routeing throughout the county, including the Dartmoor network, was previously enforced through Road Service Licensing administered by the Western Area Traffic Commissioner of the Department of Transport, but this was abolished by the 1980 Road Traffic Act. This Act also had the effect of making traffic-regulation orders more difficult to apply to coaches. Since this deregulation of coach operations, however, there have been fortunately few serious problems as many operators continue on a voluntary basis to use the routes which were established before 1980.

## Gradients

### Crawler lanes

Steep hills are a noticeable impediment to the flow of traffic. This is a particular problem in Devon where there are very many hills with gradients greater than 1 in 10, the steepest being 1 in 3. Thus the introduction of a third lane on some steep hills to act as a crawler lane and to give faster traffic a chance to overtake heavily laden lorries 'crawling' uphill at a walking pace has been a welcome improvement.

### Escape routes

Hills are closely associated with the problem of runaway vehicles, usually as a result of brake failure, so to help eliminate this danger escape routes have been provided on some of the steepest. They consist of a short length of road filled with a specially prepared bed of material which, when entered by a runaway vehicle, slows it at a controlled rate in a straight line and brings it to a halt without danger to the occupants and with minimal damage to the vehicle. However, it is a matter of concern that in the holiday season families have been observed picnicking in the escape roads while the children make sandcastles!

The movement of a 300 tonne C.E.G.B. transformer from Teignmouth to Alverdiscott in 1983 attracted onlookers along the whole length of its journey. The axle weight of this load was well in excess of the safe limits for some of the bridges on the route. This difficulty was overcome in an unusual fashion by lowering a rubber skirt (stored in the rectangular structure along the side of the trailer), enabling the trailer to convert to a hovercraft. This spread the load evenly, thereby avoiding any structural damage.

Such escape roads have been constructed on the A39 at Countisbury (two), A379 at Dartmouth, A380 at Telegraph Hill, B3192 at Teignmouth and B3234 at Lynmouth (three).

## Abnormal load movements

All lorries that weigh more than the maximum permitted gross vehicle weight of 38 tonnes or exceed certain width and length restrictions are classed as abnormal loads. The owners of these vehicles are required to give the highway authority at least two clear days' warning of any proposed movements for loads of up to 80 tonnes and five days' notice for loads of between 80 tonnes and 150 tonnes. This is to enable the loads to be checked against each structure over which they will travel to ensure that no damage will occur. All notifications are checked by the County Engineering and Planning Department in close liaison with the police who are also notified of these movements.

Over the years there has been a steady increase in the number of abnormal load movements taking place within the county, from approximately 140 in 1964 to over 1000 in 1987. This is partly a result of equipment such as excavators and mobile cranes becoming larger, and hence heavier, in the search for greater efficiency. Whilst this may bring benefits to the operators of the machinery it can result in much more difficult routeing problems, although the construction of the motorway and new dual carriageways has eased the situation in certain areas.

Before the 1939–45 war the movement of heavy loads was permitted only at night because it was such a rare occurrence. Since 1945, however, it has been a requirement for these loads to travel during daylight hours.

## The Lynmouth lifeboat

Probably one of the earliest abnormal loads to pass through Devon was the Lynmouth lifeboat, *Louisa*. She was called out one stormy night in 1899 to help a large ship, the *Forrest Hall*, which was in distress in Porlock Bay.

The sea was so rough that the lifeboat could not be launched at Lynmouth. The decision was therefore taken to haul the 3½ ton boat on its huge carriage by horses overland to Porlock Weir, where it could be launched more easily. This entailed a steep climb up the A39 coast road which was then a narrow rutted track little more than 7 ft in width and slippery with winter mud.

It took 10½ hours to complete the 12 mile 'overland launch', as this epic journey became known, and involved certain 'road widenings' en route.

The happy outcome of the story is that the lifeboat reached the 1900 ton full-rigged ship in time to save her from being washed ashore and helped the ship and the fifteen men on board to reach the safe haven of Barry Docks on the Welsh coast.

## 'Operation Caterpillar'

'Operation Caterpillar' was the name given by the police to the movement, in October 1983, of the largest abnormal load to be transported in Devon. Years of planning went into the movement of a C.E.G.B. transformer whose dimensions were a staggering 55m long, 5m wide and 6m high, with a weight in excess of 300 tonnes. The route between Teignmouth Docks and Alverdiscott near Bideford along 130 km of Devon countryside was considered by the hauliers who transport these loads on a regular basis to be one of the most difficult in the country. Improvement works totalling some £500 000 were carried out at the expense of the C.E.G.B. to ease the transformer's passage on the five-and-a-half day journey. Air-cushioning equipment driven by four gas turbine engines was used to spread the enormous load evenly over some of the bridges en route. The journey was watched by many hundreds of spectators along the route and so successful was the publicity given in the local newspapers, the hourly broadcasts on the radio and the various signed diversion routes, that traffic delays were almost non-existent.

## Holland 1

Another unusual load movement was the transport of the Royal Navy's first submarine, *Holland 1*, from Plymouth to the naval museum at Gosport. The submarine sank near the Eddystone Lighthouse shortly after the end of the First World War while en route to be scrapped. It was, however, salvaged by navy divers during the summer of 1982 with the intention of exhibiting it at the museum.

Before it could be transported it was necessary for it to be cut into three sections and for the conning tower to be removed. The metal had to be protected against corrosion after lying on the sea-bed for over sixty years but it was found to be in remarkably good condition.

The movement was carried out by the army. Such was the height of the loads that they passed under some of the motorway bridges with less than one inch clearance! The submarine was fully restored and is one of the show pieces at the museum.

## Weighbridges and height-checking equipment

Overloaded or badly loaded lorries can inflict serious damage on the highway. Therefore, a number of strategically sited weighbridges have been provided to enable the County Trading Standards Officer, in conjunction with staff from the Department of Transport, to carry out checks on suspect vehicles.

The most recent site, at Sampford Peverell, was opened in October 1986. It is used to weigh vehicles and abnormal loads on the North Devon Link Road and those entering the county along the M5 motorway. Another weighbridge facility available in Plymouth is intended primarily for continental ferry-port traffic and a site on the A38 at Kennford is used regularly to check vehicles travelling to and from the Plymouth and Torquay areas.

Consideration has been given to the provision of roadside electronic weighing equipment throughout Devon. This would indicate parts of the road network where overloading was prevalent and enable appropriate action to be taken. Such facilities could also be used in conjunction with permanent dynamic weighbridge sites, so that only those vehicles known to be overloaded would be stopped and weighed, thus avoiding unnecessary checks.

An infra-red detector system can be used to check whether a vehicle is too high to pass along a particular road. If too high it is detected when it cuts the beam of infra-red light set at the required height. In order to avoid false alarms from, for instance, birds, two beams can be used which can also determine the direction of travel. The system, by activating some form of warning, can reduce the number of incidents of lorries hitting low bridges.

## Bus priorities

In the early 1970s, Devon County Council started to take a direct interest in the declining bus industry. Subsidies from public funds were needed to support the industry and this led, after local government reorganization in 1974, to the requirement that County Councils should co-ordinate public transport. In Devon, the greatest subsidies went to support rural bus services and the methods used, many of them novel, did much to halt the decline in public transport in the county. In built-up areas, ways have been developed of improving bus services and achieving economic benefits by giving buses priority on the road network.

Bus priority is a means by which the bus traveller benefits from a reduction in travel delays, thus the drift of passengers from public to private transport is discouraged. Buses have been allowed direct access to some pedestrianized roads, and exemption has been given to buses in some traffic orders, such as Sidwell Street, Exeter, where westbound entry is restricted to buses only. Since 1975 special bus lanes have been installed on busy routes to help give an efficient service, especially in Plymouth.

High Street in Exeter is a nationally recognized example of the provision of bus priority, related to pedestrian needs (see p.138). The penetration of buses into this main shopping street from which most other vehicles are banned not only saves on operating costs of the buses but also gives the bus passenger quick access to the main shops and a pleasant environment in which to wait for the home-bound bus. The benefits derived from this situation were a significant factor in encouraging the use of minibuses in Exeter, one of the first cities in the U.K. to experiment with this pattern of bus provision which subsequently became so popular. On the other hand the very popularity of the service has increased the potential conflict between the bus and the pedestrian because of the number of buses. This problem is constantly under review.

Bus-priority techniques have been combined with the Urban Traffic Control system in Plymouth in order to give major benefits to a busy bus route. One of the two main routes into Plymouth from the north passes through residential areas and a busy shopping centre at Mutley Plain. There is considerable congestion on this route so a scheme was introduced in 1982 which limits the amount of traffic that can enter the route. Residential side roads join the route at traffic-signal-controlled junctions. Detectors keep the UTC computer informed of any congestion on the main route. The computer can in turn restrict the amount of traffic entering the route at the controlled junctions depending on where the congestion occurs. Bus lanes are provided to enable buses to bypass the queues which form at the entry points and variable-message signs can advise motorists to use the other route. This scheme has resulted in journey times for all vehicles along the route being reduced by 20 per cent.

## Future developments

Technology is advancing rapidly and the latest developments are capable of placing more information at the disposal of the driver. Route guidance through visual- and audio-advisory systems can now be fitted in vehicles and related to the changing position of the vehicle on the road. Allowance can be made for congestion and details can be provided of the quickest route in current traffic conditions. Like so many features of traffic management, however, the motorist will no doubt soon take these changes for granted and regard them as just another part of the daily routine.

## Introduction

**M**uch highway expansion has occurred this century in the three urban areas of Exeter, Plymouth and Torbay, which, prior to 1974 were all County Boroughs. Whilst Torbay escaped comparatively unscathed from the 1939–45 war, the other two were less fortunate, suffering widespread devastation to the city centres by enemy air attacks. The subsequent redevelopment resulted in considerable changes to their road networks.

This chapter deals briefly with the development of these three urban areas before the Second World War, and more fully with highway schemes after the war. However, before describing these developments in more detail it is of interest to reflect on the areas' diverse origins and functions.

Exeter is the oldest of the three, having its origins in pre-Roman times. Both the British tribe, the Dumnonii, and its Roman conquerors recognized the strategic importance of the city, particularly with regard to communications, being able to exploit the lowest crossing point on the Exe and the navigable waters of the Exe estuary. These advantages have established Exeter's position as the administrative centre of Devon.

Plymouth owes its importance to the splendid harbour and the consequent development of the naval dockyard at Devonport. Its waterside location is both its *raison d'être* and its constraining influence since, unlike Exeter, the direction in which it could develop is restricted by the Hamoaze, the Laira and Plymouth Sound. The city's origins are far more recent than those of Exeter. Whilst there are references to Sutton in Domesday Book, and whilst it developed into a thriving port subsequently, it was not until the late seventeenth century with the construction of the Royal Dockyard that Plymouth's fortunes began to soar, and it was the twentieth century before the modern city of Plymouth was created out of the townships of Plymouth itself, East Stonehouse and Devonport. It has subsequently extended to take in neighbouring settlements, notably Plympton and Plymstock.

Torbay is different again. Consisting of three main settlements all of diverse character, Torquay, Paignton and Brixham, they were not administratively combined and accorded County Borough status until 1968, only to lose that status in 1974 when local government was reorganized.

# 6

# THE URBAN SCENE

## The Road Systems of Exeter, Plymouth and Torbay

**The main road network in Exeter in the late 1980s.**

Torquay, the largest of the three settlements, owes its development to the use of Tor Bay by the English fleet in the seventeenth and eighteenth centuries. The visits were evidently protracted since the officers brought their families to the town. This laid the foundations for its popularity as a watering place and later as a holiday resort. Subsequently, the coming of the railways established that popularity and also formed the basis of Paignton's success as a holiday resort. Brixham had developed on more individual lines as a fishing port.

In general terms, therefore, it can perhaps be said that Exeter's development was based on its road communications, Plymouth's on its sea communications and Torbay's on its rail communications. Certainly Torbay is, in national highway terms, at the end of the road, and Plymouth did not enjoy good links to the west until the opening of the Tamar Bridge in 1961. The distinction is perhaps an over-simplification, but nevertheless it serves to indicate the diverse origins of Devon's three main centres of population.

Before local government reorganization in 1974, responsibility for the highways in the three main urban areas was in the hands of the County Borough Councils. In 1974 the County Council assumed responsibility for their highways, presenting an opportunity for the whole of the county's network to be managed as an entity.

# EXETER

Exeter, Devon's county town, is not only the administrative centre, but also, with its fine Cathedral, the religious centre for the county. Its importance was enhanced when, in 1955, the University College of the South West received its Charter from the Queen for it to become a university. In addition it is the shopping centre for a substantial part of the county, and is the centre of an economically flourishing sub-region for which it provides considerable employment opportunities.

Looking at Exeter's origins, W. G. Hoskins estimates that it has been inhabited for some 2100 years, thus dating from the Iron Age. An ancient British camp known as Caerwysc was located in the vicinity of Fore Street at the western end of the ridgeway which followed the route of High Street, Sidwell Street and thence over Stoke Hill. The Romans came in about A.D.50, renamed it Isca Dumnoniorum (after the local tribe), and some eighty years later converted it to a town of typical layout, with the forum being situated at the junction of High Street with North and South Streets.

Subsequent development has occurred on familiar lines, first within the city walls with its numerous gates. Whilst significant lengths of the walls have survived, regrettably the gates have not. When land was no longer available within the walls, development extended beyond them, gradually absorbing surrounding villages such as Heavitree and Wonford. More recently other early settlements, notably Alphington, Pinhoe and Topsham, have been absorbed within the city. By 1987 the city's population had reached 99 000.

Being situated at the lowest crossing, and later bridging, point of the Exe, Exeter has assumed considerable importance in communication terms. It was located at the westernmost point of the Romans' main highway network in the South West, and it is at the 'crossroads' of the present national highway network serving Devon and Cornwall.

Two major routes in the national network intersect at Exeter: the M5 motorway from the Midlands linking with the A38 to Plymouth and south Devon, and the A303/A30 from London to Cornwall. Other main roads from Exeter are the A376 to Exmouth, the A377 to Barnstaple and north Devon, the A396 to Tiverton and north-west Somerset, together with the coastal routes of the A3052 to Lyme Regis and the A379 to Dawlish and Teignmouth. Exeter is also the junction for two inter-city rail routes – Penzance to Paddington and Exeter to Waterloo – as well as two locally important branch lines. The development of Exeter airport reinforces the city's importance.

The main roads serving the city form a radial pattern converging on the central area, with the exception of the outer and inner bypasses. There are three major crossing points of the River Exe within the city – at Exe Bridges to the west of the central area, at Countess Wear on the Exeter ring road (the former outer bypass) and at Cowley, carrying the A377 to north Devon.

Before the Second World War very few new major roads

The damage caused by the bombing of the city in May 1942 marked the end of the High Street as Exonians had known it for decades; it also marked the beginning of a new central area for the city. The picture shows High Street seen from the top of the old post office immediately after the bombing. First widened to a dual carriageway, more recently it has been partly pedestrianized.

had been provided in Exeter, the only one of importance being the Exeter outer bypass in the mid 1930s. During the summer months especially, the bypass relieved the traffic congestion in the centre of the town, because until then High Street formed part of the direct route for traffic to and from south Devon and Cornwall. The route from High Street to the Exe Bridge carried the combined volume of traffic from London and the Midlands. Not long after the war, however, even the bypass became congested and achieved national notoriety for the long delays to traffic it caused during the height of the summer. This was not relieved until the M5 motorway provided a new bypass for Exeter in 1977.

## Exeter trams

To return to an earlier period, the introduction of trams into Exeter dates back to around 1880. These early trams were horse-drawn and, bearing in mind the topography of the city, they did well to last for twenty years or so. However, the problems of horse power gave rise to the need for more advanced 'motive power' and in 1903 work began on laying tram lines for the electric trams. On 4 April 1905 the first electric trams were brought into service on two routes, one between the Guildhall and Heavitree Road, the other between St David's Station and Pinhoe Road. One of the most notorious accidents that has ever occurred in Exeter involved a tram which, on 7 March 1917, crashed on Exe Bridge. The tram had lost control when coming down the steep part of Fore Street and failed

Exeter is a city of distinguished lineage. It was an ancient British settlement long before the Romans arrived. It continued as a Roman frontier town, one of the most westerly of the Empire, and blossomed with the growth of international trade, particularly in the late seventeenth century. For the greater part of its history, it has sheltered behind city walls. This map, drawn by Joseph Coles in 1709, shows buildings spreading along the major routes to and from the city. At the top right is a curious picture of the Guildhall with an extra storey built on.

An aerial view of the heart of Exeter, showing the cathedral.

to stop until it was on the bridge itself where it capsized, killing one passenger and injuring three others.

The system began to decline in the late twenties and by 1931 the tram had given way to the omnibus. The last tram was driven by the same man who had driven the first in 1905.

## The central area

Exeter's opportunity to reconstruct the highway pattern of its centre arose as a result of the main blitz on the city in the early hours of 4 May 1942. The main areas devastated were: High Street and Bedford Street from Gandy Street to, and including, Eastgate; the South Street/Fore Street area; and the south side of Sidwell Street from Paris Street to Belmont Road, extending as far as Newtown and Lower Summerlands.

The City Council later appointed a planning consultant, Thomas Sharp, to prepare a plan for the redevelopment of the city and his 1946 report, entitled *Exeter Phoenix*, was accepted as a basis for future detailed planning. Some of the earlier reconstruction was based on his overall proposals, which were supplemented by detailed proposals emerging from later reports and recommendations by the city's chief officers, mainly by John Brierley O.B.E., the City Engineer.

To mark the start of the rebuilding of the central area a commemorative feature was erected at the western end of what eventually became the new pedestrianised shopping precinct of Princesshay. The plaque, contained in the feature, was unveiled by Princess (later Queen) Elizabeth on 21 October 1949. Princesshay was finally completed in 1962 and later declared a public highway. The adjoining arcades were constructed in 1958.

Work on the new road layout commenced in September 1950, with the construction of a newly aligned Bedford Street, and most of the other roads to the south of High Street quickly followed. Provision of the service roads to the north of High Street started in 1952 with the construction of Bailey Street and Musgrave Row.

Attention turned next to the South Street and Fore Street area. Shopping development began in South Street in 1953 and at the same time the George Street service road was provided. A start was also made on the reconstruction of Mary Arches Street. The widening and reconstruction of South Street was undertaken in two stages, starting in 1955 and finishing in 1958. The length of Fore Street from South Street to Mary Arches Street was designed so that a dual carriageway could be provided later. The initial reconstruction and widening was finished in 1957 and the road network for the whole of this area was completed with the reconstruction of Bartholomew Street East in 1960 and Market Street in 1964.

The greatest expanse of wartime devastation was in the Sidwell Street area and here reconstruction was started in 1953. By 1959 several new roads, mainly intended as service roads, had been completed in an area which included light industrial premises.

The main carriageway of High Street was not replaced

Stepcote Hill, in the west of the city, was once one of Exeter's main streets. It led to the West Gate, the medieval Exe Bridge and then to Plymouth and beyond. In consequence, it saw a great deal of traffic. The centre was for carts and the steps for the wagoners and pedestrians. Its narrow aspect and cobbled surface are a reminder of the huge difference between medieval and modern traffic demands.

until the new buildings had been erected. Construction of the new road, as a dual carriageway, between Gandy Street and Eastgate began in 1961 and was completed in the following year. It had originally been intended that the dual carriageway of High Street should be continued to the Queen Street corner and then via Queen Street, Paul Street, Bartholomew Street and New Bridge Street to link with the Exe Bridge. This proposal was abandoned in the early 1960s, and so was a similar proposal for the widening of Fore Street.

Referring to the reconstruction of blitzed cities, the well-publicized Buchanan report of 1963, entitled *Traffic in Towns*, stated that one of the main mistakes seemed to have been the advocacy of the dual-carriageway street as the standard form for main shopping areas, producing the worst of both worlds, offering neither safety and comfort for pedestrians nor convenience for traffic. It cited Exeter's High Street as a typical example. On the other hand, the report was complimentary about the new Princesshay shopping precinct where, it said, something of permanent value had been created.

Perhaps the most controversial aspect in the reconstruction of the central area roads layout was the final outcome of the proposals for the Eastgate junction. Thomas Sharp had proposed a 'rectangular roundabout' but had made no allowance for pedestrian segregation. The basic proposal was, however, redesigned to provide subways and a central sunken garden. This was approved by the City Council and submitted to the Ministry of Transport. The Ministry was prepared to provide only a 75 per cent grant based on a traffic-signal-controlled crossroads. It would nevertheless have raised no objection to the submitted scheme if the City Council had met the difference in cost. This seemed a strange stipulation as the traffic figures submitted conformed to the Ministry's criteria for establishing roundabouts. Eventually, in 1957, after much discussion at Ministry level, the City Council reluctantly, and by a majority of only two votes, resolved to proceed with the traffic-signal scheme. The works commenced in 1958, involving also the realignment and reconstruction of Paris Street and New North Road, with extensive alterations to mains and services. They were completed in 1960. The choice of the traffic-signal scheme still left the problem of pedestrian/vehicle conflict at this important focal point unsolved.

Land adjacent to the inner bypass and Paris Street became the site for a new bus and coach station which was completed in 1964. In 1965 King William Street was widened and extended to provide access to Exeter's first multi-storey car park.

## The inner bypass

One of the first thoughts when planning the reconstruction of the centre area was for the establishment of an inner bypass to bring relief to the main spine road passing through the centre of the town.

The route finally chosen started at the junction of Sidwell Street and Blackboy Road, ran in a south-westerly direction across blitzed sites to the junction of Paris Street with Heavitree Road, continued through mainly private open ground to Magdalen Street and the junction of South Street with Holloway Street, finally extending to the Exe Bridge crossing. It was decided to construct a single carriageway over the entire length, and the intention was to have roundabouts at the Blackboy Road, Paris Street, Magdalen Road and South Street junctions.

The first stage from Sidwell Street to Summerland Street, beginning in 1954, was followed immediately by a second stage to Paris Street, including the roundabout. The third stage, which started in 1957, took the road as far as Magdalen Street at its junction with South Street/ Holloway Street. The final stage to Edmund Street (which gave access to Exe Bridge) completed the route.

At the same time a link was provided from Bonhay Road, to carry the eastbound traffic. Work on this section was preceded, in 1961, by a start on a widened and realigned Frog Street bridge, carrying New Bridge Street.

A well-publicized feature in clearing the way for this link was the moving, by a specialist firm, of the sixteenth-century Tudor House from the corner of Frog Street to its present site at West Gate. It became known as 'The House that Moved'.

As part of this last stage of the inner bypass a difference in levels permitted the provision of Exeter's first pedestrian subway, on the line of the old Coombe Street, to allow a segregated route from the city centre to the proposed car park at Lower Coombe Street and the Quay area. The roundabout at Blackboy Road was also provided at about this time.

The crossroads formed at the South Street junction were signal controlled, but capacity problems soon developed. A gyratory system controlled by traffic lights was established by using the road around the Acorn Inn which had originally been intended as a rear service road for new development fronting a widened Magdalen Street and Holloway Street. This gyratory system was further improved in 1974, with additional improvements planned for the late 1980s.

## Exe Bridges

Throughout its long history Exe Bridge has been important to Exeter and the two bridges there today continue to be the only major link within the city between the central part and the areas to the west of the river which include not only high-density residential development but also the expanding Marsh Barton Trading Estate. In addition, traffic between north Devon and parts of south Devon uses the route that crosses the river at Exe Bridges. They act as a funnel not only for road and pedestrian traffic but also for most of the mains and services that need to cross the river.

By 1945 the vehicular capacity of the existing bridge (built in 1905) was completely inadequate, with its four lanes controlled on each bank by traffic signals. Moreover, the flat three-pinned arch structure, although sound, was a very serious impediment to the flow of flood water and this was another reason why it had to be replaced.

Many ideas for improving the situation were considered. Thomas Sharp proposed a clover-leaf interchange on the east bank with a roundabout on the west bank, but this was considered too ambitious and extravagant in the use of land and the idea was not pursued. An alternative scheme was an additional bridge immediately adjacent to the existing one with a simple roundabout on each bank. Eventually it was decided to construct two bridges, forming a roundabout over the river, thus reducing the land requirements to an absolute minimum.

With assistance from the Hydraulic Research Station at Wallingford, the final design was drawn up incorporating the two new bridges 141 m apart, each having four 3.4 m traffic lanes. Bonhay Road traffic would travel over the bridge by way of the Frog Street underpass and Edmund Street. A system of subways would enable complete segregation of pedestrians. In addition, each bridge was to carry mains and services between the beams.

A start on the construction was made in 1959 with the dualling of a short length of Cowick Street and the provision of a small raised roundabout on the west bank to form the eventual western approach to Exe Bridge North. This bridge was opened to traffic on 30 July 1969. Two

years were allowed for the building of Exe Bridge South, owing to more extensive demolition and roadworks, as well as other associated works, and this was opened to traffic on 15 May 1972. The removal of the old bridge and the landscaping of the river banks were undertaken in 1974.

The demolition of the old City Brewery buildings during the second phase was of particular significance, for it revealed the well-preserved stone arches of the thirteenth-century bridge and exposed St Edmund's Church which was then partly demolished to be left as a ruin. The bridge is not only an interesting monument in its own right but also provides a striking contrast to its present successors.

In 1986 the Exe Bridge gyratory system and a new junction between Haven Road and Alphington Road, together with a direct link from Bonhay Road to the Exe Bridges, were included in the first phase of a comprehensive computerized signalling system in Exeter, designed to enable the maximum number of vehicles to use the roads over the bridges with the minimum of delay. In 1988 the lane arrangement on Exe Bridge South was modified to carry the Exe Cycle Route (see p.123 and p.139).

## Other river crossings

Before the M5 motorway reached Exeter it had been found necessary, because of the increase in traffic, to improve and widen various lengths of the Exeter bypass. A notable improvement was the construction, in 1972, of a bascule bridge over the Exeter canal to supplement the old

*The river bridge has always been a familiar landmark in Exeter. The pressure of traffic eventually led to the construction of the present two Exe Bridges which now form part of a large gyratory system controlled by traffic lights. The photograph was taken in 1971 during the construction of the new bridges and shows the interim arrangement when traffic used both the 1905 bridge and the first of the two new bridges.*

swingbridge and to provide for two lanes of traffic in each direction.

Over the years flood waters of the River Exe have also brought a need for road improvements, not only at Exe Bridges but also at Station Road, Exwick and at Bridge Road, Countess Wear, where viaducts were constructed across the flood plains in 1952 and 1965 respectively. Further flooding in 1974 caused the collapse of the old steel bridge over the river at Station Road, Exwick, so a new structure was provided in 1976. (See Chapter 4.)

## Transportation studies

In the mid sixties the growth in traffic and its effects on the road network made it necessary for a comprehensive Land Use Transportation Study to be undertaken. The Study, published in 1969, resulted in a package of proposals relating to a road network for the whole of the city, the scale of which proved to be financially and environmentally unacceptable.

This package contained proposals for two stages of growth: the intermediate phase up to 1981 and a second phase to 2010. The design of the first scheme included in the package, the Exe Bridge complex, was already being prepared. The next, the controversial Bull Meadow scheme, was to deal with traffic problems at the Holloway Street/South Street interchange and for this an underpass was proposed, incorporating the dualling of the inner bypass carriageway from the Exe Bridges as far as the Fairpark area. This scheme, however, failed at the public inquiry stage. Then followed the preparation of a scheme to widen and improve Alphington Street, but this was overtaken by the reorganization of local government in 1974, at which time Devon County Council, as the successor highway authority, decided to undertake a new study.

This second Study, called the Exeter and Area Transportation Study (EATS), advocated a range of strategies. These varied from making the maximum realistic provision, in environmental and financial terms, for the private car, to a public-transport-orientated strategy with severe restrictions on car users. The study proposed a balance between these objectives, including some major

Work on the two new Exe Bridges had to be completed before demolition of the old bridge could begin. For a short period during 1972, Exeter had three Exe Bridges. This aerial photograph also shows the relatively undeveloped state of much of the riverside around Exe Bridges and Shilhay.

road proposals which did not find public acceptability. The strategy finally adopted in 1978 was to use, to the best advantage, the present road system together with a measure of traffic restraint. However, at the same time the need was accepted for the Matford link road (since constructed) and for a further road, the Grace Road link, to connect the Exeter ring road with the developing residential areas to the west of the city and into the Marsh Barton Estate. The Grace Road link would also provide a more direct connection from the estate to the new length of the A30 via its link road (from Alphington Cross) which had been completed in 1976.

As a result of the study, computer-controlled traffic signals were provided at a number of important intersections and there are plans for their installation at other junctions at a later date, designed to make full use, in capacity terms, of the road network and to improve road safety.

It was also recognized that there was a need for some further major road works, especially to the radial routes. To this end there were improvements to Holloway Street, including first-stage widening, completed in 1980, and to Bonhay Road, completed in 1984, with a second-stage widening of Bonhay Road undertaken in 1986.

In 1988 the widening of Topsham Road between Burnthouse Lane and Barrack Road, together with the approaches from both directions, was completed. The

scheme involved traffic-signal control of the Barrack Road junction and the updating and modification of the traffic signals at the Burnthouse Lane junction to manage the new layout, including the cycleway which crosses Topsham Road at this point. One interesting feature of the improvement is that it resulted in Exeter's 'Second House that Moved' – St Loyes College lodge being resited bodily to allow the widening to take place without any demolition of property.

## Traffic Management

By the mid 1960s much of the programme of major road building in the central area had been completed and the era of traffic management began. This is not to say that there had been no serious attempts to control the movement of traffic in Exeter before that time. For instance, a system of one-way streets was successfully introduced in Southernhay in 1954 as part of a scheme to achieve a quiet and pleasant grassed area, for which the city received a Civic Trust Award in 1960. There was also the one-way system around High Street, North Street, Paul Street and Queen Street, brought into operation in November 1960, which, although successful for the motorist, had to be abandoned after three weeks because of the danger to pedestrians, especially at the High Street/North Street corner.

In October 1967 the first positive step was taken to

As the plants and trees reach maturity, High Street in Exeter, now partly pedestrianized, has become a pleasant place to walk, shop, meet people, or sit and listen to the buskers who frequently play here, especially in the summer. The scheme involved the paving over of large areas of the old dual carriageway and all motor traffic, except minibuses and emergency vehicles, is generally excluded.

curtail the movement of vehicles along the main shopping corridor, with the banning of west-bound traffic through High Street and much of Sidwell Street, except for buses. This enabled improvements to the scheduling of the city bus services. A greater freedom of movement for pedestrians also resulted. Then, on 8 June 1975, pedestrians were given priority in High Street between Eastgate and Queen Street as a result of an experiment prohibiting all vehicle movements with the exception of buses (and with other minor exemptions). This proved so successful that a permanent Order was made, and the environment was further improved by the removal of the central reservation and the widening of the footways, together with the provision of seats, trees, flower containers and modern bus shelters. The official opening took place on 25 July 1977. The restriction on vehicles was later extended beyond the Queen Street junction, along the front of the Guildhall to Broadgate.

Minibuses were introduced in Exeter in 1984. They are now used for all the bus services in the city, resulting in a 100 per cent increase in public transport usage. The removal of the final double-decker service from the High Street enabled even wider footways to be provided in the length east of the Queen Street junction in 1986, further improving conditions for pedestrians.

One of the most significant traffic-management measures for Exeter was the prohibition of heavy vehicles over 3 tons unladen (later changed to 7.5 tonnes maximum gross weight). A permanent Order was made on 1 March 1973 relating to the main part of the city east of the river, following an experiment introduced in 1971. Exemptions for access were carefully defined and the Order also banned the parking of large lorries in residential streets overnight as well as at weekends. There have since been modifications and extensions, in particular to include a large part of the city west of the river. These further restrictions were introduced in 1983, following a public inquiry.

As waiting restrictions were extended, the search by commuters for free on-street parking spaces broadened, leading to demands from the residents of areas immediately adjacent to the central area for some form of residents' parking scheme. Consequently in the early 1970s two-hour waiting restrictions were introduced in certain streets within the Barnfield area, but it was not until February 1978 that a residents' parking-permits scheme was introduced, initially as an experiment, in the St James area.

In 1986, a programme of highway enhancement schemes was begun in Devon. In Exeter the first schemes were the restoration of commemorative street lamps in Heavitree (described in Chapter 5) and the partial pedestrianization of Gandy Street, including its surfacing with granite setts. This has changed from a somewhat unprepossessing back street with little shopping interest into a quality street of shops, wine bars and other businesses. The Gandy Street Association, representing the commercial interests in the street, was so pleased with the environmental scheme that its members celebrated with several days of special events including music, jugglers and a Punch and Judy show.

The pedestrianization process is gradually being extended, with repaving and restrictions on vehicles at the foot of Castle Street, the northern end of Bedford Street and in Catherine Street.

The year 1987 saw the introduction of a comprehensive pedestrian signing system in Exeter which includes, in addition to attractive fingerposts, a series of interpretative panels at places of interest around the city.

Exeter was among the first cities to include a purpose-built traffic-free shopping mall as part of its post-war reconstruction plans. Princesshay continues to attract shoppers and sightseers although there are now other traffic-free shopping areas in the city.

1987 also saw the first steps taken in the redevelopment of Eastgate. The removal of a well-known local landmark, the ABC Cinema, permitted the realignment of Bailey Street (behind Boots) to form a crossroads with Longbrook Street. This is expected to be the forerunner of an extensive redevelopment of Eastgate and the bus and coach station, the most exciting prospect since the redevelopment of the Guildhall Centre, officially opened in 1976. Amongst other benefits it will resolve the pedestrian/vehicle conflict at Eastgate and maintain Exeter's claim to be one of the foremost shopping and commercial centres in the South West.

## Exe Cycle Route

In 1988 the Exe Cycle Route, linking Exwick, Burnthouse Lane, Marsh Barton and the city centre, was inaugurated. This included the attractive bridge over the Exe at Duck's Marsh, and was officially opened by Peter Bottomley, Minister of Roads and Traffic, in June of that year. This and the pedestrianization schemes emphasize that it is not only the motor car which is being provided for in the City of Exeter.

Until it was destroyed in the bombing raids of the Second World War, Bedford Street was an elegant Georgian crescent in the centre of the city. It was not the most likely place to find a car salesman! Until the early 1920s most Exonians who could afford it would probably have bought their cars from a local manufacturer of hand-built cars. The 'Clyno' cars here were early contenders in the race to capture the mass market in car sales. The marque was not a success, and the company went into liquidation in July 1929 after producing 40 000 cars.

# PLYMOUTH

Plymouth is today the largest urban settlement south-west of Bristol and serves as a sub-regional centre for south-west Devon and much of Cornwall. Its earliest recorded history appears in Domesday Book as the Manor of Sutone, with a modest population of sixty. This developed as a small fishing settlement, in the lee of the Hoe and around what is now Sutton Harbour. Plympton was a market town by 1194 and dominated the area in those early times. Sutton developed during the fourteenth century and by 1440 the population was 7000.

It was in Elizabethan times, however, that Plymouth sprang into prominence, as a result of the stirring deeds of Devon's famous seamen. Hoskins in his definitive work on Devon points to 'the emergence of Spain as the great enemy of England [giving] Plymouth a special importance as a naval base ... Thus it became a clearing-house for the disposal of prizes captured at sea in the Spanish War, partly because of its position, but partly also because it was the home harbour of Drake and John Hawkins ...' (the latter becoming comptroller of the Navy in 1589). The publication of this book coincides with the 400th anniversary of the defeat of the Spanish Armada. It was from Plymouth that Howard, Drake and Hawkins sailed in July 1588 to confront and defeat the Armada. Hoskins, incidentally, refers to the famous game of bowls on Plymouth Hoe which, he asserts, 'is almost certainly true'.

Some thirty-two years later, in 1620, Plymouth became the last port of call for the Pilgrim Fathers in the *Mayflower* prior to their historic voyage across the Atlantic. The 'Mayflower Stone' at the Barbican commemorates this event and bears witness to one of Plymouth's many transatlantic connections.

In 1691 the construction of the Royal Dockyard was begun at the entrance to the Hamoaze and this led to the growth of a township called Plymouth Dock, subsequently changed to Devonport. Increased shipping movements required expansion of the Dockyard in the eighteenth century and, by 1824, Devonport was as large as Plymouth.

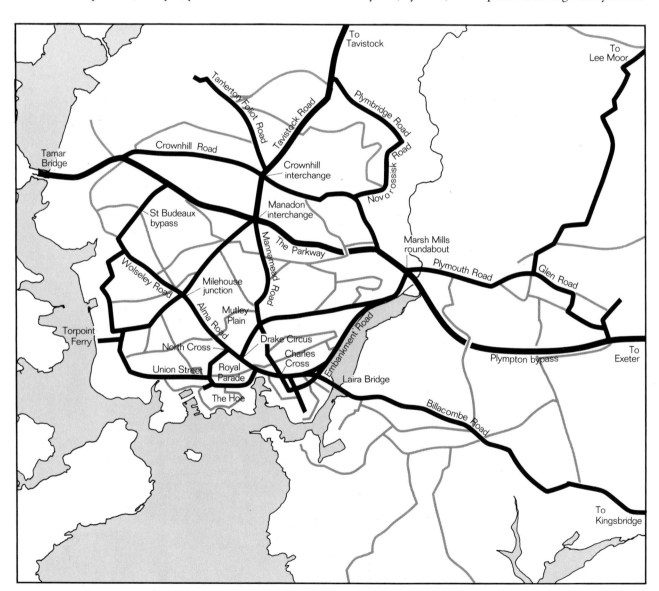

**The main road network in Plymouth in the late 1980s.**

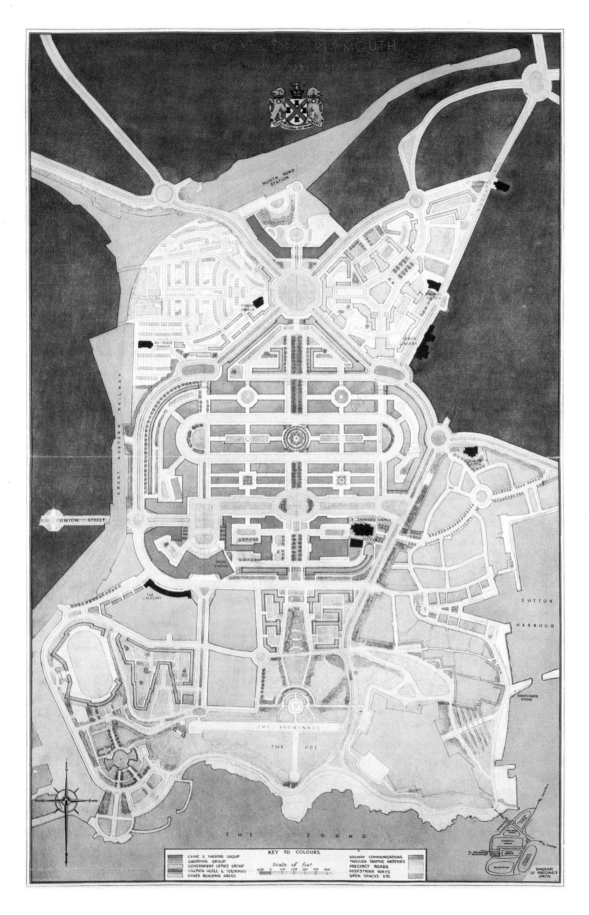

The city centre as it was envisaged in the *Plan for Plymouth*,
published in 1943. Pedestrianization of the centre was the first
major alteration since the post-war reconstruction.

By virtue of its importance as a naval base, Plymouth suffered more than anywhere else in Devon from bombing raids during the Second World War. The city endured over thirty attacks, the last and most devastating in March and April 1941. Much of the city was obliterated, including forty churches, as well as libraries, theatres, shopping streets and thousands of homes. Planning for revival was necessarily on a grand scale. *The Plan for Plymouth* included radical proposals for solving city-centre traffic problems.

A third township, East Stonehouse, developed on the peninsula separating Plymouth and Devonport; recorded as a manor in Domesday Book, by the end of the eighteenth century it had grown to a sizeable town.

By 1860 the two main rivers had been bridged. The Plym was spanned by a cast-iron road bridge over the Laira, while the Tamar was crossed by Brunel's Royal Albert railway bridge at Saltash. Ferries continued to convey vehicles and passengers to Torpoint and Saltash, whilst a passenger ferry operated to Cremyll, together with others on the Plym and Tamar. Indeed, although the Saltash ferry has been replaced by the Tamar road bridge, the others are still in use.

In contrast to its early pre-eminence, Plympton declined and, by the seventeenth century, had lost much of its former prosperity. Plymstock remained a small village even in the nineteenth century. However, in the early 1900s these two villages began to grow as suburban communities and are now substantial settlements.

The economic growth and consequent spread of development in Plymouth, East Stonehouse and Devonport led to their eventual amalgamation as the County Borough of Plymouth in 1914. It became a city in 1928. Since then the city has increased in area several times, the last extension being in 1967 when Plympton and Plymstock were included in its boundaries. In 1987 Plymouth's population had reached almost 256 000.

Plymouth's development is very much constrained by the topography as well as by the quality of the landscape of its surrounding area. To the south is the sea and the natural harbour of Plymouth Sound, magnificent when viewed from the limestone cliffs forming Plymouth Hoe. To the west is the River Tamar. To the east is the Laira, the open stretch of water forming the mouth of the River Plym. Northwards from the cliffs of the Hoe the land dips to a relatively flat area where the city centre is sited and then gradually rises over about 6 miles of hilly, and at times steep, terrain to meet Dartmoor.

Because of its location and these constraints, Plymouth has not been able to develop as would an inland town: i.e. radially outwards from its centre. Thus it consists in effect of one quadrant of a circle, with the city centre, as it were, 'off-centre'. All these factors have inevitably led to fewer radial routes into the centre compared with what would normally be expected in a city of its size, and they have limited what could be done in Plymouth to accommodate the rapid growth in traffic in the 1960s and 1970s.

However, rather than topography or location, it was the cataclysmic events of 1941 which were to shape the destiny of the city in a dramatic way. In March and April of that year, heavy air raids destroyed the old city centre and much of Devonport. The population fell from 200 000 to about 127 000, as many were driven to shelter elsewhere. After those raids the Council instructed the City Engineer, James Paton Watson, to prepare a plan for the reconstruction of the city centre, in association with Sir Patrick Abercrombie as consultant. The result was the famous *Plan for Plymouth* published in 1943, which, by its timing, was showing tremendous confidence in the future.

## The Plan for Plymouth

The origins of the *Plan for Plymouth* are briefly described in the introductory note by the co-authors Abercrombie and Paton Watson:

The Plan for Plymouth, or perhaps we should say, for a new Plymouth, became necessary because of the devastation of large areas by the enemy in the early months of 1941.

Lord Reith, when he was Minister of Works, visited the city on the 4th July, 1941. Though he stated he "did not and could not speak with authority", he advised the Council to go ahead, planning boldly and comprehensively, "go on with good planning and bank on getting financial help." Subsequent Ministers have endorsed this policy as only by so doing can the Government see in proper perspective the future machinery required for the successful re-planning of town and country.

We are fortunate, therefore, in having had such encouraging instructions which were endorsed by the local Press when reporting on the Minister's visit, as follows:–

"Good-bye to the narrow and maze-like streets of the centre; broad ways and modern buildings will replace them ... If, therefore, our proposals seem daring, it is because we know they can be realised when public opinion is so well instructed."

The Plan had as its major objectives the rehousing of those made homeless, the redevelopment of the city centre, the provision of a new road system, the expansion of the Dockyard and the attraction of new employment.

## The city centre

Looking particularly at city centre redevelopment and the provision of a new road system, the preamble to the Plan, in a few sentences, highlighted Plymouth's city-centre traffic problems before the blitz.

It was ripe for rebuilding; indeed, many individual plans were under immediate contemplation. But if these piecemeal rebuildings had taken place, the traffic congestion at the centre, already the worst in the West of England, would have been intensified almost to a degree of paralysis. The provision of a by-pass to the whole city, already projected and planned, would not have cured this central congestion, as the traffic that flows into Plymouth to shop would not and, of course, should not be diverted from its purpose....

The Plan's solutions to the problems are interesting, particularly in the light of recent events. 'The streets of the shopping centre should be especially designed for motor traffic; large car parks should be provided, and the streets made sufficiently wide to permit of continuous short-term parking without hindrance to the traffic flow.' It goes on, in what might be regarded as a contradictory way, 'Safety on the roads can only be obtained by segregation of all users of the road ... much can be done by the provision of dual carriageways, separate cycle tracks and pedestrian ways ....' Whether or not these apparent contradictions were capable of being met is a matter for consideration. Suffice it to say that in 1939 the city centre had been a random pattern of narrow streets, with tramways, even at that time unsuitable for the motorized traffic then existing. The density of traffic at St Andrew's Cross was the highest in southern England apart from London itself.

On the subject of tramways it is of interest that trams were operational in Plymouth until after the Second World War. The first tramway company in the city using horses as

Plymouth is a historic centre of naval power, and the presence, just after the war, of King George VI and Queen Elizabeth at the opening of Royal Parade showed the importance of the city. Royal Parade was a vital practical and psychological first step in the city's recovery from the war.

motive power – one of the first horse tramways in the British Isles – had been set up in 1870 (the Plymouth, Stonehouse and Devonport Tramways Company), to be supplemented by another company in 1901 (the Devonport and District Tramways Company). The latter used electric trams from the outset. Competition between the two companies caused complications in the operation of the system until 1922, by which time both had come under the aegis of Plymouth Corporation. At its peak there were 127 vehicles operating on the system. Despite modernization in the 1920s, from 1930 onwards the trams were gradually replaced by buses, and by 1939 only one route remained, that between the Theatre and Peverell. Reprieved by the outbreak of war, this service, albeit curtailed in length (from Old Town Street to Peverell), survived until 29 September 1945, when the last tram journey was made, not only in Plymouth but in the West Country as a whole.

## The Plan's proposals

The concept of the *Plan for Plymouth* was to provide for those who wanted to use their own private transport. The centre was to be so designed that there should be no through traffic among the shops, and people should be protected from the danger of traffic as far as possible. Through traffic was therefore to be on peripheral roads forming a ring road around the city centre with the radial roads terminating at large roundabouts. The roads inside the ring nevertheless were wide. New George Street was almost a full-scale dual carriageway. The footways were generously proportioned. Servicing and car parking were to be in rear courts, away from the shoppers in the busy streets. The concept was very imaginative for its day; indeed it was at the forefront of town planning.

New George Street, May 1988, just after the completion of the pedestrianization scheme.

Whatever one's views of it in the modern context, the remarkable feature of the Plan was the extent to which the implementation in the city centre followed the concept. That is the measure of the effectiveness of the Plan. The realization of Royal Parade was perhaps disappointing as compared to what was proposed, but all the main elements are there – the central feature of Armada Way linking the Hoe, the main shopping streets and North Road Railway Station, the wide parallel streets and the rear servicing areas.

The implementation of the Plan began with the building of Royal Parade, and the section from Westwell Street to Courtenay Street was opened by King George VI on 29 October 1947. He unveiled a commemorative tablet at the base of a flagpole mounted on a replica of Drake's Drum at the junction of Royal Parade with Armada Way and he officially named the two streets.

The redevelopment generally progressed northwards first with the building of Royal Parade, then New George Street, Cornwall Street and finally Mayflower Street. The ring road round the city centre was developed northwards also to Charles Church roundabout (1958), Drake Circus (1966) and North Cross (1971). North Cross and Drake Circus are interesting for the complex system of pedestrian subways, with the Drake Circus subways particularly busy because they are close to the Library, the Museum and the Polytechnic.

In general accord with the concepts of the Plan, and with the viability of the shopping area very much in mind, the City Council had cleared land in anticipation of the future redevelopment. This space was used for car parking until needed for other purposes. In the early 1960s the first multi-storey car parks were built and, because of the pressure on roadside parking spaces in the central-area streets, parking meters were introduced.

By the early 1970s, some twenty-five years after its construction, pedestrian/vehicle conflict in Royal Parade indicated the need for some positive action. In particular, pedestrians alighting at bus stops on the south side had to cross the Parade to the shops on the north side of the road. Furthermore, during the summer months there was a great deal of pedestrian movement from the city centre to the Hoe and the Barbican. The City Council therefore decided to construct a pedestrian subway under Royal Parade, on the route of Armada Way, and this was completed in 1973.

This spectacular aerial view of Plymouth says a great deal about the city's recent history. The post-war reconstruction in the central areas is easily distinguished from the rest of the city by the coherence in colour and design of the buildings, and by the shape of the road network. The older part of the city evolved over a much longer period in a haphazard manner.

The three central crossing points were removed and the two at either end repositioned as pelican crossings. The number of pedestrian crossings was thereby cut from five to three, an improvement which in turn much reduced the number of accidents. In order to give buses priority, a bus-only lane was introduced in 1978 round the whole city centre.

## 'The Regional Road System'

The Plan not only dealt with the city centre, it also made a number of proposals for improving what was called 'the regional road system', the roads approaching, and peripheral to, the city centre. Not surprisingly it refers to the 'Outer Ring Road', which had been mooted before the war (now built as the Parkway) from 'Marsh Mills to Saltash Passage at St Budeaux, where it was hoped that a high level bridge would be constructed to span the River Tamar to Saltash and beyond, thus providing a magnificent by-pass....'

To the east the Plan proposed a Plympton bypass which would have been routed between Plympton St Mary and Plympton St Maurice. The Plan comments, 'We also understand that the County Council favours an entirely new road for motor traffic between Plymouth and Exeter.' This illustrates both the perspicacity of highway planners in 1943 and the long lead time for implementation of major projects!

Another major proposal was an eastern ring road from Longbridge (Plympton), linking to the A379 road at Plymstock and terminating at Heybrook Bay. This involved the rerouteing of the A379 through Plymstock. There were other proposals for improving the local network to the east of the city, which would today give rise to considerable concern particularly from the conservation point of view.

Closer to the city centre a number of proposals were made for improving the radial roads outside the inner ring road. Principally these were:

1. the improvement of Exeter Street (to the existing Cattedown roundabout);
2. the improvement of Union Street (to Stonehouse);
3. the improvement of Cobourg Street/Saltash Road as part of the A388 route through to the Saltash ferry;
4. the construction of a new road from Pennycomequick, forming a link between the city centre and the Dockyard and Torpoint ferry.

The extent to which these proposals came to fruition is explained below. Whilst work was to proceed on the A38 'spine' road and the bridging of the Laira, many other major projects had to await the outcome of the 'Plymouth and Environs Transportation study' (PETS), started in 1973.

## The A38 'spine' road

The construction of the M5/A38 spine road, which is now taken for granted, has been achieved over a long period of time and by dint of much persistence. The main elements, so far as Plymouth is concerned, are the Tamar Road Bridge, the Plympton bypass, and linking the two, the Parkway. Although these are described in more detail in Chapters 3 and 4, a few brief comments are appropriate here.

## The Tamar Road Bridge

Until the construction of the Tamar Bridge the lowest bridging point of the River Tamar was New Bridge at Gunnislake some 15 miles (24 km) north of Plymouth. Traffic travelling directly from Plymouth to Cornwall had to rely on the Saltash and Torpoint ferries. The *Plan for Plymouth* had pointed to the need for a Tamar road bridge, and it was clear that the ferries, particularly the Saltash ferry, would not meet the demands of increasing volumes of traffic. So in 1959 Plymouth City Council and Cornwall County Council decided to fund jointly the construction of the bridge. Complementing Brunel's magnificent railway bridge opened just over a century earlier in 1859, the Tamar Bridge was opened in 1961 and was the forerunner of the Severn and Humber Bridges. The bridge has been extremely successful and the amount of traffic using it has far exceeded expectations.

## Plympton bypass

In former times the main route into Plymouth from London and Exeter had been through Plympton, past Plympton Marsh to the south of Longbridge, thence to Lipson and Tothill. The embankment by the side of the Laira was not constructed until the early nineteenth century.

The Plym could be forded at Longbridge, depending on the state of the tide, and a bridge was built here in 1753.

This road eventually became the A38 trunk road and its traffic, despite increasing enormously in volume, continued to thread its way through the narrow streets of Plympton, including the Ridgeway shopping centre. Although in the 1960s Glen Road had been built, affording some relief to Ridgeway from local traffic, it was still in environmental terms wholly unsatisfactory. Thus when plans were drawn up to improve the A38 between Plymouth and Exeter to dual two-lane carriageway standard, they included proposals to bypass Plympton. It was suggested that, unlike the proposals in the *Plan for Plymouth*, this section should pass through Saltram estate, owned by the National Trust, and thus to the south of Plympton St Maurice. Despite a strong rearguard action by the National Trust, the route through the estate was chosen and the bypass was opened in 1971, thereby providing a further substantial road crossing of the River Plym.

## The Parkway

With the construction of the Tamar Bridge and Plympton bypass the intervening link now became essential. Until the opening of the Tamar Bridge in 1961, through traffic from the A38 to Cornwall principally used the route from

Plympton via Royal Parade and Devonport to the Torpoint ferry. After the bridge was built this traffic was directed to the Forder Valley/Crownhill Road route, still an unsatisfactory road since it passed through heavily built-up areas, with the very steep Forder Valley Hill forming part of the route.

A corridor had been reserved for the road since the late 1930s. As a result there was land ready for use, with very little need for property acquisition. The road was conceived as a generously proportioned parkway whose function was to take trunk-road traffic through the city away from other, less suitable city roads: this was the nearest Plymouth would get to a true bypass. Construction work began in 1982 and the Parkway, as it was christened, was opened in 1985. Apart from 9 km of dual carriageway, it also includes the Manadon flyover which is a very substantial structure (see Chapter 4), directing traffic towards Outland Road and Milehouse and away from the congestion of Mutley.

## Laira Bridge

Only twelve months after the opening of the Tamar Bridge, another major project, the new Laira Bridge, was completed. The first Laira Bridge was built in 1827 at the expense of the Earl of Morley, using the then innovative system of cast-iron arches on wooden piles, sunk into the silt of the Laira. It was 16 ft wide, quite enough for those days. However, the continual pounding of traffic fractured some of the cast-iron segments and weight and speed limits had to be introduced. Clearly it had to be replaced, and a pre-stressed concrete bridge to dual-carriageway standard was built and opened in 1962.

The eastern abutment of the old bridge still exists, with the commemorative plaque of the original bridge built into it. The Latin inscription reads:

Hunc Pontem
Senatus Auctoritate Susceptum
Novas et Commodas
Vias Recludentem
Johannes Comes de Morley
Suis Sumptibus
Struendum Curavit
Opus Inchoatum A.D. 1824
Absolutum A.D. 1827.
J.M. Rendel, Architecto.

The translation is: 'Lord Morley, with Parliamentary Consent by public wish, undertook at his own expense the building of this bridge which opens new and suitable roads. The work began A.D. 1824 and completed A.D. 1827. J.M. Rendel, Architect.'

## Transportation studies

The Plymouth Land Use/Transportation Survey (LUTS) completed in 1966 was the first major study of traffic in the city to take account of predictions of the future growth of the city and the economic activities that generate traffic. It proposed an extensive framework of major roads in the city

to accommodate the traffic pressure, including a route, bypassing St Budeaux, as a north-west radial linking to the Tavistock Road. These proposals were later reviewed by a more detailed study initiated by the City Council in 1973 and taken over for completion by the County Council in 1974. The Plymouth and Environs Transportation Study (PETS) gave greater consideration to the potential contribution to be made by public transport and the likely availability of resources for road building, much reduced from those of the previous study. The completion of these studies was the next major milestone in the planning of Plymouth's road system over thirty years after the publication of the *Plan for Plymouth*. It is interesting that both the Studies and the Plan pinpointed similar problems, but, as one might expect, the solutions were not necessarily the same. Four strategies resulting from PETS were examined and a preferred strategy was adopted by the County Council in 1976. The means of dealing with the through traffic on the A38 had already been implemented or identified so the Study was concerned primarily with solving traffic problems in the city centre and on the approach radials. In summary these problems related to: the roads from Plympton and Plymstock; the city centre/Crownhill/Tavistock corridor; relief of the city centre and its pedestrianization; the city centre/St Budeaux corridor and the relief of St Budeaux.

Proposals to overcome these problems were later included in the County Structure Plan.

## The roads from Plympton and Plymstock

In order to deal with traffic from Plympton to Plymouth city centre a number of improvements have been made to this corridor. Before the Study, and indeed over a number of years, improvements had been made to Exeter Street as well as subsequently to the road alongside the Laira (from Marsh Mills to Embankment Road), which was widened in 1974. Further improvements came with the construction of the Embankment Road relief road along an old railway cutting – an imaginative scheme which was completed in 1981 – and the dualling of Plymouth Road, Longbridge between Marsh Mills and Plympton in early 1987. Travellers on this corridor, however, will be looking to the flyover at Marsh Mills on the A38, to reduce their journey times to and from the city centre. For travellers on the A379, including those from Plymstock, improvements to the road had been made in 1974 when the length between Laira Bridge and the city boundary was widened to dual-carriageway standard. They also have benefited from the construction of the Embankment Road relief road.

## The Crownhill/Tavistock corridor

To the north of the city are new areas of housing development, with some light industry and the city airport. Beyond this is Dartmoor National Park and villages which have become dormitory areas for the city. The route to these areas, the A386, subsequently passes through Tavistock, linking to the A30 and ultimately Okehampton.

In the early 1980s traffic entering Plymouth on the A386 was encouraged by means of signing to reach the city centre by way of Milehouse and Pennycomequick rather than through Mutley Plain which was badly congested and incapable of substantial improvement. Improvements are proposed to the length of road between Milehouse junction and North Cross. This will also benefit the A388 corridor, which is described below.

Another link which is being improved is Outland Road which joins Milehouse to the A38 at the Manadon flyover.

North of the Manadon flyover on the Parkway is Crownhill. In the 1950s it was a busy shopping centre at the junction of the main east-west and north-south traffic routes through the city, both single-carriageway roads. The solution to the problem at Crownhill was conceived as a two-level clover-leaf dual-carriageway interchange. The road scheme, with six subways for complete pedestrian segregation, was completed in 1968, with an immediate environmental improvement at Crownhill shops and the removal of long traffic queues in the rush hours.

In due course Tavistock Road, north of Crownhill, will be improved to dual-carriageway standard to serve not only the commuters from Tavistock but also the additional traffic resulting from development at Roborough. The village of Roborough itself has already been bypassed, enabling it to regain relative tranquillity.

There was, however, still a need to manage the traffic on the busy Mutley Plain route to improve its capacity. Computer technology was introduced and a scheme for the implementation of a series of traffic signals from the city centre through Mutley Plain to Manadon, linked to a central computer at Exeter, was completed in 1982. This is described in Chapter 5.

## Relief of the city centre

Abercrombie and Paton Watson recognized that it was necessary to separate traffic destined for the city centre from that which had no need to be there. They perceived it in simple terms as traffic needing to bypass the city and that visiting the city. A modern, less easily soluble, difficulty is that of separating traffic visiting the city centre from that travelling around the periphery. PETS proposed the construction of a northern relief road between Tothill

The two photographs on these pages tell a remarkable tale of destruction and revival over a period of nearly fifty years. On the left is a view of Plymouth as it looked before the devastating bombing attacks of the Second World War. On the right is a picture taken from an almost identical viewpoint in 1985.

Avenue and Western Approach. However, after considerable local and political pressure, it was decided that the environmental cost of the scheme was not justified and it was abandoned in 1987. An alternative solution is to introduce traffic management measures which will meet requirements to 1996. These include 'variable message car park' signing, which directs motorists to the nearest car park where spaces are available, and increasing the capacity of key junctions by the introduction of traffic signals, as well as improving Buckwell Street to the south of the city centre. After 1996, major junction improvements or a one-way gyratory system around the city centre will be necessary.

## The city centre/St Budeaux corridor

Abercrombie and Paton Watson had identified the need to improve the A388 corridor from Pennycomequick to the Tamar Bridge, and PETS confirmed this need. The importance of the route increased as Saltash grew rapidly from the time that the bridge was opened, as a dormitory area for the city. As mentioned above, the principal need for improvement is at the corridor's eastern end which also serves the Crownhill/Tavistock corridor.

## St Budeaux bypass

St Budeaux has suffered from the effects of greatly increased volumes of through traffic, and in 1988 a bypass was constructed in the Weston Mill valley, providing a direct link from the Parkway to the Dockyard. Much-needed relief was afforded to St Budeaux, especially its shopping centre, as a result.

H.R.H. Queen Elizabeth in the new pedestrianized central area of Plymouth to open the 'Sundial' fountain on 22 July 1988.

A view of St Andrew's Cross at the junction of Old Town Street and Bedford Street. This picture appeared in the *Plan for Plymouth* to illustrate the pre-war traffic conditions on the 'busiest corner in the west'. The scene is made to look even busier by some faked extra vehicles on the right of the picture.

## Pedestrianization

Abercrombie and Paton Watson felt that it was important for shoppers to be able to move freely through the streets of the city centre and to park their cars easily within those streets. This dictated the width of the streets in the Plan. They were planning for the age of the motor car; what they clearly did not foresee was the rate at which car ownership would increase. Had they done so they might have pursued their ideas of segregation one stage further and kept vehicles and pedestrians as separated as possible. Some thirty years later the need for that segregation was recognized, as a result of PETS, and in 1987, some forty years later, pedestrianization became a reality. Although not achieved without much, at time acrimonious, public and political debate, its completion, together with proposals to redevelop the prime shopping area between Royal Parade and New George Street, has surely brought significant benefits to both shopkeepers and shoppers alike. In July 1988 the acrimony and controversy were set aside, when, as part of the celebrations for the 400th anniversary of the Armada, the Queen unveiled a plaque commemorating the realization of the pedestrianization proposals. Thus the *Plan for Plymouth* had been updated to meet the challenge of the twenty-first century.

# TORBAY

Because Tor Bay provides a magnificent natural shelter and anchorage its history is as long as man's association with the sea. Ships sheltered there during the Armada campaign in 1588; William of Orange landed at Brixham in 1688; and during the Napoleonic Wars the British fleet used Tor Bay as an anchorage. In 1944 it was a Second World War assembly point for the Normandy invasion fleet, while in peacetime Tor Bay has been the setting for many prestigious yachting events, including the 1948 Olympics, the start of the Tall Ships Race and several royal reviews of the fleet.

The first real growth in the area took place during the seventeenth and eighteenth centuries, but not until the coming of the railway in 1848 was there an upsurge in its popularity as a watering place. Since that time the growth of the three towns of Torquay, Paignton and Brixham has been rapid, centred almost entirely on tourism. In 1968 they were combined to form the County Borough of Torbay, which today enjoys the reputation of being one of the country's leading resorts. Such was the rate of growth

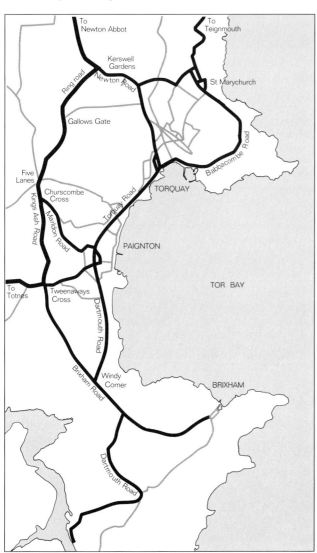

**The main road network in Torbay in the late 1980s.**

that Torbay became the second largest urban area in Devon and the third largest in the south-west peninsula. By 1987 its population had reached 118 000. The Engineer to the newly created County Borough throughout its short six-year existence prior to local government reorganization was Michael Hawkins, who subsequently became County Engineer and Planning Officer.

As a result of Torquay's comparatively recent origin, its highway network was exceptionally well landscaped with wooded drives and terraces following the contours of the hills. Its present attractiveness owes much to the foresight of the landowners at the time. Paignton does not share Torquay's advantages in terms of its setting and topography, while Brixham's street pattern is typical of an older established fishing port.

## The increase in road traffic after 1900

With the advent of motor transport, the first problem encountered in Torbay was damage to the road surfaces caused by traction engines with their large cleated iron wheels and heavy trailers. These were soon followed by motor vehicles and, in 1909, to overcome one of the problems of dust nuisance which plagued pedestrians at the time, the first experiments were made in Victoria Street, Paignton with limestone chippings and tar. Nearby Palace Avenue was tar painted at the same time. In August of that year a tar-sprayer was bought for £90, and the 'watering of the street', necessary several times a day in dry weather, was no longer required. In common with urban areas elsewhere, the first steps were being taken to cater for the effects of the motor vehicle.

## Trams and buses

In 1905 the Torquay Tramway Company was authorized to build a tramway in various parts of Torquay. Two services were provided from Beacon Quay, one to Torre station, St Marychurch and Babbacombe on a circular route through Wellswood and Ellacombe, with a second to Torquay station. It was decided not to use 'overhead trolleys' but to install the 'Dolter' surface-contact system instead. The 'Dolter' system operated by means of 'studs' between the rails. The 'studs' were activated by a 'skate' under the tram as it passed over them, thereby bringing them into contact with a live rail beneath the ground. This propelled the tram forward.

When the Tramway Company decided to extend to Paignton in 1910, Paignton and Torquay Councils were at odds with one another. Paignton preferred the overhead system, and Torquay wanted 'Dolter' for the whole system. The dispute went to arbitration and it was revealed that, in Torquay, horses had been electrocuted by stepping on 'live studs'. Not surprisingly Torquay lost the dispute: 'overhead trolleys' went into operation from Torquay station to Paignton, and the rest of the system was converted at the same time.

Trams operated in the two towns for over twenty years.

By the 1920s traffic congestion was serious and the replacement of trams by a more flexible form of transportation became urgent. Trolley-buses were then in vogue and an attempt was made to introduce them in Torbay. The Torquay and Paignton Traction Bill was submitted to the 1929/30 Session of Parliament but it failed at the committee stage. Trams were finally replaced by Devon General omnibuses early in 1934.

## The coast road between St Marychurch and Paignton

The first major improvement to the coast road was made possible when the Great Western Railway doubled the tracks between the two towns in 1909–10. As part of this, the tunnel (145 yards long), which had existed on the Torquay side of the gasworks since 1859, was 'opened' out. This enabled the road to be regraded and realigned on its present route from the entrance to Livermead Cliff to Hollicombe, thereby eliminating Breakneck Hill which had caused considerable problems to the early motor-buses with their small engines and uncertain braking systems. At the same time the bridge over the railway was constructed. (It was reconstructed in 1936 and the familiar pink concrete carriageway was put down.)

The Marine Drive at Hope's Nose was built and opened in 1924. The finance for this came from a fund set up to provide work for the unemployed.

In 1933, just before the trams ceased running, the building of the new sea-wall and promenade was started between Princess Pier and Belgrave Road. The carriage-

The photograph shows the opening of the Torquay tram service on 4 April 1907. These early trams were powered by the 'Dolter' system, which used a pair of magnetized skids mounted under the tram to draw up a metal arm fixed beneath two metal pads in ceramic 'Dolter pots'. These were set into the road surface at regular intervals. A pair of electrical contacts were closed by the movement of the metal arm and the power then flowed through the metal pads and the skids to the tram motors. Unfortunately the sea air affected the free movement of the metal arm on occasions, causing some of the pads to remain live after the tram had passed. In the interests of public safety the system was replaced after a short time by the more conventional overhead cables.

way, which had changed little since the turnpike days, was extended to almost twice the existing width. The opening of Abbey Park in 1924 and the later purchase of Torre Abbey together with its grounds, enabled the widening of Torbay Road to be carried out in 1939 between Belgrave Road and the Grand Hotel.

## The post-war era

Although Torbay suffered aerial attack during the Second World War, causing casualties and damage to property, the scale of destruction was far less than that experienced in Plymouth and Exeter and so it provided no opportunity to improve the highway network. In the years following the war there was a steady increase in the volume of traffic, as elsewhere. More families in and around Torbay became car owners, and an increasing number of visitors to the area travelled by private car rather than rail. By the late 1950s congestion during the summer months in the Torbay area was seriously impeding the movement of essential services.

The Dean of Bristol made a prediction in 1814 to his friend Sir
Lawrence Palk, that Torquay would one day become a fashionable
watering place. Sir Lawrence, who owned Torquay and the
surrounding lands, made several improvements to the village, but
the number of visitors did not increase. 'What more can I do?' he
complained to a friend. 'Make a road' was the reply, 'the place is
inaccessible.' The next morning Sir Lawrence, his friend and a
woodman staked out the Newton Road! Torbay's expansion has
been almost entirely due to tourism, but the resort would never have
developed at all had the roads around it not been improved. The
photograph shows how residential expansion has now linked the
towns of Torquay and Paignton.

In the late eighteenth and early nineteenth centuries, public transport in Torquay was provided by sedan and bath chairs, and later by donkey carts. So common a sight were these chairs that in 1845 the Commissioners instructed their Surveyor to 'appoint a convenient place between the hotels for the chairmen to stand with their chairs'. The increasing popularity of the resort generated a lively market for public transport services of all kinds; the arrival of motorbuses popularized outings into the surrounding countryside as well as increasing the mobility of the tourists within the town. The picture shows two Chelmsford steam buses in The Strand in 1904.

For instance, ambulances were taking between one and two hours for journeys between the Brixham and Paignton areas and Torbay Hospital in the Lawes Bridge (Shiphay) area. The A379 road along the sea front was the only route available other than a single-track lane about 8 ft wide between Shiphay and Marldon where vehicles would need to reverse into gateways frequently during busier times of the day. It was decided to develop this route into a ring road and by 1961 it had been opened up to a minimum width of 18 ft between Shiphay and Marldon. As soon as this route was available, as many as 13 000 vehicles per day were using it.

## Torquay and Paignton central areas

Considerable emphasis was given to traffic management during the 1960s, and in May 1965, after much public debate, a one-way system was introduced in the central area of Torquay. This comprised four interlocking 'cog-wheels', three of which still remain essentially as originally devised,

There have been no substantial changes in the main road network in Torquay since the middle of the nineteenth century. The most rapid period of development occurred between 1815 and 1840 when the town was becoming a popular resort. The Torbay road, shown here in 1933 undergoing its first major improvement, was built in 1840 by the local Turnpike Trustees at a cost of £13 000.

Brixham harbour became the centre of tremendous excitement in the spring of 1944 as American forces gathered at sites along the coast between Weymouth and Land's End in preparation for the Normandy landings. In the harbours of both Brixham and Torquay concrete 'hards' were built for tanks and other military vehicles to be loaded on to the landing ships. The Brixham hards in the foreground of the photo are still useful for launching sailing boats.

covering the central area of the town between the main Post Office in Fleet Street and the Technical College in Newton Road. The principle behind the system was that there should be no conflicting traffic flows requiring control by traffic signals. Apart from signal-controlled pedestrian crossings, the only signals necessary were those retained in Union Street at the junction with Market Street, plus those installed later in Abbey Road at the junction with St Luke's Road, in both cases to deal with access to the central multi-storey car park.

A number of traffic signals at other locations in Torquay had been introduced in the mid 1960s. A temporary traffic-signal arrangement on the gyratory system linking Fleet Street, The Strand and Torbay Road, was made permanent, using the most advanced form of technology then available. A master controller was used to co-ordinate the six individual controllers operating various signals to give vehicles a progression around the system.

In Paignton, a one-way system, incorporating Eugene Road, was introduced in 1966 to deflect through traffic from the Torquay direction away from the Preston shopping area. A one-way system in Paignton town centre was brought into operation in April 1968. In 1970 a modification was made to this one-way system to remove through traffic from Victoria Street and provide a small pedestrianized area at its junction with Torquay Road. This involved the demolition of property to enable an extension of Commercial Road from Dartmouth Road to Totnes

Torquay was among the first places in Devon to convert a shopping street that carried traffic into a pedestrian area. The Fore Street precinct in St Marychurch was opened on 15 December 1978 by the Chairman of the County Council, Councillor Goodrich. The occasion was marked by the installation of the decorated lamp visible in the foreground, which had been sited at various locations in the town before being restored and given a permanent home in the pedestrianized street.

was improved to its present modest standard over the years, mainly as a result of frontage development. In 1959 Middle Street was widened, as an unemployment relief scheme, to enable easier access to the harbour.

A modest scheme arising from the operational needs of the Second World War (Brixham was a major embarkation port for the United States Forces) resulted in the demolition of three houses in Berry Head Road to provide a turning space for tanks and transporters as they boarded landing craft near the lifeboat station; it was later used as a turning space for buses.

In post-war years traffic management, in the form of parking restrictions and one-way streets, has been progressively introduced to make the best use of road space available, not only for the domestic needs of inhabitants and visitors, but also to sustain local industry, the foremost of which is a fishing fleet which has regained prosperity in recent years. The landing of fish at Brixham requires large refrigeration vehicles to pass from the harbour through the town centre to distribute the fish catches to markets and processing depots far afield.

Of particular note is a pedestrian-priority scheme introduced in 1971 in Fore Street (the main shopping street) to preclude all vehicles between 10 a.m. and 6 p.m. throughout the summer months when the town is overwhelmed by visitors. This was one of the first of its type in the county.

Such a high proportion of visitors are car-borne that in 1978, a park-and-ride scheme was introduced whereby visitors were invited to leave their cars in a car park on the outskirts of the town and to travel by special bus service, thereby relieving traffic pressures in the harbourside and central areas of the town. During the first year of its introduction, some 9300 cars used this facility, which is financed jointly by the County and Borough Councils.

## Highway planning

During 1965 a transportation study was started, covering an area slightly larger than Torbay itself. Information provided by this was used during 1968 and 1969 when a Traffic and Transportation Plan was prepared, as required by the Ministry of Transport from all urban authorities with a population over 50 000. Torbay's plan was one of the first to be prepared in the country.

In the course of drawing up a Development Plan for the new County Borough, a more detailed transportation study of the possible options for a highway network for Torbay was carried out between 1969 and 1972. This broadly identified two options as the basis for consultation. One

---

Road, and following negotiations with British Rail the highway was widened through Station Square. This entailed the removal of the original gates and the wrought-iron footbridge which had become a familiar landmark in the town centre. This decision at the time caused much dismay, particularly among railway enthusiasts.

As described in Chapter 5, the opportunity arose for Torbay to become a Ministry of Transport demonstration area for the first compact Urban Traffic Control (UTC) system in the world, whereby a network of traffic signals in a small urban area is controlled by computer. Before the introduction of this UTC system in 1979 the existing traffic-management systems were thoroughly re-examined. It was realized that the Torquay central-area one-way system was now capable of improvement. As a result traffic signals were installed at the junctions of Abbey Road/Tor Hill Road and East Street/South Street and the one-way flow in the road between these junctions was reversed. Traffic signals were also installed at the junction of Torbay Road/Belgrave Road in place of the previous roundabout arrangement. A number of new signal-controlled pedestrian-crossing facilities were also provided.

## Brixham

Brixham is at the end of the main road system and it does not suffer from the effects of through traffic. It is a compact coastal community, tightly packed with buildings making the best use of land in an area of unusual topography and providing a refuge from the marine elements to which the town is exposed. Conventional road building would have been destructive to the very essence of the town. New Road, linking the town centre with the main road network,

was based on an improvement of the coastal route southwards from Torquay through Paignton; the other envisaged the construction of a high-quality dual-carriageway ring road. After considerable public consultation and debate the Council decided to adopt the ring-road option, and also recognized that the improvement of traffic conditions in the town centres would require widespread traffic-management measures.

In parallel with the transportation studies, the County Borough Council commissioned planning consultants to prepare policy plans for the central areas of Torquay, Paignton and Brixham. Following extensive public consultation, town-centre plans were approved to complement the highway plan and form the basis for future planning in Torbay.

## Ring road improvements

Work began on the first stage of the upgrading of the ring road, between Kerswell Gardens on the A380 Newton Road and Gallows Gate, immediately after the formation of the new County Council in 1974. This new route, largely to dual-carriageway standard, was completed in 1975. Other improvements to the ring road were carried out during the next decade, pending the provision of the remainder of the high-specification route. Improvements were introduced in 1976 at the Five Lanes junction at Marldon to provide a twin mini-roundabout system, and a major improvement of the intersection of the ring road with the main Paignton to Totnes road at Tweenaway Cross was implemented in 1983 to increase capacity and to

More than 200 000 tons of rock had to be removed to make this 60 ft deep cutting for the Quarry Bend road improvement near Waterside, Paignton. When completed, in early 1969, the £142 000 scheme provided 500 yards of dual carriageway, replacing a notorious double bend which wound round the top and edge of the rocky outcrop. The former Paignton Urban District Council started the scheme in late 1967 and it was completed by the new Torbay County Borough, formed in 1968.

The modern harbour at Torquay shows how the resort has expanded its facilities specifically for the seafaring tourist. The marina in the foreground was completed in 1987. The square concrete ramps in the old harbour are the 'hards' mentioned on p.155.

The conflict between pedestrians and motorists is exemplified by the sea front at Torquay. People using Shedden Hill car park caused serious delays to traffic as they walked to the sea-front promenade. To improve both traffic flow and safety, the footbridge shown here was designed and built in 1971 for Torbay Borough Council by the Butterley Engineering Co. of Derby. In the following year, it gained a prestigious award from the British Constructional Steelwork Association. The intricately shaped deck is a steel box girder.

provide signal control for pedestrian movements. The improvement of the Windy Corner junction at the Brixham end of the ring road followed in 1984.

The plan to upgrade the ring road envisaged improved highway links between the ring road and Paignton. Marldon Road and Preston Down Road were typical Devon lanes, outside the urban area, until they were reconstructed to modern highway standards in 1982 and 1985 respectively, thereby encouraging Paignton traffic to use the ring road rather than the coastal route.

## Pedestrian priority

The construction of the first stage of the St Marychurch bypass in 1974 paved the way for comprehensive pedestrianization of Fore Street, St Marychurch in 1978. The building of service roads at the rear of properties on both sides of Fore Street permitted the total exclusion of all vehicular traffic and the creation of an attractively landscaped shopping centre.

The Town Centre Plan for Torquay envisaged pedestrian priority in the main shopping streets of Union Street and Fleet Street. A determined effort to introduce an experimental scheme in Union Street in 1979 failed largely as a result of fears for the commercial success of the town centre expressed by the trading community.

Nevertheless the need for redevelopment of a large central area site in Torquay, in the vicinity of Swan Street with a prime frontage on Fleet Street, had been recognized over a period of many years and various attempts made to redevelop the area comprehensively without success. Meanwhile the Borough Council had over the years purchased a large amount of property in that area and also controlled the bridges over Swan Street, but the inability to make progress resulted in a decline in the shopping standard in this prime area. In 1975 the Borough Council

again reviewed the opportunity for redevelopment and in 1977 adopted yet another scheme as a basis for consultation with local traders, landowners and interested parties.

No firm proposals emerged until 1983 when a revised plan was prepared, which included the creation of pedestrian priority in Fleet Street between Union Street and The Strand, in accordance with the established policies of the Borough and County Councils. It was envisaged that access to the redevelopment area, including a multi-storey car park, would be from Cary Parade and that vehicles needing to service other properties in Fleet Street would be allowed access. No other traffic would be allowed in Fleet Street between 10 a.m. and 6 p.m. except mini-buses.

A review of bus services resulted in an improved service to Torquay's central area and proposals for the removal of bus stands on both sides of The Strand, which had been a cause of concern over a long period. The redevelopment plan incorporated the provision of a dual carriageway at Cary Parade and the closure of Vaughan Parade to all traffic except service vehicles. The plan included a pedestrian footbridge linking the new shops and stores in Fleet Street with the Cary Green area, and the landscaping of the latter in association with the repaving of Vaughan Parade to provide an attractive pedestrian-priority area.

A major development company was selected to carry out the redevelopment scheme and detailed plans were prepared in consultation with the Borough and County Councils. The town waited anxiously for the long overdue redevelopment to begin, but as the date of starting drew near, rumours began to circulate that the firm was going to withdraw from the arrangement. Despite denials, this eventually happened just prior to the contract being made in 1986.

Against a background of bitterness and a continuing and vigorous campaign to 'Save Old Torquay', as the opponents of the redevelopment marketed their cause to refurbish the existing buildings, the Borough Council set about recovering the position. In 1986 proposals were again invited from interested developers and agreement was reached with the Rosehaugh Heritage plc for the comprehensive redevelopment of the area. Again the population waited anxiously for the start of the work. Eventually demolition began in October 1987 and construction got under way the following January. On 25 April 1988 the Mayor of the time, Councillor Eloise Armes, laid the foundation stone. The whole of the western side of Fleet Street was razed to the ground and the long awaited 'Fleet Walk' development began, with completion planned for midsummer of 1989.

In the meantime, the nearby Pavilion was refurbished to provide a splendid shopping centre, and the English Riviera Centre was constructed, thus providing the resort with its long-awaited and overdue specialized conference facilities. A major part of the Fleet Walk redevelopment was the creation of Fleet Street and Vaughan Parade as a pedestrian-priority area of high quality and which, together with the enhancement of The Strand and Victoria Parade, heralded the recovery of Torquay as one of the nation's major holiday resorts.

## Development of the Organization

**7**

On 18 August 1791, the poet Coleridge left the mail coach at Cullompton to complete the journey to his destination, Plymtree, on foot. He clearly did not enjoy the experience, which prompted him to write the poem 'Devonshire Roads', which begins thus:

> The indignant Bard composed this furious ode
> As tired he dragg'd his way thro' Plimtree road.
> Crusted with filth and stuck in mire
> Dull sounds the Bard's bemudded lyre;
> Nathless Revenge and Ire the Poet goad
> To pour his imprecations on the road.
> Curst road! whose execrable way
> Was darkly shadow'd out in Milton's lay.
> Where the sad fiends thro' Hell's sulphureous roads
> Took the first survey of their new abodes;
> Or when the fall'n Archangel fierce
> Dar'd through the realms of Night to pierce.
> What time the Bloodhound lur'd by Human scent
> Thro' all Confusion's quagmires floundering went.
> Nor cheering pipe, nor Bird's shrill note
> Around thy dreary paths shall float;
> Their boding songs shall scritch owls pour
> To fright the guilty shepards sore.

It was not until the next century, however, that Parliament took action to improve road conditions; the present arrangements for maintaining the highway network in Devon may be said to originate from the Highway Act 1862. This gave the Justices in Quarter Sessions the power to combine parishes in rural areas into highway districts under a highway board. In east Devon in 1864 such an arrangement existed whereby the parishes of Bicton, Clyst St George, Clyst Honiton, Clyst St Mary, Colaton Raleigh, East Budleigh, Farringdon, Littleham, Lympstone, Otterton, Sowton, Withycombe Raleigh and Woodbury formed the Woodbury Highway District Board, the District Survyor being Henry Dagworthy.

Dagworthy's accounts for the month of December 1864 state the amount of expenditure from the funds of the Board for repairing and maintaining the roads in each parish. The heads of account include manual labour

# IN GOOD REPAIR

## Maintaining the Highway Network

(number of days), breaking (number of yards), materials for surface repairs, cart hire (by the day), tradesmen's bills, incidental expenses and total expenditure. While the sum of £1.5s.0d. was spent in the parish of Clyst St Mary, £25.16s.2d. was incurred in the parish of Otterton. The expenditure for the thirteen parishes was £166.17s.10½d. The work was done by contract after having been put out to competitive tender.

In the late 1800s the principle evolved that roads should be divided into lengths with a man in charge of each. Such men became known as 'Lengthmen' and their typical duties are described later in this chapter.

## Creation of new authorities

In 1888 County Councils were established and became responsible for 'main roads' and thus for road maintenance. They were authorized to charge all the expenses of their work to the general County Account which was financed from the County rate. In 1894 Urban and Rural District Councils were formed and these, together with Municipal Boroughs (which dated from 1835), were responsible for all highway maintenance except on 'main roads'.

It was not until the Local Government Act 1929 that the term 'county roads' came into being for those roads for which the County was responsible. These then comprised all roads in Rural Districts, and all classified roads in Municipal Boroughs and Urban Districts although Borough and Urban Authorities with populations of 20 000

**The first serious attempt to raise money for the maintenance of the roads came with the setting up in the mid 1700s of the Turnpike Trusts. Among the ninety or so surviving tollhouses in Devon the Copper Castle tollhouse on the A35 at Honiton is a rare example with its gates still intact.**

or more had the right to continue to maintain their roads if they wished, and many did so. The maintenance of unclassified roads could also be delegated to Rural District Councils.

The more important roads which had developed to be of national significance were designated as trunk roads and became the responsibility of the Ministry of Transport in 1936, although maintenance work was delegated to the County Councils as agent authorities.

## Maintenance during the Second World War

At the outbreak of the Second World War in September 1939 as the younger men joined the armed forces, older men had to carry on the maintenance work. Labour on farms was similarly depleted and during the busy harvest period roadmen were diverted from time to time to help with agricultural work.

In the early days of the war, when rumours of invasion were in the air, direction signs were removed and destinations on milestones obliterated 'to confuse the enemy'. In 1940 roadmen were instructed to abandon routine jobs and to proceed to certain parts of Dartmoor where they were to place stakes to prevent the landing of German gliders. Brent Moor is one area where these stakes can still be seen.

Towns and villages were occasionally subjected to 'hit and run' raids by low-flying German aircraft. On one such occasion, when the village of Dittisham was machine-gunned, Arthur Finch, a road foreman with Totnes Rural District Council, had a lucky escape when the gallon tin of white paint hanging on the handlebars of his motorcycle took a direct hit. He said, 'I came closer to it then than in the 1914–18 war.'

Relief from the menace of invasion and daylight aerial attack came in 1942, to be followed in 1943 and 1944 by the friendly invasion of American forces. Many roads in Devon were subjected to heavy military traffic and although the normal programme of improvements was suspended a large amount of work was undertaken for the government.

In December 1943, parts of six parishes in the South Hams coastal strip backing Slapton Sands had to be completely evacuated within a period of six weeks when the area was required for the battle training of American forces. Roadmen were sent to help with the exodus. Many roads suffered damage from the influx of tank transporters and other heavy military equipment. Bridges were also damaged, particularly parapet walls. A foreman's diary dated 2 February 1944 reads, 'Parapet wall of East Cornworthy Bridge (west side) has been damaged. Cracks about 16–18 feet overall and showing to road level. The keystone appears to be slightly shifted, the arch appears sound, wall has been struck and severely shaken in 2 places.' An entry dated 23 March 1944 reads, 'Some surface damage has been done at Westerland and by Staverton turning by military caterpillars (American).' There are also several references in the following months to damage by tanks, damage to roadside fencing, damage to road surfaces, tarmac ripped by tracked vehicles, and so on.

Roadmen were allowed extra rations and one also finds reference to cheese-ration forms and tea and sugar coupons. Foremen were issued with petrol coupons for their motor cycles. Road maintenance gangs were provided with small triangular black and yellow metal signs with the letters RP/R painted on them which they displayed while working and which identified them as a 'Repair Party/ Roads'. These signs were also fixed to rollers and other plant and vehicles.

In the battle-training area itself roads suffered badly not only from military traffic but from damage caused by aerial and naval bombardment, activities carried out to give troops experience of conditions under fire.

During February and March 1944 there was a flurry of activity to re-establish signposts. Before the 'D' day landings in Normandy on 6 June 1944 many roads leading to the embarkation points along the south coast of Devon were strengthened and improved, the work being financed by the government. Immediately before the invasion the temporary storage of live shells and boxes of ammunition was a common sight on the roadside verges of south Devon.

## Post-war reclassification and reorganization

When the war ended in 1945 the County Council decided to withdraw the delegation for the maintenance of unclassified roads from sixteen rural districts, resulting in the transfer of 5448 miles of unclassified roads, of which 2179 miles were upgraded to a new category, Class III.

Before 1947 there had been two separate County Road Divisions, North/West and South/East, but on 1 April in that year, the County Roads Department was brought together under one County Surveyor and a new headquarters was established in the old County Police Headquarters in New North Road, Exeter.

## The divisional workforce

For some years after the end of the Second World War, the number of workmen employed remained fairly constant at around 1300. They were amongst the lowest paid in the country which deterred younger men from joining and by 1963 almost two-thirds of the men were aged over fifty-five. Financial restrictions in the late sixties necessitated severe cuts in the size of the workforce and these were accomplished by retirement or by people leaving of their own accord.

By 1971, the labour force had reduced to 1054 men and drastic action was required to bring about an appreciable increase in productivity. A nationally agreed work-study-based incentive-bonus scheme was therefore introduced and was in full operation by the autumn of that year.

## The effects of national recession

Road maintenance had always been vulnerable in times of national recession and was particularly so during a series of economy measures imposed by the government starting in 1968/69. A reduction of 15 per cent was required in maintenance expenditure, followed by a similar cut in 1969/70. With its high road mileage and large proportion of minor roads, Devon was bound to suffer more than most areas from such savage cuts. The *Daily Telegraph* of Wednesday, 27 August 1969 carried the headline 'Disrepair of minor roads worries Councils' and it was clear from the number of authorities mentioned that the deterioration resulting from the cut in maintenance funds was to become a national problem.

## The Marshall Committee Report

The government recognized that a common approach to road maintenance was long overdue and in 1967 a national committee was set up to consider every aspect of the subject, under the chairmanship of Dr A.H. Marshall, C.B.E., who was the Associate Director of the Institute of Local Government Studies at the University of Birmingham. In 1970, the Marshall Committee Report marked the emergence of highway maintenance as a national concern and was an important stage in its history. The one basic message was that highway maintenance must be seen as a modern, complex and mechanized activity which absorbs large resources and must be subject to modern business methods. It defined road maintenance as 'those activities designed to preserve rather than to improve the highway'.

The report contained a large number of recommendations concerning the maintenance of roads. It was received by many with the hope of at last achieving what had been advocated for many years, but with considerable doubts that the high funding necessary to realize the standards suggested would be forthcoming. Nevertheless, in 1971 the Department of the Environment (now the Department of Transport) allocated £1.6 million (later increased to £2 million) to bring its own trunk roads in Devon up to the Marshall standard of maintenance. This large volume of work was carried out by contract and completed in 1975. A number of the other recommendations in the report had to some extent already been implemented in Devon.

The Marshall Committee Report was an important milestone in setting a framework for determining maintenance needs in a consistent manner, but it looked for ideal solutions which in reality proved too expensive to carry out.

## Local government reorganization, 1974

The most significant changes in the maintenance of roads in Devon followed the passing of the Local Government Act 1972. On 1 April 1974 the County Council became responsible for all maintainable roads within the county, including those in the Cities of Exeter and Plymouth and the County Borough of Torbay as well as many previously maintained by the smaller local authorities. The maintenance of trunk roads remained a government responsibility but the County Council was still required to undertake work on these roads as agent for the Department of Transport.

The length of county road to be maintained increased from 10 608 km in 1973 to 12 845 km on 1 April 1974. In addition, 317 km of trunk road were maintained for the Department of Transport. This became the largest road network of any county in the United Kingdom and the County road maintenance budget for 1974/75 was £5.7 million. These changes were to mean a fundamental rethink of the traditional approach to highway maintenance in Devon and resulted in many staff being required to change their responsibilities and place of work.

## The divisional structure

In order to manage this increased network of roads, a new area and divisional structure was drawn up. Co-ordination of the divisions, joint appointments and agent authorities was to be achieved through Area Engineers based at Plymouth, Exeter, Torbay and Barnstaple, with the allocation of maintenance funds, policies and standards being administered by a central policy team. The number of county highway divisions increased from thirteen to seventeen and included 'joint appointment' Divisional Surveyors/District Engineers in Exmouth, Teignbridge and Bideford/Northam, these being employed partly by the County Council and partly by the District Councils. In Torbay and Exeter agency arrangements were negotiated. This allowed for the work to be carried out by the District Council staff to policies and standards laid down by and with funds allocated by the County Council. In Plymouth what was probably a unique arrangement was agreed whereby the manual workforce remained in the employ of the City Council, but controlled by County-Council-employed divisional staff. This was possible because the City Engineer also jointly held a County Council appointment as Area Engineer (West). Despite the potential pitfalls, the arrangement worked well for some years before a formal agency arrangement was entered into between the two authorities.

Since 1974 the challenge of safeguarding the enormous investment in the highway network with the limited funds available has been met successfully and maintenance in Devon has emerged from being the 'Cinderella' of highway engineering to be in the forefront of the development of new techniques, which were to stand maintenance engineers in good stead to deal with what was to follow.

Maintenance has been subject to many pressures and influences, not least of which were progressive financial cuts of some 20 per cent between 1975 and the mid 1980s. By 1988, the county road length being maintained had increased to 13 909 km because of the construction of new roads and the growth in housing developments. The annual budget for the maintenance of county roads was £31 million which was still about 12 per cent lower in real terms than it was in 1974. Also, in 1988, 32 km of motorway and 299 km of trunk road were maintained by the County, as agent for the Department of Transport, with an annual budget of some £2.5 million.

In addition to financial restraints and the increase in road length to be maintained, a number of other factors have influenced the management of highway maintenance in Devon. Not least of these factors is the substantial increase in volume and weight of traffic using the roads, frequently in excess of their designers' calculations. Other factors have been changes in the financial systems, the introduction of new materials and plant, the major input of new technology, and the damaging effects of bad winters.

## The motorway

The completed M5 motorway in Devon was officially opened on 27 May 1977. Its maintenance is the direct responsibility of the Department of Transport and as the Department's agent, the County Council set up a specialist Motorway Maintenance Unit (MMU) to maintain the 32 km of the M5 in the county west of Sampford Peverell (Somerset County Council maintains the M5 east of Sampford Peverell), and also the high-speed dual carriageways, such as the A38 to Plymouth and the A30 to Okehampton.

The principal depot for the MMU is at Sowton, Exeter. During the winter months it is able to respond 24 hours per day to emergencies and adverse winter conditions. It has a particularly close working relationship with the Devon and Cornwall Constabulary through the police headquarters at Exeter. In liaison with the police, the MMU deals with all vehicles abandoned on the motorway; from 1975 to 1987 it had to remove some 530 vehicles.

## Maintenance policy changes resulting from financial restraint

The progressive cuts in highway maintenance funding of some 20 per cent announced by the government in July 1975 had a serious impact on Devon's roads, coming on top of the restraints of 1968/69. The cuts were imposed despite protests and the Minister of Transport's suggestion was that the greatest impact should be on the less heavily trafficked roads, but that operations affecting road safety should remain unchanged, and that the effects of the cuts should be chiefly noticeable in reduced riding quality, less footway maintenance and a deterioration in overall appearance.

Following a substantial review of its policies, the County Council decided to concentrate maintenance funds on the higher categories of road, with a 'make-do-and-mend' approach to the lower categories. The use of surface dressing was increased although it was recognized that this was no substitute for traditional blacktop surfacing. The use of expensive hot-rolled asphalt was virtually eliminated. In addition, the use of concrete paving on footways was restricted to town centres only and the frequency of grass cutting and sweeping was drastically reduced. These policies provided an impetus for the development of new ways of assessing maintenance needs, the more accurate allocation of available funds to meet these needs and the collection of evidence to demonstrate what was happening to the condition of the roads.

A substantial review of the maintenance organization followed in 1978 and brought about a major change in the way things were done, including considerable management restructuring.

## Changes in the volume and type of traffic using Devon's roads

The number of vehicles in Great Britain rose from 11 million in 1971 to 18 million in 1986 and the Transport and Road Research Laboratory predicted that the figure will rise to 25 million in the year 2000. There has been an increase in gross vehicle weight from 32 tonnes to 38 tonnes (on five axles instead of four), together with an increase in the maximum permitted length to 18 metres for vehicles with trailers, and to 15.5 metres for articulated vehicles.

Added to these national effects was the extra traffic generated by the opening of the M5 into Devon, together with an increase in heavy traffic following the opening of the Plymouth to Roscoff, Brittany, ferry link in 1975.

Changes in agricultural policy in the late 1960s meant the phasing out of the small milk-churn lorries in favour of bulk milk tankers weighing some 19 tonnes laden. The trend towards larger fields, larger herds and the use of bulk grain, fertilizer, feed, fuel and cattle transportation, together with modern farm equipment such as large balers and combine harvesters, further increased the number of heavy vehicles using rural roads.

As if this were not enough, minor roads have increasingly been used by other heavy industrial vehicles such as clay lorries and larger buses. The closure of some branch railway lines has also generated more road traffic in some areas.

## Competition and its impact

On 1 April 1981, Part III of the Local Government, Planning and Land Act 1980 came into effect, governing the operation of local authority direct labour organizations (DLOs). This Act, with the aim of improving services, increasing the efficiency of the DLO and lowering the cost to the ratepayer, required the DLO to compete for some types of work with private contractors, and also to achieve a prescribed level of profit.

Without doubt the competition regulations heralded greater changes in the way works on the ground were organized and carried out than had any previous legislation. It is to the credit of the workmen and their managers that these changes have been seen as a challenge and the DLO has consistently succeeded in achieving and surpassing the requisite rate of return of 5 per cent on the value of capital assets held. It has been said to have been a surprise to competitors that the DLO has been successful in winning a high proportion of the work for which it tendered, yet it is hardly unexpected that an organization skilled at roadworks should be competitive.

The late 1970s, with the DLO legislation imminent, saw a major reappraisal of procedures. It was decided that there would be a separation of the 'contracting' and 'client' functions which was accompanied by the rationalization and combination of certain divisions. At about this period the joint appointment arrangements in Exmouth, Teignbridge and Bideford/Northam, referred to earlier, were ended. By 1981 the seventeen divisions of 1974 (excluding agencies and the MMU) had been reduced to eight, and by 1987 to seven.

In 1984 it was decided to change over to a separate contracting DLO responsible to an Assistant County Engineer (Works Management), who was also responsible for the operations of the Mechanical Engineering Division. The total labour force of the DLO in 1987 was 692 men, managed and supported by 120 staff. The organization was run as a large business which in 1986/87 had an annual turnover of £20 million and made a 6.8 per cent return on the value of capital assets held. At the same time the number of depots and offices operated by the DLO was reduced.

In 1988 the Government increased the competition requirements, with more areas of highway work that did not previously need to be the subject of competition having to be put out to contract; these included road sweeping, gully emptying, grass cutting, together with vehicle repair and maintenance. The County Council was ready for this development and an entirely separate contracting organization was created to be known as Devon Direct Services.

## Roadmen and training

It is apparent from all these events that the men who work on the roads, and their unions, had, over a relatively short period, to face major changes in the way things were organized and carried out and therefore had to adjust their attitudes to new technology and the requirements of competition. That they met these challenges in a positive way is reflected in the success of the DLO in a competitive market place.

Training is of course vitally important in a time of rapid change and in 1975 the County Council, jointly with Plymouth and Cornwall, set up a Training Centre at Notter Bridge in Cornwall which has proved invaluable. As well as academic work it also provides training in a wide range of practical skills and new techniques.

**Loading salt at the Motorway Maintenance Unit at Sowton. In a bad winter salting crews can work around the clock, clearing snow and spreading thousands of tonnes of salt. Even in less severe weather, 1200 km of the county's priority routes are treated whenever icy conditions are predicted. Over 50 000 tonnes of salt are held in stockpiles around the county.**

Several roadmen have moved on from training at Notter Bridge to undertake courses at the South Devon Technical College and have progressed to become foremen or highway superintendents.

## The highway divisions a hundred years on

The Divisional organization has come a long way from the days of the lengthman and has changed out of all recognition from the organization of 1974. In 1988 the annual budget for motorway, trunk-road and county road maintenance was almost £34 million. Seven large Divisions (together with the MMU and agencies of Exeter, Plymouth, Torbay, and Mid Devon) were managed by the four Area Engineers acting as a corporate group. The work force had shrunk from over 1000 men to less than 700. Each Division was managed by a Divisional Surveyor responsible for the maintenance of road lengths of up to 1800 km.

The Divisional Surveyor's role is to safeguard the county's highway network for the benefit of road users, to respond to emergencies, to identify and respond to needs using the modern technology at his disposal, to specify modern materials and methods and above all to ensure that the work is carried out at the most competitive price, either by the DLO or by contractors. His task is to seek value for money and the task of the DLO and other contractors is to provide it.

## New technology

Nowadays, Divisions take full advantage of modern information technology in order to stretch limited budgets to fund the maximum amount of work. 'Value for money' has become the key phrase.

The new systems are capable of processing, sending and receiving vast quantities of information. They have revolutionized the handling of financial information, and have the benefit of enormous computing power and instant electronic communication between remote offices.

New technology develops rapidly and the original 'Datapoint' machines installed in Divisions in the early 1980s soon proved too slow and were supplemented by terminals directly linked to the County Council's main-frame computer at County Hall. This arrangement has been overtaken by a new breed of powerful personal computers that are 'network linked' so that they can communicate with each other and form the basis for Divisional and DLO systems into the late 1990s. Computer keyboards and screens have become nearly as common in Divisional offices as they are in High Street banks.

The 'state-of-the-art' DEVONET system (see p. 171) was the key to managing the vast quantities of data of the Highway Inventory and led to the concept of a Highway Information Management System (HIMS). Plans of the highway network can now be produced by computer at any specified scale. The system can relate skidding accidents to skid resistance of the road surface, plot the position of highway features such as gullies, or summarize work required for particular needs in a defined area, as well as many other uses. Carriageway areas can also be identified from the system for inclusion in surface-dressing and surfacing contracts, removing the need to visit and measure the site each time work has to be done.

Together with the weather-monitoring equipment, described later in this chapter, the systems available to the Divisional Surveyor ensure that Devon County Council is equipped to extend the management of highway mainte-nance forward into the twenty-first century.

## Maintenance Policies and Practices

The current arrangements for maintenance of roads had their origins with the 'Lengthmen' system mentioned earlier. In Devon such men were each responsible for the maintenance of 4 or 5 miles of road, to which they were required to give constant attention.

Typical duties of lengthmen were set out in a small instruction booklet produced in October 1913 and supplied to every man then employed on the main roads throughout the county. The text was as follows:

### Ditches, Channels and Side Drains

1. All ditches required for taking surface water from main roads, or for intercepting water from adjoining land, must be kept scoured, cut, cleaned out, and deepened whenever necessary. All drains and culverts for conveying water under the roads must be kept clear and in repair.

   The cross-grips and side ditches should be cut out twice a year, or oftener if necessary, and at all times kept clear of grass and other obstructions; the inlets should be kept lower than the water tables, and sufficient and even fall provided. All outlets, gullies, catchpits and grates must be kept clean and in suitable condition to take surface water at all times.

   It is only in wet weather that the required work to drains and grips, etc., can be properly observed and resulting damage prevented.

2. The grass, weeds and dirt shall be removed from the channels, watertables and quarters twice a year, or oftener if necessary, and the edging of the grass margin carefully trimmed, care being taken not to cut it back. Any soft places in the channels or quarters should be made strong and good with road stone. Long lines should be used to make neat and even edges. All soil-heaps, scrapings or sweepings should be at once removed from the metalled carriageway and in no case should they be left in such a manner as to obstruct traffic or impede the flow of surface water.

### Patching

3. Great care should be exercised in the patching of waterholes with material of suitable quality and size, and unless tarred material is used, it should be only done when the roads are sufficiently soft and wet. Merely filling ruts or potholes with loose unrolled material is wasteful and ineffectual, and must on no account be done. During or immediately after wet weather the surface of the road where water stands should be loosened with picks and hacked out to a depth of not less than one inch, and the holes patched with 1½ in. metal, which must be covered with fine material, water if required, and well rammed immediately with an iron rammer, unless a steam roller is working near and available at once. Patches in waterholes should always completely fill the hole so that water will not stand at the edges, and the edges should be trimmed and the patch consolidated to as near the level of the surrounding surface as possible.

   Under no circumstances should large material more than 1½ in. gauge be used for patching, and it should not be less than 1 in. gauge.

   Where tarred material (which may be from ⅜ in. to 1 in. gauge) is used, the patching must be done when the road surface is dry, after loosening the waterholes sufficiently to form a key for the material, which should be well rammed or rolled at once; all fine stuff and dirt should be swept out before the patching is done.

### Stone Breaking

4. All stone depots and yarding places shall be kept properly levelled up, and provided with measuring posts or walling 3ft in height, and no metal measured until properly yarded 3ft (or 4ft 6in.) high.

No stone, broken or unbroken, must be deposited or heaped in such a manner as to project on to the metalled surface of the road. It should be placed as far back as practicable, but not allowed to obstruct any ditch or drain. When stone is being broken by the roadside, suitable screens must be used to prevent stone and splinters flying on the road.

Unless otherwise ordered, limestone, sandstone and flints to be used for coating should be broken to 2¼in. gauge, and granite, basalt or quartzite to a 2 in. gauge.

### Scraping and Sweeping

5.  Mud, leaves, or other rubbish must be scraped and removed from the roads where necessary, especially during wet weather, and particularly in shaded or damp places. If dust is swept and removed from the road in dry weather, it will prevent so much mud forming when the roads are wet. All accumulations of scrapings or sweepings should be immediately removed from the roadways and channels.

### Coating

6.  (a)  All mud and dirt must first be scraped, swept and cleaned off. Where the road is of sufficient strength, the old surface should, where necessary, be scarified or loosened for the full width and a proper shape and cross-fall obtained. Roads with thin weak crusts should not be scarified. If necessary the quarters should be raised and strengthened and the centre lowered where there is sufficient thickness of crust to allow for this. If the centre of the road is hollow, or the whole width weak, it should be strengthened and properly shaped. Local or approved stone may be used for strengthening and shaping the road, and this should be steam-rolled before the coating material is applied. The cross-fall from the centre to the side of a water-bound macadam road should not exceed one in twenty-four, or ½ in. to a foot, except on steep gradients where this may be slightly increased to prevent water coursing down the road surface. The cross-fall should be frequently checked by the use of a straight-edge and spirit level. At curves, the outside of the turn should be slightly raised instead of sloping from the centre as stated above.

    (b)  Road scrapings, soil or dirt must on no account be used for binding stone. Clean gravel, chippings or quarry siftings preferably of the same quality as the stone used for coating should be used.

    (c)  When the width of the metal carriageway exceeds 15 feet, the stone must not be spread over the full width at once, but a width of at least 7 feet left clear at one side for traffic until the remaining width is thoroughly consolidated.

    (d)  All stone spread during each day must be rolled in before the roller leaves at night sufficiently to allow vehicles to pass over without danger or inconvenience. On Saturdays and the days preceding general holidays all stone spread on the metalled road must be thoroughly consolidated before the roller leaves the work.

    (e)  When any loose stone is left overnight for any reason on any portion of the road, a danger-lamp must be placed at each end and arrangements made for them to be kept lighted from dusk to daylight.

    (f)  It is essential that all workmen in the carrying out of repairs should cause as little obstruction, inconvenience, or risk of damage as possible to all users of the road.

    (g)  Great care should be taken to avoid inequality in surface at the ends of re-coated lengths. The old surface for the full width of the road and a length of not less than 4 feet should be scored and loosened at an angle of 45 degrees and coated with a tapering layer of stone to be rolled with special care. Straight and uneven joints to new work are to be specially avoided.

    (h)  Full loads of stone should not be tipped on the road close to the point of spreading, but the material gradually unloaded as the carts are drawn along. All metal should be well and evenly spread and turned over so as to equally distribute the smaller material. No material must be spread more than two stones thick without each coating being separately steam-rolled. No large patches must be put in without the surface being well scarified or loosened in order to properly form or preserve it in suitable shape.

    (i)  When repairing ruts, the full width of each rut must be scarified or loosened with a pick to a sufficient depth to allow of the road metal being rolled and consolidated to the same level as the surface adjoining each side of the rut.

### Trenches, etc.

7.  (a)  Roadmen should report to the District Surveyors any opening or disturbances of main road surfaces done by any persons whatever.

    (b)  The roadmen should immediately inform the District Surveyor of any trenches on main roads that require levelling, or if they are such that the Highway Authority should repair they must be kept properly levelled with stone well rammed and consolidated.

At that time, the three County Surveyors – C.G.S. Acock, W.P. Robinson and E.J. Stead – charged their District Surveyors with the duty of seeing that the roadmen strictly adhered to these instructions.

In the early days the County Surveyor would travel in a horse-drawn carriage to meet his District Surveyor whose usual conveyance was a pony and trap. Roadmen were required to place a red flag at the junction of the main road with the road on which they were working so that the County Surveyor would know where to find them. These labourers, who were mostly recruited from the agricultural industry, were a race apart and took great pride in the appearance and general maintenance of their length. They were of necessity subject to the minimum of supervision. Some are known to have concurrently followed such sports as rabbiting or other country pursuits and to have suffered instant dismissal when caught.

Entries in their timesheets have often brought a smile to office staff. For instance, a man cleaning watertables (channels) would write 'Cleaning Mary's Bottom', or 'laying in hedgegrowth' when paring banks and verges, or if sick 'In bed with the District Nurse'!

## Patching and minor repairs

It has long been recognized that efficient patching of carriageways and footways is an essential element of maintenance work and the old adage 'a stitch in time saves nine' is particularly apt in this respect. It has proved vital that preparatory work is carried out in the early spring in advance of the surface-dressing programme.

Many miles of road in Devon are devoid of a piped drainage system and water is the greatest enemy of the road structure. Inadequate side drainage, coupled with the increase in size, weight and number of vehicles, is often the principal cause of damage.

Until 1964 liability for accidents caused by a defect in the highway could be denied under the rule of 'non-feasance' (which was established in the case of Russell *v*. The Men of Devon, heard in 1788 before the Chief Justice). Non-feasance applied where the authority had simply failed to carry out repairs; but they could be held liable for damages by reason of mis-feasance, ie. where repairs had been attempted but not satisfactorily carried out. This non-feasance rule was abrogated by the Highways (Miscellaneous Provisions) Act 1961, though this did not come into effect until 3 August 1964. It did not mean that the County Council then had no defence against a claim for damages, but it had to consider the options of either paying for higher insurance premiums or establishing a better system of inspection whereby the condition of the road could be monitored at a frequency related to the usage, classification and character of the road. A system of inspection was therefore introduced to ensure that the state of repair of the highway was that in which a reasonable person could be expected to find it. Clearly more frequent inspections are required in busy urban areas than on country lanes.

## Holes in the road — responsibilities and repair

Most statutory undertakers – British Gas, Electricity Board, Water Authority and British Telecom – probably regard a road as a convenient corridor in which to lay a main or cable. Reinstatements following statutory undertakers' main laying rapidly became one of the chief problems of carriageway maintenance after the Second World War. Ostensibly it was intended to bring this under control by the Public Utilities Street Works Act 1950, but while regular co-ordination meetings were, and still are, held with all statutory undertakers to programme the works of all parties, the system is by no means foolproof. Difficulties have arisen because of delays or when 'emergency' work has been required to mains and services. What is certain is that once a road surface, which has probably been consolidated over a long period, is disturbed it is virtually impossible to restore it to its original condition.

The scale of the problem in Devon is considerable. For instance, in 1966/67, over 5000 road-opening permits were issued and the total length of highway openings in that year amounted to nearly 74 miles. The encasing of gas main joints as a consequence of the introduction of natural gas in the 1960s presented particular problems.

Statutory undertakers are encouraged to use shared trenches wherever possible and a good deal of success has been achieved in this direction; an example is the renewal of mains in conjunction with sewerage schemes. Cross-country mains have also been located in adjoining fields rather than in the road itself where practicable, care being taken to leave room for possible future road improvements.

The problems of damage caused by openings in the highway by the public utilities has continued to grow, and the effects on traffic became more noticeable as traffic flows increased. By 1987 the annual number of recorded openings of highway in Devon had risen to over 9000. The County Council tries to ensure that these works are carried out with as little disruption and danger to the travelling public as possible and that openings are satisfactorily reinstated. Trench inspectors are employed to supervise these works and the cost of these inspectors is recovered from the utilities.

In the light of national concern about the inadequacies of current arrangements for dealing with the activities of the public utilities, the government commissioned an investigation by Professor Horne who recommended in 1986 that substantial changes in legislation and procedure were required. Where possible, some of these recommended changes are being introduced in Devon with the co-operation of the utilities, but regrettably most await parliamentary time for the debating and passing of new legislation.

## footways and kerbs

One result of the reductions in maintenance expenditure in recent years is that the use of flagging for footways has been restricted, except in busy town centres, conservation areas and other approved sites. Here considerable success has been achieved in dealing with the problems of vehicle damage by using small slabs and concrete or brick pavers.

The introduction of pre-formed concrete channel blocks to replace the old cast-iron channels which were supposed to take roof water across footways but which were invariably blocked, has made the footway a much safer place in the winter.

Footways are maintained with the needs of prams, wheelchairs and blind people very much in mind. In large urban areas a special arrangement exists whereby the local Association for the Blind is kept informed of the location of all maintenance work including that affecting footways.

## Drainage

Road drainage in Devon takes many forms and often roads themselves serve as natural drainage channels for adjoining land. Open ditches adjoining the road are fairly common, particularly in the east of the county. Some have been piped with open-jointed pipes surrounded by clean stone filling, in the interests of safety, to support the carriageway and to provide additional width and passing places.

The responsibility for ditch cleaning varies across the country and is dependent upon historic rights and responsibilities. Although in some counties the owner of adjacent land has to keep highway ditches clear, in Devon in most cases the County Council has to carry out the work.

The topography of Devon means that many roads follow precipitous courses along the sides of valleys and combes. Many miles of these roads have to be supported by high retaining walls. The task of keeping these walls in good repair demands the special skills of stonemasons.

The County Council has a prescriptive right to drain roads on to adjoining land by way of drainage channels known as 'easements'. In Devon this often takes the form of an opening bored through a high bank, and is known locally as a 'buddle hole'.

Piped drainage systems range from small-bore drains to large pre-cast concrete culverts. It was agreed in the early 1960s that culverts under high embankments should be not less than 48 in. in diameter to permit easy access. Old stone culverts still exist in many places and give way from time to time.

In some villages, for example Bampton, streams now flow in underground culverts that run through the whole length of the street and these culverts are subject to periodic inspection for maintenance.

The County Council has a prescriptive right to drain roads by way of existing easements, which in many cases are simply holes through the hedgebanks (commonly known in Devon as 'buddle holes') on to adjoining land. This right extends to the cleaning of the easement and so much as is necessary of the outfall on private property to prevent the road from flooding. It is estimated that there are as many as 36 000 easements on minor rural roads alone. Years ago many of these drains were formed by landowners themselves for the purpose of irrigating their land or watering their stock but they are now considered to be an encumbrance by many farmers. Attempts to stop them up have led in at least one case to High Court proceedings and injunctions have been upheld by the Courts to enable the County Council to continue to use them.

In some areas deep natural drainage channels exist in close proximity to the road and the erosion created in time of flood can lead to expensive maintenance work. The use of stone-filled gabions (heavy-gauge galvanized or plastic-coated wire baskets, 2 m × 1 m × 1 m) is a fairly common form of construction for retaining the road in such circumstances.

Nowadays adequate waterways are provided on new construction and there is a steady investment in the provision of new drainage systems on existing roads, in order to avoid future maintenance problems and the hazards created when wet road surfaces freeze in the winter.

## Watertabling

In an agricultural county such as Devon the seasons have a direct bearing on road-cleaning operations, a wet winter resulting in mud being carried on to roads by natural drainage, vehicles and animals.

It is an offence to deposit mud on the road from the wheels of vehicles and as a last resort police assistance has sometimes been enlisted in the enforcement of these laws where the owner fails to co-operate. The County Council prefers to obtain the co-operation of farmers and landowners and has produced a guidance leaflet entitled *Farming and the Public Highway*, jointly with the National Farmers Union. No such remedy exists, however, for damage done by cattle to banks and verges and in carrying soil on to the carriageway.

'Watertabling', a term probably unique to the West Country, refers to the cleaning of the road surface and channels, grips, buddle holes and ditches and is all part of an operation that is vital to ensure that the highway remains free of water. The spoil is disposed of on the adjoining verge or loaded into lorries and tipped.

## Gully emptying and road sweeping

The regular emptying of gullies and catchpits is essential to the good maintenance of road-drainage systems and is carried out to a regular schedule. It is performed by a fleet of vacuum gully-emptying machines, each operated by a two-man team. Special attention is paid to gullies in hilly areas with heavy storm-water run-off and to roads where industrial or quarry traffic is predominant.

To the layman the cleansing of gullies during long dry summers, such as those of 1976 and 1983, may appear to be unnecessary but it is essential to replenish them with clean water and so avoid drain odour.

Road channels are swept on a regular basis in urban areas, and on main rural roads, to prevent dirt and debris accumulating and eventually blocking gullies and drains. Sweeping is also carried out as part of the preparation for, and during the course of, surface-dressing works and also in emergencies, such as oil spillages, when the road surface sometimes has to be scrubbed with detergent.

## Retaining walls, embankments and cuttings

The topography of Devon is such that there are many retaining walls and the maintenance of these can be an expensive item. The roads of coastal towns such as

Ilfracombe, Brixham and Dartmouth are in many cases supported by old high stone retaining walls which have to be repointed, pressure grouted, or rebuilt from time to time.

There is a very considerable mileage of road, where the carriageway immediately adjoins a precipice without the support of a retaining wall and lacking the benefit of a properly designed drainage system. The provision of stone-faced mass-concrete retaining walls and gabion retaining structures has therefore become a common feature of maintenance work.

Some roads in Devon rise to about 1500 ft above sea level while others are several feet below spring-tide level. The hilliness of the county has meant that deep cuttings and embankments have had to be formed in many places.

All slopes and rock cuttings are regularly inspected to detect incipient slides, falls or springs. A watch is also kept on slopes not owned by the highway authority where falls or failure might cause damage or injury to road users and where, if potentially dangerous conditions are found, the owner or occupier of the land can be requested to take the necessary action.

## Roadside verge grass cutting

On county roads grass cutting has been considerably reduced and is restricted to a maximum of six times a year in urban areas and normally a single-swathe width cut twice a year on rural roads. The background to the development of these policies is dealt with in Chapter 8. The policies are

When a road is in constant use, the surface can become polished and therefore dangerous, particularly when wet. Part of the regular duties of the materials laboratory staff is to undertake skid-resistance tests on selected sites. Where the results of the tests prove unsatisfactory, remedial treatment follows.

summarized in a booklet which has been praised by parish councils and conservation bodies as an example to others of the correct approach to verge management. The implementation of these policies has ensured that Devon's verges look attractive, especially during the main flowering periods of the spring and summer. (Methods of cutting are described on p. 183.)

As far as the motorway and trunk roads are concerned, grass cutting has ceased as a general practice except in certain restricted places and circumstances, on the instructions of the Department of Transport.

## Monitoring of road conditions

For many years the structural condition of roads in Devon was assessed by Divisional staff who had a wealth of practical personal knowledge and experience of their region. However, visual inspection alone does not always reveal the whole story and of course there was no way of ensuring that each surveyor used the same criteria in determining need. After much research, both in this country and abroad, more scientific methods for the measurement of structural road conditions evolved. Two machines developed in the early 1970s to further this assessment were the Deflectograph and the SCRIM. These machines were introduced into Devon in 1975 and are now used on a regular programmed basis. Owing to the high cost of the machines several counties in the South West formed a consortium and arranged with a specialist contractor to undertake the surveys at a low overall cost.

### The La Croix Deflectograph

As its name suggests, this was pioneered by the French and enables deflection of the carriageway under a slow-moving loaded wheel to be accurately measured and recorded on magnetic tape. This gives a continuous record of the structural state of the road. With traffic-flow information and knowledge of the existing road construction, readings are interpreted by computer to calculate the residual life or the need for reconstruction or overlay and the thickness required. The use of the Deflectograph in Devon, which is confined to the motorway, trunk roads, principal and other important routes, gives valuable information to the engineer about the lower unseen layers, to enable him to determine accurately maintenance priorities.

### SCRIM (Sideways Coefficient Routine Investigation Machine)

This provides a mechanical means of measuring the resistance of a wheel to skidding on the road surface, where the wheel is free to rotate but has a sideways as well as a forward motion. A large proportion of Devon's main-road network is examined by SCRIM surveys and the results are analysed by computer, in conjunction with accident statistics, to identify lengths of road where skidding resistance is declining. Remedial surface treatment can then be carried out before the problem becomes serious.

## Visual Condition Surveys

Deflectograph and SCRIM provide detailed information about specific lengths of road, but there are many other characteristics which need to be evaluated in order to assess overall maintenance requirements, so a systematic approach to visual inspection and measurement is also needed.

A system of maintenance rating, known as CHART, was adopted in Devon in 1976 on the motorway and on trunk roads. The information collected by small inspection teams (two or three men) is fed into the computer for processing. The results indicate the lengths of road which are substandard, the apparent treatment needs and the relative priorities of remedial work. These are then interpreted to determine the reasons for failure and the extent, type and timing of treatment needed. It is a requirement of the Department of Transport that all requests for money to strengthen or reconstruct the motorway and trunk roads are supported by CHART, Deflectograph and SCRIM information.

These surveys are relatively expensive and could not be justified for use on all of Devon's large road network, so a 'sample survey' based on CHART was developed for use within the county. This provides a broad basis for ensuring that funds for structural maintenance are distributed throughout the county in accordance with needs.

Devon has supported the National Road Maintenance Condition Survey (NRMCS) since it was set up in 1976. This is a CHART-based sample survey of a random selection of all classes of roads in each county (selected by the Department of Transport) and was designed to give a national indication of the trends in road conditions and to enable each member county to compare its roads with the national picture. Initially it was a purely visual survey but in 1981 it was enhanced to include Deflectograph information.

## DEVONET and the Highway Inventory

The surveys described above give valuable information on the condition of roads, but it became clear in 1978 that if funds for cyclic maintenance were to be properly allocated and managed then there was a need to know what in the highway had to be maintained. In other words an 'inventory' of highway features and fixtures was required. Expenditure allocations could then be based on identified needs instead of the traditional historical pattern.

First attempts to collect inventory information were promising but it soon became clear that the task was of a scale that would necessitate a computerized database. A decision was therefore taken to delay the inventory collection and concentrate efforts on creating the database. The Devon road network plans were first divided into sections, related to the ordnance survey grid, then every section was given a unique number which fixed its position in the network. A powerful computer programme was developed to handle the data. So DEVONET was born and not only provided the key that was needed to allow the

Highway Inventory to proceed, but, equally important, provided the database to enable many other computerized highway-management systems to be developed.

An extensive inventory collection operation was started in 1984, which was to last three years. This represented a major investment and brought the management of highway maintenance into the high-technology age. Funds can be allocated to known needs in accordance with County policies and the location of works required can be scheduled and plotted on maps by computer, resulting in improved efficiency and cost saving.

Various methods of collecting the inventory data were considered, including aerial survey and video recording, but in the end the most effective and accurate method was found to be the use of temporary survey assistants, who were trained to collect the data using electronic notebooks. These devices were pre-programmed with a self-checking capacity and at the end of a day's work the data collected was sent to the central computer by telephone line. The system became affectionately known by those taking part as 'Pedestrian Logging of Data' or PLOD!

An early benefit of the DEVONET system was the analysis of accident statistics that enabled potential skidding sites to be identified and relatively inexpensive remedial works to be undertaken, resulting in a reduction in accidents.

The system is marketed commercially to the benefit of the Devon ratepayers.

## Results of the surveys

Analysis of the results of these surveys in the early 1980s showed up distinct trends in the condition of the county's roads and the need to review policies.

The policy of concentrating funds on the higher categories of road proved successful in that the condition of principal roads had not deteriorated. However, the state of minor roads and particularly rural roads, had by 1985 declined to the extent that funds had to be transferred from the higher to the lower categories of road in an attempt to arrest the deterioration. The very high mileage of minor roads in Devon (over 90 per cent of the network) made it clear that some rationalization was required and a decision was therefore taken to extend the concept of the road hierarchy down to the very lowest level of road.

## The minor-road network

In the early 1980s, Divisional Surveyors and Traffic Engineers made a preliminary assessment of the function of every rural minor road in the county, having regard to its importance to the community. This was the start of a major consultation exercise involving all parish councils and bodies such as the National Farmers Union. After more than twelve months of consultations, a hierarchy of rural roads in Devon was drawn up. The roads were placed into seven classifications, ranging from those serving as the main access to communities down to those serving only fields. In addition many were identified as candidates to be reclassified as byways.

Broad maintenance standards were determined for each category and a signing policy initiated to direct traffic on to the most appropriate route. The development of the Devon Road Network has rationalized the maintenance of this major part of the network so as to ensure that funds are directed where the need is greatest.

## Stone, Tar and Concrete

The work of such men as Thomas Telford (1757–1834) and Robert Macadam (1756–1836) resulted in great improvements in road construction and maintenance throughout the country. The system evolved by Telford for making and maintaining roads was based on a foundation of large stones, covered by a layer of smaller broken stone and blinded with dust or gravel. In Devon a similar system was known as 'hand pitching'. Stones passing a 9 in. ring were usually bedded on 3 in. or 4 in. of sand, gravel or clinker laid to correct line and camber with the largest, flattest face downwards. The spaces between the points were filled with 1½–3 in. stone and the projections knocked off with a knapping hammer. The surface was watered, to wash the smaller stones into the gaps between the bigger stones, and then blinded as necessary and compacted by a 10 ton steam-roller working from sides to centre. This system persisted well into the 1950s.

Macadam's system was to lay a consolidated thickness of about 4 in. of graded stones (none larger than 3in.). Another layer of about 4in. of broken stone was then added, watered and rolled. A final layer of stones not larger than 1in. was then laid to a consolidated thickness of 2in. This was then watered, rolled and blinded with fine gravel and sand or 'scalpings', depending on the type of material available locally. The resulting construction became known as waterbound macadam.

Roadmaking and maintenance in the early nineteenth century greatly increased the need for materials from the Devon quarrying industry, while in the towns natural-dressed-stone kerbs, channels, setts and paving flags provided additional business. Dartmoor granite was in great demand and the setts for many Plymouth roads were produced at Staple Tor Quarry near Merrivale.

## The development of the quarrying industry

The increased need for road maintenance, together with the rapid railway developments in the latter half of the nineteenth century, naturally led to growth in the quarrying industry.

Devon is rich in minerals and stone has been quarried for centuries. Granite, gritstone, quartzite, basalt and limestone are all quarried in the county and used for various purposes in road-making.

In the early days stone was obtained from a large number of relatively small quarries and disused pits can still be found on some farms, though most have long since been filled in. The stone for setts, kerbs and channels was split with wedges, a highly labour-intensive job. Stone for repairs and waterbinding was also broken at the quarry face by hammer and large numbers of men were employed. The stone was brought by horse and cart to roadside 'landings' where it was further broken by hand with a knapping hammer to a maximum size of about 2½ in. The work was often done by older men too inactive for other work and the 'pirate's patch' worn over one eye by some of them indicated the high price they had paid for not protecting their eyes with wire-mesh goggles. The broken stone was roughly graded and formed into piles to be measured by the Surveyor and paid for by the yard. Some of the oldest surviving lay-bys are those which were used as temporary storage areas for stone. Many were surrounded by walling to enable the 'yardage' of stone to be more easily measured.

The introduction of portable mechanical crushers into the quarries made 'stone cracking' by hand at the roadside obsolete. In the 1920s and 1930s quarrying operations consisted of drilling, blasting, loading, crushing and screening. The blasting operation entailed drilling short shot holes, charging (filling the holes with dynamite) and firing. However, in some quarries, such as Fenacre at Burlescombe in east Devon, 'tunnel' blasting was later adopted. This method consisted of driving a T-shaped adit into the quarry face and charging the extremities of the T. The shock wave produced by the explosion was quite spectacular and thousands of tons of fissured limestone would be dislodged. Large stones were reduced to manageable size by 'popping' (the application of explosive to the face), a somewhat noisy process.

## Dust problems and the advent of tar

With the advent of motor vehicles around the turn of the century dust became a severe problem and a familiar sight was the horse-drawn water cart with perforated sprinkler bar used 'to lay the dust'. As the number of motor vehicles increased (10 000 Model T Fords were being produced per annum before the First World War) and the pneumatic tyre enabled higher speeds to be achieved, dust became an intolerable nuisance.

Tar was first produced in the second half of the nineteenth century as a by-product of the carbonization of coal for the manufacture of gas. The use of this gasworks tar initially as a palliative to the problem proved to be a great step forward in road maintenance in Devon and indeed throughout the country. Its use not only cured the dust problem but also provided a waterproof seal to the road surface. The process was commonly known as 'tar and chips' or 'tarring' and is now more generally called 'surface dressing'.

Tar was delivered from the gasworks to the roadside in barrels and heated in a horse-drawn coal-fired 'tar crock'. It was applied to the road surface from buckets, watering cans or from a hand lance and then squeezed or brushed in by hand. The surface was blinded with ¾ in. or ½ in. stone chippings, 'racked up' with ¼ in. stone chippings from small heaps along the roadside, and rolled in. A road gang would often use some 400 to 500 gallons of tar in a day.

**This road gang are laying waterbound macadam. It is probable that they were carrying out a repair to the road surface by filling depressions with 1½ – 3 in. stone, then brushing the surface with fine gravel and sand, watering it in with water from the horse-drawn bowser (left of picture), and finally, rolling with a 10-ton steam-roller.**

While undertaking this operation, the roadmen wore protective clothing consisting of strips of old corn sacks tied around their legs and a 'West of England' sack secured around their middle with binder cord.

Cold emulsions were also developed and had certain advantages over hot tar; for example, it was not essential for the road surface to be absolutely dry. The material was delivered to railway sidings in 40 gallon drums which were placed at appropriate intervals along the roadside. Each drum was then carried on an iron-framed barrow with cast-iron wheels and the emulsion poured on to the road surface and spread with stiff bass brooms (made from tree bark) at a rate of about 1 gallon to 6 square yards. It was then 'shovel scat' by hand with ⅜ in. or ¼ in. chippings or sand dredged from local rivers, the latter giving a sandpaper finish and not needing to be rolled. A schoolboy at Ashburton was once accused of setting a drum of emulsion rolling; it landed and burst in a reservoir where its contents caused some discomfort to the local inhabitants. When brought to court he claimed that the drum was so delicately balanced on the roadside verge that his dog, an ardent 'ratter', had inadvertently set it rolling. He was acquitted.

Another process emanating from the use of tar to bind the chippings together was known as 'grouting'. This was done by gangs of men spreading a layer of 1½ in. or 2 in.

dry stone aggregate on the road, pouring on a measured quantity of binder (about 1½ gallons per square yard), blinding with chippings and rolling in.

## The use of tarmacadam and asphalt

The next logical step from this method was the incorporation of tar (and later bitumen, a by-product of petroleum) as the binder with graded stone, forming tarmacadam, a name that will probably live for as long as roads exist. The introduction of portable crushing and screening machines and later fixed crushing, screening and mixing plants in the quarries led to the greater availability of coated macadam. From the 1920s to the 1940s this was laid by hand from small heaps by a gang of six or eight men and the average daily output was about 40 tons.

Hot-rolled asphalt (which uses natural asphalt or pitch as a binder for the chippings) was first manufactured in Devon in 1928 at Mill Road Depot, Barnstaple. The material was mixed, then transported up to 20 miles to site where it was hand laid. A typical laying gang consisted of three spreaders, one raker, one rammer (for edges), one flagman, one man heating forks and one screeder. The material was consolidated with a steam roller to a thickness of 2 in. giving a coverage of about 12 sq. yds per ton. Outputs of 60 tons per day were achieved and the costs worked out at about 5s. 0d. per sq. yd. for a very long-lasting surface.

Some of the men developed great skill and became 'leading hands' whose characteristics were a good eye, a strong arm and the ability to organize and motivate a small number of men. The work was of course seasonal and the winter months were principally spent in watertabling, cleaning 'buddle holes' and easements, ditching and keeping other forms of drainage in good order, and repairing potholes.

A finely graded asphalt known as 'Damman' became popular for some work. It was laid in Fore Street, Kingsbridge in 1936 on a fairly steep gradient to a depth of ¾ in. consolidated thickness; it lasted for twenty-five years. Similar work was done in other parts of the county and sometimes on steep gradients the roller had to be winched up and down. Timesheets would read 'Spreading Dammit' – which was open to two interpretations!

Local limestone was, and still is, widely used for road making and maintenance in Devon where it exists in abundance. However, it has one serious fault: it tends to become slippery with wear and this has been the source of many accidents in the past, particularly in wet weather. In the early 1930s many surfaces resembled glass and King Street in Plymouth was notorious for this problem. Steam-rollers would not climb on steep limestone gradients, so blue elvan and other hardstone not susceptible to polishing had to be used. Needless to say, limestone is no longer used for road surfaces.

## The retread process

A method of reconstructing minor roads on a large scale in the immediate post-war period was known as 'retread'. This involved scarifying (breaking) the existing road, adding more stone, harrowing to mix the added stone then blading to the correct profile. The loose material was then 'grouted' with cold bitumen emulsion from a bulk sprayer, reharrowed, sprayed again, rolled, sealed and chipped. The whole process cost about 3s. per square yard at that time and was much cheaper than a new tarmacadam surface. This method put many miles of neglected Class III and unclassified roads into reasonable order. It soon waned in popularity but is re-emerging as a cost-effective method of maintaining minor roads, using specially designed plant.

## The road improvement programme and the quarrying industry

The end of the 1950s saw the beginning of an upsurge in expenditure on the improvement of both trunk and county roads so that there was less emphasis on general maintenance until the publication of the Marshall Committee Report (see p. 161) in 1970. To cope with the increased workload the quarries began to equip themselves with modern processing plant capable of high output of stone and macadams for laying by machine. This also had great benefits in the maintenance field.

Before the Second World War, commercial quarrying in Devon was primarily a family business, but like many other industries this has followed the modern trend of amalgamations into bigger companies and takeover bids have been commonplace.

Since the war blasting techniques have gradually become more sophisticated, full-depth drilling of shallow quarry faces being employed and secondary breaking carried out with the drop ball or hydraulic impact hammer. Fixed plant and machinery for crushing, screening, conveying and drying stone, together with equipment for heating tar and bitumen and for mixing and weighing 'blacktop' materials, have also been considerably improved. Today modern methods and control systems involving electronics and microprocessors have greatly reduced manpower levels and completely changed the role of the quarry master of fifty years ago. The considerable capital investment involved has resulted in higher output, improved quality of product and reduced cost of production.

In addition to coated materials many quarry companies have also installed modern plant for the production of ready-mixed concrete and pre-cast concrete products, including kerbs, paving slabs, channels and blocks.

## Devon County Council quarries

It is not surprising to find that, as a highway authority, the County Council at one time owned its own quarries. Immediately after the Second World War the County Council was operating ten such quarries, but by 1959 only three remained. They were located at Wilminstone near Tavistock, at Rydon near Kingsteignton and at Barton Wood near South Molton. In 1960 the annual output from these three quarries was over 78 000 tons and supplied about one quarter of the tonnage required by the County Council at that time.

Plymouth City Council operated its own limestone quarry at Prince Rock until the late 1960s and also mixed bituminous road materials.

### Wilminstone Quarry, Tavistock

In 1960 part of the plant at Wilminstone was still being driven by steam but electrification was completed during 1962 and at that time the costs to drive any item of quarry plant by electricity were 50 per cent less than if driven by steam. Up to then Wilminstone had been worked by the County Council for forty years and had produced 1½ million tons of elvan roadstone. The quarry continued to supply the Tavistock, Okehampton, Plympton, Holsworthy and Torrington Divisions until 1969 when it was becoming apparent that the high-quality blue elvan stone was running out. Extensive surveys were carried out by deep drilling and seismic methods over a wide area of land owned by the County Council adjoining the quarry but the results were disappointing. Further lowering of the quarry floor was not possible owing to flooding. The production of stone ceased on 30 October 1970. Some of the plant was transferred to Barton Wood Quarry and the remainder dismantled and sold.

### Rydon Quarry, Kingsteignton, Newton Abbot

This limestone quarry was reopened in 1952 after a period of closure and continued to operate until 1968. The old and obsolete plant was then sold off or removed.

The worked-out area now houses the offices, stores and workshops for the Newton Abbot/Teignbridge Division, offices and the main depot for bridge maintenance, a local depot for the Mechanical Engineering Division, and a large barn for storing winter salt.

### Barton Wood Quarry, Brayford

The freehold of Barton Wood Quarry (29 acres), together with an adjoining farm of 80 acres, was purchased in 1963, thus securing a large deposit of gritstone for the future. New plant was provided in 1965/66, electricity providing the motive power and also being used for the heating of tar and bitumen. The plant was again modernized in the 1970s and 1980s and continues to service mainly the north Devon area. The annual output is about 42 000 tonnes.

Barton Wood is the only quarry owned by the County Council still in operation.

## Materials testing, research and trials

The quality control of materials to ensure compliance with specification requirements began in Devon in 1954. At that time one man was installed in a small laboratory at the Central Repair Depot in Exeter to perform analytical tests for aggregate grading and binder content on bituminous materials used by the Divisions.

In 1960 a Devon Fire Service vehicle was converted to a mobile laboratory. This enabled routine testing of bituminous materials to be carried out on site or at the mixing plant in the quarry and allowed adjustments or corrections to be made rapidly. Mixing, delivery, laying and rolling temperatures could also be closely controlled.

The appointment of additional staff in the early 1960s and a materials engineer in 1963 enabled the scope of the laboratory's work to be considerably widened. Soil-testing and concrete-testing sections were established and the laboratory was temporarily relocated in 1964 at the St Thomas divisional depot in Elm Grove Road, Topsham. A 200 ton compression machine was purchased for crushing-strength tests on concrete and to enable crushing values to be determined on quarry aggregates.

The work of the laboratory was further expanded to cover most areas of materials technology, particularly in soils and concrete, whereas previously the prime emphasis had been on bituminous materials testing. Work was also undertaken for other County Council departments, principally that of the County Architect to determine

Barton Wood Quarry, at Brayford, near South Molton is the only quarry owned by the County Council still in operation. It produces about 42 000 tonnes of gritstone every year for use on Devon roads.

bearing capacity (the strength of the underlying ground) for foundations of new buildings, as well as to inspect and test materials employed on resurfacing contracts and the construction of school playgrounds. Work was also undertaken for the County Land Agent as he was then called. Other work was done for the former Devon River Authority and also for some other local authorities in the county.

In 1966 the laboratory moved to its first permanent site at Denver Road, Topsham, when a new mobile laboratory was purchased, and in 1969 an engineering seismograph was acquired for use in preliminary site investigations. The Pilcon Wayfarer earth-boring rig was modified to enable it to be towed instead of transported on a low-loader. The expansion of the road-building programme in Devon in the 1960s and early 1970s considerably increased the laboratory's workload of soil surveys, testing of bituminous materials and roadstones, concrete testing and checks of skidding resistance and riding quality.

The skid resistance of road surfacing, particularly in wet weather, is of vital importance in the reduction of accidents, and research was carried out on the extent to which various roadstones polish under traffic. A polished stone value (P.S.V.) test developed by the TRRL was used and a wide variation found to exist between limestone at the lower end of the scale with a value of 0.39 and gritstone at the higher end of the scale with a value of 0.70. Limestone was therefore expressly excluded from the wearing course of surfacings used in Devon.

Investigation of highway materials is increasingly important, particularly with the development of new products, and a wide range of tests is carried out by the County Council's Materials Laboratory. The laboratory moved from Denver Road to its present location at the site of the former Divisional Office in Elm Grove Road, Topsham in 1979 and has since been developed into one of the best-equipped materials laboratories in the West Country. It is run on commercial lines and staff costs and overheads have to be covered by income from tests carried out.

## Structural maintenance – developments

### Reconstruction and haunching

The lack of adequate construction depth of many of Devon's older roads, coupled with the increase in size, weight and volume of vehicles and the devastating effects of severe or wet winters has led to the need for a considerable amount of repairs to be undertaken.

Deformation caused by wheel tracks has been evident on many principal roads and complete breakdown has occurred on a high mileage of narrow minor roads where the heavy wheel loads of carriers of milk, grain, fuel and other bulk materials have been confined between high hedgebanks. These commercial vehicles, together with large balers and combine harvesters, have also been responsible for damage to the base of hedgebanks, rutting of verges and edge of carriageway failure, requiring expensive repairs. 'Haunching' is the term used to describe repair and strengthening of the carriageway edge, and a comparatively inexpensive system of haunching with concrete has been developed. Relatively cheap retread methods have been resurrected using old road material 'planed off' from elsewhere mixed with bitumen emulsion to deal with some of the worst problems on minor roads.

**Surface dressing of a housing-estate road in Tiverton 1988. Bitumen emulsion has been spread on the road surface by a special tanker fitted with spray bars. A lorry, in the foreground, is reversing to spread the final surface of chippings, using a tail-board-mounted metered chipping spreader.**

## Resurfacing and overlays

Road surfacing is the most costly aspect of maintenance work. Since the introduction of natural gas, tar from the old gas works has no longer been available and coated materials used in Devon, collectively known as 'blacktop', have contained bitumen to bind the stone together. The correct binder content is critical since a high content can present difficulties in laying and lead to slipperiness and deformation, whereas a low content can produce easily crumbled and permeable material which is difficult to compact and prone to disintegration under traffic.

Specifications have gradually been improved and there have been two significant changes in recent years: first the requirement for high-strength mixes to meet the needs of specific sites instead of the former standard recipe mixes, and secondly the Department of Transport requirement of a highly skid-resistant finish created by raised chippings to provide a texture depth of 1.5 mm. Experience has shown that the policy of restricting the use of expensive materials was counter-productive and resulted in premature failure of inadequate materials. Hot-rolled asphalt, which is very expensive but lasts a long time, is now generally specified where its use is regarded as worth the extra expense in certain locations.

## Surface dressing and skid treatment

The surface dressing of roads by the application of a film of bitumen covered by a layer of chippings continues to be the backbone of road maintenance in Devon and is still the cheapest form of surface treatment. The operation is essentially a preventative measure, the objective being to seal porous surfaces against the ingress of water, to arrest disintegration and to provide a durable roughened non-skid surface.

Each year the programme for surface dressing is prepared in the preceding summer and a contract let by Christmas, enabling the successful contractor to obtain materials in good time for the following season's work. The areas requiring treatment are obtained, for estimating and contractual purposes, from the Highway Inventory which also provides sound historical records.

Cut-back bitumen and bituminous emulsions are now the binders in general use in Devon. High-performance binders containing polymers are also successfully used on heavily trafficked roads.

Chippings can be used clean or lightly coated with bitumen; 20 mm, 10 mm and 6 mm are the sizes normally used in Devon. High-quality roadstone with a good skid resistance is readily available and elvan, basalt, gritstone and quartzite all give good results and have an attractive colour.

Difficult sites, such as very sharp bends, roundabouts and approaches to traffic signals, which are all subject to heavy braking, sometimes justify special treatment. A sophisticated and very expensive anti-skid treatment employing epoxy resin binder blinded with calcined bauxite chippings has proved successful on several sites in Devon such as at Countess Wear swingbridge and the traffic signals in

The steam-roller was the first major item of mechanical equipment available to the road menders. The photograph shows a typical road gang of the 1920s equipped to scarify an uneven road surface, reshape it by hand, brush in dust, water it and finish the job by rolling with the steam-roller. Another interesting feature is the caged bird hanging near the driver – apparently a common sight in those days.

Exeter Road, Teignmouth. This treatment is now generally specified at the approaches to all pelican and zebra crossings.

One further method of surface treatment that should be mentioned is the use of slurry seals. This is a method of surface sealing in which a slurry of fine aggregate and bitumen emulsion is laid through a specially designed spreader box. The process is very useful for the maintenance of roads in built-up areas, particularly those on housing estates, since the roads can be opened to traffic within 2–3 minutes of laying. Modern developments of the process provide very strong materials and, because they can be laid thinly, they are frequently used where the carriageway level is critical. This form of surface treatment has been extensively used throughout the county with considerable success.

## Concrete

Concrete is widely used nationally in road construction and repair though it has not been extensively used in Devon for carriageway construction, mainly because coated materials from local quarries have been cheaper. Concrete roads give a very long life, but against this, when maintenance is eventually required it can prove very expensive. Many residential roads and some main roads built in Plymouth and Torbay at the end of the Second World War are of concrete construction and some of these were built by prisoners of war. There are also a number of concrete roads in Barnstaple. These roads have given good service but there have been problems of rocking and cracking slabs, low skid resistance and poor ride characteristics. Such problems have been dealt with by replacing defective slabs and many of these roads have since been overlaid with bitumen macadam or slurry sealing. Whilst this has been generally successful, 'reflective' cracking of the new surface occurs above the joints in the concrete slabs.

The first section of the M5 motorway in Devon was constructed in concrete and has given rise to problems at the joints which have necessitated regular repairs with epoxy resins. It has remained otherwise sound, although grooving of the surface to reduce the risk of aquaplaning was carried out some years ago and has resulted in high levels of tyre noise.

Many of the early problems with concrete carriageways have been overcome with new continuous-laying machinery. In 1987, the A30 dual carriageway from Whiddon Down to Tongue End Cross was constructed using this technique.

Concrete products are extensively used in road maintenance: hydraulically pressed concrete kerbs and paving slabs, concrete pipes, gully pots and manhole sections are all in everyday use. *In situ* concrete is used for bedding kerbs and slabs. This used to be mixed with shovels on site, before petrol-engined concrete mixers were in use, but now it is almost invariably supplied ready-mixed in purpose-built mixer trucks operated by commercial organizations.

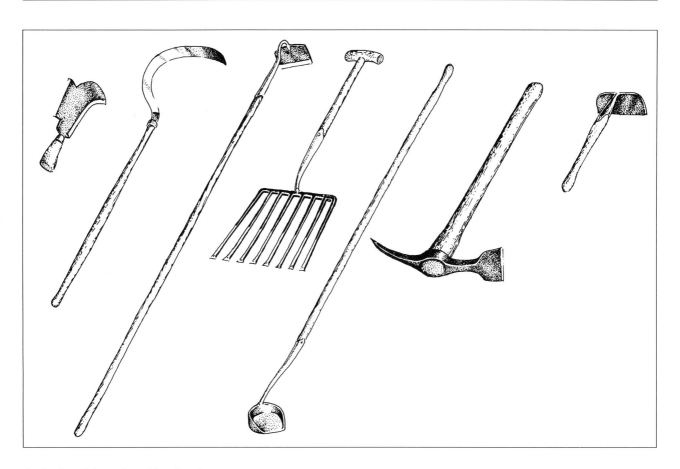

A selection of the tools used by a lengthman.

## From Shovels to Surfacing Machines

In the early days all road repairs were carried out manually using hand tools. Typical tools used by lengthmen included Devon shovel, broom, scraper, pick, turnip hoe, slataxe, mattock, stone scoop, stone fork, scythe with sned and barker, staff hook, bill hook, paring hook (together with protective sleeve for use with a short forked stick to hold down growth) and wheelbarrow. Loosening the surface of a waterbound road to carry out repairs was done by men wielding picks which was a slow and costly method.

The first major item of mechanical equipment available to the road menders was the steam-roller, the earliest of which was built in the middle of the nineteenth century.

The steam-roller became the principal item of mechanical plant associated with road maintenance and many were equipped with scarifiers which could loosen a road surface, enabling it to be reshaped with added stone and rolled to the original level in a fraction of the time possible with hand tools. The scarifier attachment comprised two or three steel spikes or tynes capable of being raised or lowered by handwheel and worm-screw and usually set to cut to a depth of about 2 in. The number of tynes used depended on the hardness of the road and sharpening them provided regular business for the local blacksmith.

On steep hills rollers sometimes ran away and in the mid 1920s such an accident occurred in Salcombe when the driver lost control and his roller went into a nearby plantation where it broke in two!

Before the war the steam-roller towing a living-van and water-cart, often followed by a gaggle of excited children, was a common sight in rural Devon. At the outbreak of the Second World War, Devon had a number of steam-rollers which were more than fifty-five years old. As late as 1944 these steam-rollers would have a roadman 'pilot' with red flag to conduct them from one parish to another. The steam-wagons which carried stone from the quarries to the roadside also aroused great interest as they rumbled along on chain-driven solid rubber-tyred wheels.

A roller driver by the nature of his employment led something of an itinerant existence and when working some distance from home used a living-van equipped with bunks, bedding, cooking stove and utensils. Sometimes he would be accompanied by his wife. The wooden van had a curved corrugated-iron roof and cast-iron wheels. A feature of the steam-roller was its brass bindings and fittings which were kept well polished; indeed the roller as a whole was tended with considerable pride.

One such driver suffered great distress when the boiler lagging of his roller caught fire. He reported to his foreman that 'the poor old girl' had been 'burnt to ground' and for years afterwards his wife was referred to as 'Mrs Burnt to Ground'!

In the 1920s the operation of spreading tar and chippings (surface dressing) became mechanized with the introduction of a coal-fired tar tanker mounted on a lorry which fed a 'flapper' machine. The tar fell by gravity on to a revolving beater driven by the road wheels, which broke up the liquid and distributed it uniformly over the road surface. The spray pipe was divided into sections which could be used separately to cover varying widths of road. An improved flapper machine was used at Okehampton and Tavistock up to 1947.

In the mid 1920s a tar tank mounted on a Foden steam wagon was used in north Devon. The sequence of operations followed a set pattern. First, two men swept off the road surface by hand. Immediately following was a 7-ton-load-capacity Foden steam wagon, fitted with a 1000-gallon tank filled with tar and with steam-heated jacket to maintain the contents in a fluid state. Apart from the driver and mate, one or two men manned the valve wheels on the spray bar mounted at the rear of the vehicle. The operation proceeded at walking pace followed by a Foden 6-ton three-way tipper steam-wagon with the body raised in the rear-tipping position to allow its load of granite chippings to fall into the hopper of the attached 'Wrafton' gritter. This latter device was invented by R.M. Stone, the County Surveyor for North/West Devon at that time, in conjunction with a firm of agricultural engineers by the name of Messrs Isaacs of Wrafton (near Barnstaple), whence the gritter's name was derived. This second assembly drove in reverse, the gritter being actuated by a chain drive from its two road wheels to the internal mechanism. Apart from the driver and mate of this second vehicle, two were at the controls on the gritter. A further two men swept the edge of the treated road surface before

it was finally rolled with an Aveling and Porter 10-ton double-crank compound steam-powered roller of 6 nominal horse power.

The chippings were produced at Wilminstone and Wallabrook quarries near Tavistock and sent to many railway sidings including Mill Road Depot siding at Barnstaple. There they were hand loaded into the Foden 6-ton steam-wagon by four men. The wagon was then taken to the site of the works to have the Wrafton gritter attached. The tar was sent by steam-heated rail wagon from Plymouth to the siding nearest to the site, there to be transferred to the 1000-gallon tank lorry with its steam-heated jacket.

A width of approximately 7 ft 6 in. could be treated with such equipment (approximately half of the road width) and a road 15 ft wide and 3 miles long could be treated in one day. By a system of valves on the spray bar and controls on the Wrafton gritter, narrower widths could be treated, as

**Surface dressing with bitumen or tar and chippings became an effective means of sealing the road, and at the same time providing a good surface. Early development of lorry-mounted tankers fitted with spraybars were the forerunners of modern equipment. The photograph shows a proprietary bitumen emulsion known as 'Colfix' being used for the first time on a road near Okehampton in the 1920s.**

not all roads were exact multiples of 7 ft 6 in. in width. The treated road surfaces gave, and still do to this day, excellent quality in road-holding characteristics, typical of the roads in the county.

When the Second World War began, many of the County Council's vehicles were six or seven years old and some items of plant such as compressors and concrete mixers were as much as ten or twelve years old. Spare parts became unobtainable and had to be made in the Council's workshops; it says much for the ingenuity of the mechanics that all the Department's vehicles and plant were kept on the road at that time.

After the war, the expansion in road mileage and expenditure, coupled with increasing costs of labour and materials, led to increased 'mechanization'. The average weekly wage rate of 15s. in 1914 had increased to £2 in 1938 and by 1954 was £6. Likewise tarmacadam, one of the basic materials for maintenance, had increased from 12s. 4d. per ton in 1938 to 26s. per ton in 1954. Haulage costs had increased in the same period in the same ratio. As grants from the Ministry of Transport, and also the County rate, had increased by only 30–40 per cent since 1938 it was obvious that economies had to be made in order to maintain roads to a reasonable standard. This was achieved largely by the introduction of mechanization which had the effect of increasing daily output with a consequent reduction in the labour force required. The labour force in 1954 was only half the total force employed by the County Council and the Rural District Councils to maintain the same lengths of roads in 1938.

The introduction of the tracked American Barber-Greene mechanical surfacing machines into this country on airfield construction during the Second World War, and the appearance in the mid 1950s of the pneumatic-tyred Blaw Knox machine, revolutionized surfacing techniques. Devon purchased its first Barber-Greene machine in 1951 which was able to lay surfacing material up to a 10 ft width in one operation. This was followed by the purchase of two junior machines, each capable of laying material to a 7 ft width. The standard machine was replaced by a Blaw Knox PF90 in 1964 at a cost of £7000, and the junior machines were later replaced by Blaw Knox PF65 machines. These machines could lay up to 300 tons per day. Later the machines were sold and surfacing work was carried out by contract.

It is surprising how easily men, many of whom had been drawn from an agricultural background, adapted themselves to the use of the new machinery. Their enthusiasm can perhaps best be judged from an entry on one of their timesheets which read 'out with Barbara Green'!

Even the junior machines were too wide for many of the narrower county roads and in 1953 experiments were carried out with the Phoenix-Edwards box spreader. This had no moving parts but ran on skids and bladed the material over the width of the machine to the thickness

**Between the wars, steam-powered wagons like this 1920 Garrett were used by the County Council to transport stone from quarries or railway sidings to road-repair sites. Some of these lorries were converted to carry 1000 gallon steam-heated tanks filled with tar to spread on the road before the laying of stone chippings.**

Increasing mechanization resulted in the need to move heavy plant between sites and back to depots for repair and maintenance. Originally, plant would have moved around under its own power, but this was a very slow process. In 1952, the Central Repair Depot (now the Mechanical Engineering Division) was equipped with this 20 ton A.C. Mammoth Major low loader, which was able to transport even the heaviest plant. It went out of service in 1972.

required. It also had rubber-tyred wheels for quick and easy travelling between sites. The experiments were successful both as regards cost and riding quality and this equipment was used for very many years. Output increased to 150 tons per day, three times that of hand spreading.

A significant post-war development was that of heating and planing, a technique employing oil burners for heating the road surface and oscillating cutters for removing an inch or so of the surface to enable a new wearing course to be laid where existing threshold levels were critical, where material had become slippery, or where a badly corrugated surface needed regulating.

By the mid 1950s, diesel-rollers were being purchased to replace the old steam-rollers. One of the last occasions on which a steam-roller was used was on the A380 Telegraph Hill–Rushycombe Corner improvement in June 1958. At Rushycombe 'Bessie II', driven by Daniel Saunders, was lowered into the deep ravine by wire rope to consolidate a new embankment rising to a height of 70 ft and worked her way out again.

However, six steam-rollers were retained from the original fleet of eighteen and in 1976 it was decided that the veteran machines should be preserved as they had become collectors' items and quite valuable. In order to keep them in working condition and general good order the rollers were offered for lease to responsible steam-engine enthusiasts. People who expressed an interest were

naturally concerned at the high cost of repairs, particularly to boilers and fire boxes which need high-quality steel and the work of highly specialized craftsmen. Despite these difficulties, however, leases were entered into, with the result that some of these rollers can be seen in the Devon County green livery of their time at steam-engine rallies, looking their best for competition.

The details of these rollers are:

| Type | Chassis No. | Registration No. | Date of Registration |
|------|------------|------------------|----------------------|
| Greens III | 1968 | TA 2431 | 25/10/21 |
| Marshall 127 | 78153 | TT 1855 | 1/12/24 |
| Marshall 131 | 85106 | DV 4005 | 20/2/30 |
| Aveling Porter 138 | 4873 | TA 6120 | 27/4/23 |
| Wallis Stevens 139 | 7904 | OT 3167 | 1/12/26 |
| Aveling Porter 144 | 11599 | TT 9449 | 17/8/26 |

Surface dressing, or 'tarring' as it was called, became highly mechanized with the introduction in the 1950s of bulk pressure sprayers of 1000 and 2000 gallons capacity, lagged to keep the tar or bitumen hot and with their own adjustable spray bars. Bulk pressure sprayers were the forerunners of sophisticated machines in the maintenance field which now have capacities of up to 3600 gallons. They can be used to control accurately the rate of spread of binder on to the road surface and are fitted with telescopic spray bars which will expand from 7 ft 6 in. to 12 ft 6 in. wide in 6 in. increments with automatic cut-in valves.

Tailboard attachments to lorries for spreading of chippings have been considerably improved and the gravity-fed metered-roller type is now in general use. These machines keep to a minimum the amount of loose chippings and those remaining are removed by mechanical sweeper. A large self-propelled chipping spreader operated by one man can also be hired for use on wide roads. A good deal of skill is required by lorry drivers who have to reverse along many miles of country lanes and who have to negotiate gradients as steep as 1 in 4. Multi-wheeled pneumatic-tyred rollers have been in use for many years and have advantages over the steel-wheeled type in that the crushing of chippings is avoided, and movement from site to site is easier and quicker.

## Further improvements in machinery and techniques

All coated material, except in patching and reinstatement work, is now laid by machine. Daily outputs of 1000 tonnes of 28 mm basecourse and 800 tonnes of hot-rolled asphalt wearing course have been achieved on dual-carriageway work.

Laying machinery continues to be improved and automatic ancillary equipment controlled by sensor units and laser beams is available to give accurate control of level, crossfall and joint matching to ensure a much higher standard of finish than previously possible. The Telescreed is another major advance and adjusts the laying width automatically from 2.5 m to 4.75 m wide at the touch of a switch. Diesel rollers have long since superseded the steam-roller and are equipped with disc cutters for the clean and accurate cutting of centre-line joints. Modern rollers can now be specified not only with plain steel drums but also with rubber-coated drums and vibrating equipment to increase compaction well above that achieved by a non-vibrating or dead-weight roller. The self-propelled side-loading chipping spreader for hot-rolled asphalt work is also widely used.

Wherever possible roads are overlaid to increase construction depth and so add strength, but it is sometimes necessary to remove material. The old oil-fired heat/planing machine was superseded by the infra-red heat/planer which in turn has largely been replaced by a continuous-drum cold planer capable of removing 100 mm of material in one pass. Planing work is carried out by contract in Devon and is carefully programmed to accord with subsequent resurfacing work. Smaller versions of the planing machines have been recently acquired which can be used for the removal of defective material prior to patching and trench reinstatement.

In the late 1970s a section of the A38 at Heathfield was laid as a trial by the 'Repave' method. This used sophisticated equipment that planed off the old surface, recycled it with fresh bitumen and relaid the surface in a continuous operation. Though an expensive process, the resulting surface performed well. The cost and size of this operation, however, means that it can only effectively be carried out on long lengths of wide road, making its use very limited in Devon.

The use of modern laying machinery has contributed in no small way to improved smoothness of ride on main routes in the county. Machines for measuring surface irregularity have been available for many years. Two such machines – 'the bump integrator' and the 'rolling straight edge' – have been used in Devon. However, neither of these has been entirely satisfactory since the long wave-length irregularities which affect high-speed vehicles are not measured. A high-speed profilometer, now being developed by the Transport and Road Research Laboratory, will represent a major step forward when it is available for general use.

## Road cleaning and grass cutting

Ditching and watertabling (the cleaning of road channels), the traditional work done by hand by the lengthmen, also became mechanized. Some very ingenious machines were tried in various parts of the country but they were expensive and of limited use. However, soon after the war a County Council employee developed the 'Porter-Hill Scoop', an inexpensive loading attachment for a tractor, and this, together with a rear-mounted disc plough, enabled the work to be done in a fraction of the time.

The cleaning of ditches situated at the back of grass verges has always been a problem and their depth, width and position in relation to the road may present difficulties which can only be overcome manually. However, the advent of 360° slew excavators such as Hymacs and Poclains enabled much of the work to be mechanized.

The sweeping of channels by hand on kerbed urban roads and main rural routes has been almost totally transformed by the mechanical road sweeper, which is

Keeping the roads open for traffic in the winter now accounts for a significant proportion of the money spent on maintenance. The photograph shows a road near Princetown in the winter of 1946-7 and provides a graphic demonstration of the way in which the county can be paralysed by bad weather. One particular difficulty was the 'ammil', a thick coating of ice which formed on all exposed surfaces, bringing down power and telephone lines.

The winter of 1977–8 produced remarkable scenes in the exposed parts of the county. In spite of persistent efforts, it proved impossible to keep Haldon and Telegraph Hills open to traffic in the face of the blizzard of 18–19 February. People were forced to abandon their cars and spend the night in a local hotel. Abandoned vehicles were covered with up to 10 ft of snow in some places, making the task of clearance awkward and slow. The photograph shows abandoned vehicles on Telegraph Hill.

equipped with rotating brushes and acts rather like a giant vacuum cleaner. Similarly, road gullies which had to be cleared using special narrow shovels are now emptied and refilled with water by the gully emptier, these vacuum machines having a capacity of about 1200 gallons.

In the immediate post-war years verge trimming was carried out mainly by hand, but on properly levelled verges small hand-operated machines were used; the Allen scythe with reciprocating blade was a typical example. Equipment for attaching to tractors gradually came on to the market, with flexible blades capable of cutting at almost any angle and with a mechanism for throwing the machine out of gear when it encountered an obstruction, thereby preventing damage to the blade. The levelling of verges enabled considerable economies to be made by mechanical cutting, permitting the use of ordinary tractors fitted with flail mower attachments.

Grass cutting has become a mechanized operation and machinery has been much improved. The modern flail-type hydromowers and turbomowers, both side- and rear-mounted, with hydraulically operated cranked arms carrying the cutting head, have long since replaced the flat-bed reciprocating-blade machine for rural grass cutting, with various types of pedestrian-controlled mowers being used in urban areas.

## Dealing with Emergencies
### Snow and ice

Devon is not normally subject to heavy snowfall and winter maintenance has mainly involved the treating of roads to deal with ice and light snow. This was originally done by lengthmen spreading grit from roadside heaps. It gradually became more mechanized with men spreading the grit from a moving lorry and later by a towed 'spinner' gritter. In the early 1960s the advantages were recognized of using ground rock salt as a road de-icer and specialist bulk spreading vehicles are now used.

Although not a frequent problem, blizzards have in some years caused considerable disruption. During such conditions, many miles of road become completely blocked by deep drifts of snow trapped between high hedgebanks, and even coastal roads have become impassable. In his report to the Woodbury Highway Board in January 1875, Henry Dagworthy reported that 'Mr Searle the contractor for Littleham was compelled to hire a number of men to clear away the snow which completely blocked the road between Exmouth and Budleigh Salterton. The expense incurred amounts to 15 shillings which I consider a reasonable charge and the work absolutely necessary to be done.'

In recent years blizzard conditions across the whole county were experienced during the winters of 1946-7, 1962-3, 1967-8, 1968-9, 1970-71, 1977-8 and 1978-9, although every year snow occurs on the higher ground.

The severe winter of 1947 was the worst in living memory at that time and Devon had only twenty-nine snowploughs and three mechanical loaders. The disruption to the community lasted for many weeks. As a result, the newly appointed County Surveyor, R.B. Carnegie, who had

previously been County Surveyor of Inverness-shire, made considerable improvements to winter maintenance arrangements for subsequent years.

During 1963, snowfall was recorded at Exeter airport on twenty-seven days and heavy snow fell on at least seven occasions. Snow fences were erected in 1968 adjoining the A35 between Honiton and Axminster at Springfield Corner, the A373 Honiton to Cullompton road at Hembury Fort and the A385 Totnes to Plymouth road at Marley Head. These proved to be effective. In 1970 the Dartmeet to Ashburton road was blocked by 9 in. of snow and Boxing Day that year was the coldest since 1938. These conditions were combined with gale-force winds which meant that virtually every minor road became blocked to a greater or lesser extent, with miles of snow drifts up to 10 ft deep. In these conditions snow blows off fields and moorland and completely fills roads between high hedgebanks so clearance work carried out the previous day can be nullified overnight.

## Blizzards, February 1978

At 7.30 a.m. on Saturday, 18 February 1978, the following weather forecast was issued by the Meteorological Office at Mountbatten, Plymouth: 'Moderate to heavy accumulations of snow are expected today over much of Devon, particularly over the moors. Severe drifting is expected in the strong to gale force east to south easterly winds.'

This forecast was the prelude to one of the severest blizzards experienced in Devon and was to result in a major emergency operation being mounted by staff and the County Council's own labour force. They were already dealing with the effects of drifting from heavy snowfalls earlier that week.

A subsequent forecast issued at 1.55 p.m. on that day read: 'Road surface temperatures already sub-zero in most areas by dusk with formation of icy patches. This extends snow warning until 10.00 a.m. tomorrow.'

By this time Divisions were fully operational and a decision was taken to open the Emergency Control Room at County Hall at 7.00 p.m. on the Saturday evening. During the evening and night a blizzard raged over the whole county and almost every road, including the M5, became blocked with many feet of snow and in places drifts were up to 9 metres deep. At one stage during the night the Divisional Surveyor for Okehampton reported that drifts on the A30 near Sourton Cross had reached the tops of the telegraph poles! Such conditions made further work futile, as many snow ploughs became snowed in and had to be abandoned. Numerous motorists had to leave their vehicles and many were rescued by County roadmen.

Sunday, 19 February dawned to reveal almost total closure of the county's highway network. During the course of the following week or so the task of restoring communications was probably the largest operation of its kind undertaken by the County Engineer's Department. At the peak of the operation, 1683 men were employed, of whom 714 were hired from outside sources. A total of 1042 items of machinery and plant were used including all the County Council's resources and 796 hired items. This included snow blowers from the Department of Transport and Bedfordshire County Council and large rubber-tyred articulated loading shovels from local quarries. Helicopters were used to fly some drivers back to their stranded snow ploughs and also proved invaluable for reconnaissance to determine the extent of the problem to be tackled.

The cost of the snow-clearance operations was over £1.2 million, against a budget of £344 000. Subsequent repairs of road damage caused by snow-clearing plant and frost cost a further £1.6 million.

Significant lessons were learnt and acted upon about the need to improve winter-maintenance arrangements and the performance of plant, as well as the need for better advance weather information. This experience resulted in the first two snow blowers (Rolba R400s) being purchased by the County Council.

## Blizzards, January 1979

Unusually, for the second year in succession heavy snow and severe freezing conditions were experienced in January 1979 and many main routes were closed for long periods. Snow fell on about fifteen days in January and February and, although depths were nowhere near as great as in 1978, strong winds caused drifting of up to 1.5 metres. The main problem in 1979 was the severe cold, with temperatures as low as −13°C being recorded. This meant that the snow lasted longer and there was severe frost damage. The problem of dealing with persistent frost led to stocks of salt falling to only 13 per cent of their pre-winter level, at a time of national shortage. The County Council resorted to importing salt by sea from Germany and Sicily. As a result of this experience stock levels were subsequently increased to allow a reserve capacity. Problems were aggravated by a national work-to-rule by local authority workers which meant that for a period no pre-salting took place.

The cost of this operation was £1.9 million, with subsequent remedial works costing in excess of £2.5 million.

## The winter of 1984–5 – 'the big freeze'

The winter of 1984–5 was significant, not because much snow fell (snow was recorded as lying at Exeter airport on seven days) but because of an extended period of exceptionally low temperatures throughout virtually the whole of January and part of February. Salting and snow-clearing operations cost £2.4 million against a budget of £1.2 million, but the major effect of the sustained period of low temperatures was a subsequent frost-damage repair bill of over £5 million which could only in part be met from

One of the county's Rolba R400 snow blowers at work near Totnes in early March 1986. These high-volume clearance machines (800 tonnes per hour) are particularly well suited to clearing the deep drifts that can cover the roads between the high Devon banks in rural areas. To make sure that the main routes remain clear, the county also has a Rolba R1200 snow blower, which can clear 1500 tonnes of snow per hour.

reserves and had to be largely funded by deferring planned maintenance works.

These problems were compounded by the winters of 1985 and 1986 which, though not exceptionally severe by previous standards, resulted in blizzard conditions on two successive years in the South Hams, a part of the county which normally escapes the worst of the weather.

## Modernization

The experiences of several severe winters and the increasing public expectation that roads will be cleared and maintained in a safe condition at all times, have led the County Council continually to update and improve organizational arrangements and to invest in modern plant, improved salt storage facilities and new technology such as ice-detection sensors and weather radar.

Operational procedures are reviewed annually and identify routes for priority of attention. At the top of the list for treatment and snow clearance are the M5 motorway and the all-purpose dual carriageways. However, other principal roads, main routes in urban areas, most scheduled bus routes and the main access roads to villages and farming communities are also afforded a high priority.

### Spreaders, ploughs and blowers

Salt-spreading, gritting and snow-clearing equipment became very much more sophisticated in the 1980s and the

**On the night of the storms which flooded Lynmouth, quantities of floodwater cascaded down the narrow lanes leading from the moors. The effect on the fabric of the roads was cataclysmic – in this instance a deep trench had been ripped out of the road by the scouring action of the water. In some places these scoured-out trenches reached 18ft in depth.**

ability of specialist vehicles to respond to severe winter emergencies in terms of power and performance increased tremendously.

Five large Swiss-built snow blowers are based at depots at Okehampton, Barnstaple, Parracombe, Honiton and Moretonhampstead, and over twenty tractor-mounted blowers are operated by farmers on pre-arranged routes in the more remote areas. These blowers have proved their worth in recent years and the largest in the County fleet, the Rolba R1200, has a cutter width of 2.1 m and can move 1500 tonnes of snow per hour.

In addition to the snow blowers, there are about two hundred other items of equipment ranging from mechanical shovels to six-wheel-drive salt-spreading vehicles fitted with snow ploughs. In serious blizzard conditions this impressive fleet can be supplemented by a vast array of hired machines.

### Salt and grit

Ground rock salt is used to deal with ice and light snow but this is supplemented with grit to provide better grip for vehicles when snow becomes hard packed. The store of

1100 tons of salt held in 1963 was soon found to be inadequate and had been increased to 20 000 tons by 1970. In the 1980s pre-winter salt stocks have been held at just over 50 000 tonnes. The salt is stored in purpose-built barns or in large stock piles protected by sheeting.

## The use of technology

Devon led the country in the development of ice detection on highways in the early 1980s. This equipment enables engineers to see at a glance, on a visual display screen, surface and air temperatures and moisture levels, together with 'surface alert' and 'surface critical' warnings. The first ice-detection sensor was installed on Haldon Hill in 1980 and its use proved successful in the winter of 1980–81. The installation of sensors was progressively increased as the operational benefits and savings in unnecessary salting became more apparent and by 1987 a total of thirty-six remote sensing units had been installed making this the largest system in the country at that time. Certain routes have been thermally mapped to relate their thermal fingerprint to the ice-detection sensor location and this technique is to be used in future to determine the need for and location of further sensors. In addition, the need to have early information on approaching weather systems resulted in a decision to install a weather radar system in 1982. This proved invaluable in giving forewarning of snow, making it possible to initiate action just before snow arrives and also to stand men down earlier when the problem is seen to have passed.

In order to get the maximum benefit from this new technology, a central Information Room has been developed which is also manned out of normal hours whenever adverse conditions are expected. Weather forecasts are

Devon led the country in the early 1980s with the introduction of an ice-detection system for highways. At thirty-six sites throughout the county, special sensors, which are in effect miniature weather stations, constantly monitor and feed back to County Hall detailed information on prevailing atmospheric and road surface conditions.

received daily from the Meteorological Office and sent out electronically to Divisions and Agents. Decisions on appropriate action to be taken are then made in accordance with prescribed procedures and the Information Room acts as a reporting centre for Highway Superintendents of actual conditions experienced and action being taken. The Information Room personnel are thus able to provide accurate information to the police, motoring organizations and the media about road conditions.

In extreme circumstances an emergency control room is opened in the basement of County Hall to co-ordinate operations. It is manned twenty-four hours per day if necessary by senior staff of the County Engineering and Planning Department and representatives of the police and motoring organizations. The ability to deal with weather emergencies has come a long way since the limited primitive equipment of 1947 and frequent visits are made to Devon by engineers from home and abroad to see the facilities the County Council has developed.

## Wind and water

### Highway flooding

From time to time, after periods of heavy rain, roads can be affected by flooding. Local highway flooding often results from water run-off from adjoining land and can become a problem particularly in the autumn when fallen leaves block gully gratings and drainage inlets.

The information and control room in County Hall provides electronic monitoring of weather conditions and urban traffic control systems (UTCs). Normally, information obtained is passed to relevant personnel to assist in day-to-day operations, but at times the information room becomes the control centre for the co-ordination of operations.

Winter is hard on road surfaces. Not only does the clearance of snow and ice take considerable time and effort but severe frost leaves a legacy of major repair work to be carried out. The picture shows the type of damage that may be found on a rural road following a period of severe conditions. In 1984–5 damage was so extensive that it resulted in an abnormally high repair bill of over £5 million for the whole county.

The large steep-sided rainfall-catchment areas of Devon can result in extremely rapid run-off after periods of intense rain. This has sometimes proved to be of disastrous proportions, with normally placid streams, rivers and estuaries bursting their banks causing widespread flooding and damage. After the Lynmouth flood of 1952, the east Devon flood of 10 and 11 July 1968 must rank as the most serious experienced (see Chapter 4). This occurred after exceptional rainfall on the Blackdown Hills (5 in. of rain fell between 4 p.m. and 10 p.m.) resulting in widespread flooding, the loss of ten bridges and extensive damage to roads, retaining walls, drains and culverts. The cost at that time of making good damage to roads alone was of the order of £500 000. More recently, on 27 December 1979, serious flood damage occurred in Newton Abbot and other towns and villages surrounding Dartmoor, when torrential rain followed a period of freezing conditions.

Nowadays, flood warnings are issued by the South West Water Flood Warning Office and if necessary the County Control Room is opened and operates in close liaison with South West Water and the Meteorological Office at Plymouth. Weather radar and satellite data now play an invaluable part in enabling rainfall patterns to be monitored as they develop and warnings of danger to be issued earlier.

The engineer deals with the immediate effects of flooding by arranging road closures and diversions and he also provides support and technical advice to the County Emergency Officer and to District Council Officers, who are responsible for dealing with the flooding of property and relief work. When waters have subsided, the engineer begins the work of clearing mud and debris from road surfaces, inspecting and cleaning drainage systems, and

ensuring that all bridges and culverts are clear and that any damage is repaired.

Such events seem to be inevitable from time to time. As long ago as 18 January 1875, Henry Dagworthy reported to the Woodbury Highway Board, that 'Many of the roads have been greatly injured by the recent snow and heavy rain'.

## River erosion

Erosion by rivers can cause local maintenance problems. For example, one case on the River Exe in the 1960s was the subject of a public inquiry. The reason for this was that the County Council, whose view was upheld, felt that the public footpath affected could be diverted for about £400, whereas the owner of the adjoining land was insisting on a protection scheme at a cost of £7500, which was considered to be too expensive.

In the 1960s the River Plym above Cadover Bridge was diverted from its original course over a length of 150 yards because it had encroached to within 12 ft of a county road. The work was carried out jointly with the River Authority.

An interesting situation exists just upstream of Dart Bridge, Buckfastleigh where the River Dart has eroded the soft rock, leaving sections of the adjoining road to Buckfast Abbey cantilevered on a shelf of limestone about 20 ft thick. This is supported at river level by concrete piers approximately 3 ft square. This area is of course well known for the large caves in the well-fissured limestone.

## Coastal erosion

Erosion of the 154 miles (248 km) of coastline in Devon is a relatively slow process but is more pronounced in the soft shales of the south Devon coast than elsewhere. At times it has threatened county roads and footpaths and indeed in some cases, such as at North Hallsands, Hope Cove and Thurlestone, public roads have been lost to the sea; at North Hallsands a contributing factor was the long-term effect of removal of shingle from the sea-bed off Start Point for the construction of Devonport Dockyard. There is no statutory requirement, however, for the County Council to reinstate public roads lost to the sea as a result of the forces of nature: it would be quite unreasonable if it were so.

Under the Coast Protection Act 1949, maritime District Councils have the primary responsibility for coast protection work. Only where it is necessary to safeguard a highway is the County Council itself entitled to execute coast-protection work without consulting the appropriate District Council, though it is of course consulted as a matter of courtesy.

In January and February 1963 a major problem occurred at Blackpool Sands on the south Devon coast where the main Dartmouth–Torcross road was threatened. This road, the A379, was built in 1855 by Arthur Howe Holdsworth, Governor of Dartmouth Castle. Serious erosion of the soft shale at the centre of the cove occurred where the road is some 70–80 ft above beach level and where the distance between the edge of the road and the top of the cliff had been reduced from 50 ft in 1906 to 24 ft. The provision of a 'wall' of large stone blocks (blockstone) down to the underlying clay and to 20 ft above mean sea level was carried out at a cost of £29 000. The fill for the embankments was obtained from local road improvements. At Matts Point, a short distance away on the Torcross side, the road had to be relocated further inland in 1947 and a constant watch is kept on this location where large fractures exist in the adjoining cliff. It has been suggested that some of the movement at Matts Point may have been due to the shelling of this particular length of coastline when the American forces occupied a large part of the South Hams as a battle-training area prior to the Normandy landings in 1944. Certainly the scars left by bursting shells are still clearly visible in the limestone walls between Matts Point and Strete Gate.

The blockstone form of construction has also proved successful at the villages of Challaborough and Beesands. It is not only effective in dissipating wave action but has the advantage that repairs can be easily and quickly undertaken between tides.

Where relatively short sections of erosion have had to be bridged, such as in Cliff Road, Salcombe, a ladder type of construction, consisting of simply supported reinforced-concrete beams tied together by similar cross members approximately 2 ft square at 10–12 ft intervals, has been used.

Coastal footpaths are also prone to erosion and although in some cases it has been expedient to retain them, usually it has been cheaper and easier to divert them.

Such a procedure was followed in 1969 when approximately 1½ miles of the coastal footpath between Seaton and Lyme Regis became untenable because of continual and serious movement of the cliffs. This particular stretch of coastline is notorious for landslips which have occurred several times over a very long period. Blue lias clay visible at beach level is overcapped by greensand surmounted by high chalk cliffs rising to about 300 ft above sea level. The infiltration of water into the greensand during particularly wet winters has given rise to large areas of land movement. Such a landslip is recorded as having occurred on Christmas Day 1839 when the greensand collapsed under the weight of the overlying chalk and 45 acres of arable land at Bindon and Dowlands slid towards the sea and was lost to cultivation. Two cottages in the lower region of the cliff were destroyed and a great chasm 300 ft wide, 150 ft deep and ¾ mile long was formed.

## The storm of January 1979

Between 30 December 1978 and 5 January 1979, together with other winter problems in the county, the villages of Torcross, Beesands and North Hallsands were battered by enormous seas when severe south-easterly gales coincided with high tides. The sea defences were struck by huge waves and while boulder protection at Beesands was damaged but held the sea at bay, the gabions at Torcross were breached and the old sea wall completely washed away, resulting in many houses being destroyed or badly

Coastal erosion is usually a gradual process, but at Hallsands and Beesands in south Devon a series of storms washed away the road and destroyed most of the houses. It is widely thought that the sudden change in the pattern of the coastline in this area was due to the effect of large-scale removal of shingle from the sea-bed off Start Point in 1897, for use in construction of Devonport Dockyard.

In the winter of 1977–8 heavy snowfalls followed by freezing conditions and high winds caused spectacular snowdrifts in some of the exposed parts of Devon. The example here is a road in the Okehampton area, where a mechanical digger struggles to clear drifts of up to 5 metres.

*Above:* **A combination of high tides and severe south-easterly gales between 30 December 1978 and 5 January 1979 resulted in the complete destruction of the sea defences at Torcross. This picture gives a vivid impression of the storm at its height.** *Top:* **The immediate aftermath of the storm reveals the extent of the damage. The remains of the sea defences completely cover the footway and have crashed into the front room of the property on the left of the picture.**

damaged. Many properties had to be evacuated and at the height of the gales one old Beesands fisherman lying awake in the early hours of the morning, said to his wife, 'Mother, I can hear the sea', meaning that it was literally washing under the floorboards and he knew it was time to 'abandon ship'.

With the co-operation of the Devon quarries, some 10 000 tonnes of blockstone were brought in throughout day and night as an emergency measure to provide immediate protection to the A379 along Slapton Ley and to the public road fronting Torcross, together with repairs at Beesands and North Hallsands, in an operation costing over £250 000. This saved the road and further houses from being washed away. A permanent protection scheme was carried out by South West Water in 1981, with substantial grant aid from the Ministry of Agriculture, Fisheries and Food.

It is in times of emergencies such as these that engineers, skilled operators and roadmen use their resources in working together to protect the community and maintain its highways.

Devon's environment is its most priceless asset, with its two National Parks – Dartmoor and Exmoor – its Areas of Outstanding Natural Beauty and elsewhere a landscape which by any standards is consistently attractive. Its varied coastline makes it perhaps Britain's premier holiday area. These attributes have considerable implications in highway terms. The rolling landscape means that it is both important to integrate the highways into the landscape and difficult to do so.

Despite a considerable programme of new road-building in recent years, particularly the M5/A38 and A30 spine roads, sensitive routeing and landscaping have by and large ensured that these new highways have fitted well into the landscape. The increase in traffic, including that resulting from tourism, has been absorbed without irreparable damage to Devon's environment. Indeed, as the pressures have increased so the techniques have improved to deal with them.

The rest of this chapter explores the relationship between Devon's countryside and the very intricate highway system within it. The more detailed elements of the highway network are described, including those features and amenities which combine to create Devon's unique roadside environment. The text takes the reader along ancient roads and coastal footpaths. It describes roadside features and street furniture, some commonplace, some unusual. It describes how water features complement the county's roads. It points to the importance of the Devon hedgebank both from a visual and a nature conservation point of view. It endeavours to emphasize the role which roadsides play in wildlife conservation, a role not always readily recognized.

Much of the chapter indulges unashamedly in nostalgia, but it concludes by describing some recent contributions to the roadside environment, illustrating that roads are a constantly evolving feature of the landscape.

## Ancient Roads, Unusual Streets and Village Greens and Squares

### Green lanes

In Devon the term 'green lane' tends to be applied to any track which has been completely grassed over. The Countryside Commission has defined a green lane as 'an

# 8

# THE HIGHWAY ENVIRONMENT

## Features of Interest, Past and Present

Many green lanes follow ancient routes through some of Devon's most delightful countryside. Not all of them form part of the highway network maintained by the County Council, and they are not necessarily public rights of way.

unmetalled track, which may or may not be a right of way for the public either on foot, horse, bicycle or motor vehicle, including a motor bicycle, and which is usually bounded by hedges, walls or ditches'. Thus defined a green lane could therefore be a county road, a byway, a bridleway, a public footpath, or none of these, and may be passable or impassable to all or some forms of traffic. Therefore, although the term will include many rights of way shown on what is known as the statutory definitive map (see p. 197) and some lightly trafficked county roads, there is no presumption that a green lane is a public highway.

Of all the types of highway that exist in Devon, green lanes are the most evocative of the past. Just by stepping on to the unmade surface and brushing against the overhanging branches the walker may begin to imagine all the past travellers who have used the lane and kept it open, not by volume of traffic but by continuity of feet, 'truckamuck', packhorse, wagon, traction engine and tractor. (A 'truckamuck' was a crude form of sledge initially consisting of nothing more than two uprooted trees tied together. In its more sophisticated form – and it survived in many places until the early 1900s – the sledge was mounted on wooden or iron runners.)

Most people in Devon know where to find a green lane; and whilst it may be little used now (or so it seems), centuries ago it may have been a busy thoroughfare. Prehistoric man descending from the moors carved ways into the lush vegetation as he moved towards the fertile river valleys and coasts. Some green lanes run near ancient religious sites or prehistoric monuments. Some lead up to ridgeways from which flints and pottery were traded. In the Saxon *burh* town of Lydford there are some fine examples of lanes dating from the original grid-pattern layout of this once important town. Other lanes show the characteristic 'dog's-leg' shape of access lanes to Saxon strip farms. Some ancient boundary lanes form part of parish divisions, but were probably in existence before as manorial or hundred divisions.

For centuries 'truckamucks' were used to transport goods along these narrow lanes. Some green lanes became known as sledge ways. The habit of shovelling up the 'trucked muck' on to the tops of hedgebanks resulted in a deepening of the lanes and the flourishing of the hedgerows. Baring-Gould in *Devonshire Characters and Strange Events* suggests that lanes around the coast were made deliberately sunken so that coastguards could not see the free-traders passing.

Sunken lanes, so-called because the surface is below the level of the adjoining ground, are characteristic of Devon. The green lanes survey (see below) revealed that about 17 per cent of those recorded fell into this category. A number of suggestions have been made for their existence. That they were dug out to provide the material with which to form the hedgebanks on either side seems the most logical explanation, but natural attrition, the physical scraping away and removal of mud over centuries, or the formation of drainage channels are other possibilities.

Some ancient market towns in Devon still exhibit evidence of green lanes used to bring goods to the centre of the town during the growth in trade in the fourteenth century. Packhorses brought goods into town along the country roads at great danger to all: 'For it was no joke in the old days to meet a train of packhorses. They occupied the whole of the road, leaving no room for a mounted man to pass, and they plodded on steadily, nose to tail without a thought of stopping before any living obstacle.' (From a contribution made by Sir J. Fortescue to W. Harding Thompson's *Devon: A Survey*, published in 1932.)

The terrain of Devon has always presented problems to transportation. The illustration of a carrier in the eighteenth century shows the difficulties involved in manoeuvring packs through the lanes. The packs were supported by Devon crooks or crubs (vertical wooden supports for goods carried by pack horse), whereas in other areas of the country the packs were just slung up across the donkeys and mules. Some lanes reveal evidence of packhorse ledges along their sides; these were carved out to allow packs to pass undamaged (see top picture opposite).

The wheel came late to Devon. New lanes were built for wagons, leaving some of the old green lanes for pedlars, solitary travellers and horses. But wagon ruts still exist in some lanes, showing the exact axle width of the old wagons and carts which worked the 'truss' ways, the lanes which were once chiefly used to bring corn to the county's many mills. Though arable farming has declined, many of these lanes continue to be used today as access to fields for cattle and tractors.

Apart from their agricultural importance, green lanes

were also used as routes for the transport of metalliferous minerals when Devon was an important supplier. The many green lanes which weave up and down the Tamar valley on both sides of the border once rang to the sound of boots as miners went to and from the tin, copper and arsenic mines. There are also many stone quarries throughout Devon and these too are surrounded by systems of footpaths and green lanes which once led workers to the workface.

Although it is known that some are prehistoric in origin, it is not always easy to date green lanes. Where there is no positive evidence, such as that relating to the mineral-extraction industries, it is difficult to find the necessary historical data.

Occasionally a lane will reveal evidence of its antiquity in a more positive form than even documentary evidence can provide. For instance there is a small hump-backed bridge in a recently restored lane at Washbourne near Totnes. The bridge bears the following inscription:

> New built at the
> Counties Charge
> 1687 Richard
> Kelley Treasurer

The Washbourne and Harbourne valleys were once extremely busy places: milling, paper making, lime burning and quarrying, cider making, charcoal burning, wool spinning, all took place here; there is a medieval dock at Tuckenhay and a tannery was said to operate at Allaleigh. So maybe this bridge, possibly once referred to as Perch, Prarch or Perchwood Bridge in documents dating back to 1653, was much used in that prosperous period. But industries decline and routes change to accommodate new transport needs: there is no mention of this bridge after 1703. Today it is a tantalizing reminder of how lanes which were once thoroughfares can be so easily lost. The discovery of this bridge should inspire all those who enjoy the challenge of an overgrown lane glimpsed through a car window. It is always worth going back.

Green lanes are important in nature conservation terms. Along with the trees and shrubs in the hedgerows, which are often remnants of ancient woodland, come a variety of plants and flowers. Regional differences in lane construction, layered hedges, overgrown tunnels, stone walls, sunken lanes and ridgetop lanes all support different habitats and many insects and birds can be found. Foxes, badgers and various small mammals all use lanes as their highways or dwelling places.

Some green lanes have specific links with the past, such as Runaway Lane at Modbury where, during the Civil War, the Royalists escaped into Plymouth pursued by the Roundheads. Others are reputed to be haunted. In a sense they all are haunted by people and events whose stories will never fully be known.

In 1983, following a study of green lanes carried out by the Dartington Amenity Research Trust, a Manpower Services Commission scheme was set up to identify, survey and compile a record of green lanes in Devon. Data collected comprised historical, documentary and physical

This illustration shows a packhorse loaded with goods on wooden 'crooks', or 'crubs'. These were made out of two willow saplings which were bent ('crooked') when green, then dried in that shape. The two bent poles were joined by horizontal bars, and the whole assembly slung over the pack saddle. Writing in 1874, Samuel Smiles reveals that packhorses were still in use in some parts of north Devon at that time.

evidence, including status, width, lane users, access and hedgerow species. In addition a note was made of remedial tasks required to enable clearance and repair work to be undertaken subsequently.

## Ancient trackways

There are a number of ancient trackways in Devon. Indeed they could easily be the subject of a separate chapter or even a book. Dartmoor in particular has a considerable network, including some with such evocative names as the Lich Way, Mariners' Way and the Abbot's Way.

One particularly interesting relic is the ancient trackway built with large stone cobbles at Avonwick about 1½ miles downstream from South Brent. Constructed alongside the River Avon, it was probably used by farmers taking their cattle from that valley up to the western slopes of Dartmoor. It is also suggested that it might have served as a parish boundary. There is evidence of considerable wear from wagon wheels, and in the eighteenth century it became a sliproad by the side of the tollhouse on the Totnes to Ivybridge turnpike. It fell into disuse with the advent of new roads constructed above flood level.

It appears likely that a section of the trackway at the

**This delightful little bridge carries a green lane over a stream near Washbourne in south Devon. The area was once the centre of a variety of industrial activities and this lane once carried considerable traffic.**

South Brent end was lost as a consequence of the building of the South Brent to Kingsbridge railway in 1863. The part which now remains between two beautiful old stone bridges – Avonwick Bridge by the old tollhouse and Horsebrook Bridge – was restored in 1984 and is now a bridleway.

## Unusual streets

Devon's towns and villages contain a large number of streets of character. In coastal towns such as Brixham, Dartmouth and Ilfracombe, where houses are perched high on the cliffs, some streets are simply narrow flights of stone steps. In other places, particularly Appledore, there are streets that are little more than open surface-water drains beautifully built in granite setts, with the main channel down the centre rather than at the sides. Certainly their width is such that only pedestrians can use them. Four interesting streets are particularly worthy of mention.

Parliament Street, Exeter, is claimed to be one of the narrowest streets in the world and varies in width from 25 in. to 45 in. The origin of the name is not clear; some connect it with the fact that Edward I held a Parliament in Exeter in 1285. (The people of Crediton support the same premise for the name of Parliament Street in their town.) However, others say the name may derive from its proximity to the Guildhall. Whatever the origin of its name, it is to many simply 'squeeze belly alley'.

Stepcote Hill, Exeter, although narrow and steep, was, until about the sixteenth century, the main thoroughfare leading to Exeter's West Gate and the old bridge over the River Exe, part of which has now been restored. Close by is 'The House That Moved'. This old timber-framed building was moved bodily to enable the construction of part of Exeter's inner bypass. This street, together with the old bridge, St Mary Steps Church and the small group of Tudor buildings, forms an attractive reminder of old Exeter.

Castle Street, Tiverton, has a cobbled channel in its centre carrying a stream known as the town leat, which rises on Norwood Common some 8 km away. It provided the town's original water supply, given by Isabel, Countess of Devon in about 1262. The channel is one of the oldest of its type still to contain water.

Probably the best known is the cobbled street of Clovelly, the picturesque and romantic village on the north Devon coast, and it is perhaps unique. It is formed in terraces with flights of some 650 steps as it extends from the small harbour up the precipitous side of the sea cliff and is flanked by attractive houses stepped, as it were, in sympathy. Obviously motor vehicles cannot use the steps so goods are still carried by donkey and on wooden sledges. Moving house must be a particular problem, not to be undertaken lightly!

## Village greens and squares

An historic feature of the road network is the village green or square. This originated in an age when villages were places of refuge in an often hostile environment. The siting of dwellings around a 'central place' provided a secure area both for the inhabitants and for their animals when danger threatened. Alternatively it may have developed as a meeting place and as the location for commercial activities such as markets and fairs. In such instances the activity may have pre-dated the buildings which subsequently would define the area of the meeting or market place.

Over the centuries village greens and squares have taken on a less exciting role, serving now as a setting for the surrounding buildings and sometimes as a car park. Village greens have also served other purposes, perhaps for recreation, and in this way the villagers have often acquired customary rights. These were not, however, formally established in modern times until as late as 1965, when the Commons Registration Act came into force. This enabled the registration of village greens in exactly the same way as common land. In Devon over 100 village greens are registered.

It is perhaps invidious to pick out individual village greens, but there are three particularly fine examples in the Dartmoor National Park – Widecombe-in-the-Moor, North Bovey and Manaton. Newton St Cyres, near Exeter, has a village green with modern origins. In the 1950s the centre of the village was demolished to improve the A377 road between Exeter and Crediton. Nowadays this would be regarded as an act of vandalism, but it must be acknowledged that the redevelopment round a village green has been attractively achieved.

Among the villages with interesting squares are Broadhembury in east Devon, Bradninch and Thorverton (with its cobbled pavements) in mid Devon, Drewsteignton in the Dartmoor National Park and Chittlehampton in north Devon. This last square contains a village pump and sets off what is acknowledged to be one of the county's finest church towers.

## Street Markets and Fairs

Although not so numerous as before the advent of the motor car, there are still many markets and fairs held in Devon. Whilst not a permanent feature of the roadside scene, these markets and fairs, held on certain days or times of the year, are an important part of the highway environment since streets and squares of the county's market towns provide the natural place for such activities. In addition, many towns and even some villages still hold annual carnivals which, unlike markets and fairs, are not commercial in origin.

Even in the past, Devon had fewer village ponds than other regions, and many of these have now disappeared. At Halberton, shown here, the pond is reputed to be fed by warm springs and, as a result, never freezes over.

Street markets have existed from the earliest times and the butterwalks of Totnes and Dartmouth, which were built in the seventeenth century, are lasting monuments to what is perhaps a fading tradition. Dartmouth Butterwalk, built between 1635 and 1640 is probably the finer, with its granite pillars and exquisite wood carving. Its counterpart in Totnes, possibly built first, is in its own way equally spectacular but quite a length of the original is missing. Nevertheless it has a charm of its own with pillars of granite, wood and masonry in varying shapes and often at peculiar angles. The colonnaded Poultry Walk on the opposite side of the street carries the slate-hung upper storeys, for which Totnes is famous, over the Yorkstone pavement below. An archway just below the Poultry Walk, which gave access to the old pannier market, has long since disappeared but the market continues to thrive in the civic hall square on Fridays. On Tuesdays in the summer its charity stalls are graced by local people in Elizabethan costume, a great attraction to visitors.

Another covered way in quite a different style can be found in Butchers' Row at Barnstaple, a survival of the medieval custom whereby shops selling goods of a similar kind were all placed together.

Street markets continue to thrive in many of Devon's towns and a new development is the one-day market held in a rural roadside location. These, alas, lack the character

**Built on land recovered from the River Dart, the Butterwalk (1634–40) in Duke Street is a fine group of houses erected at a time of great prosperity for Dartmouth. This was based on the Newfoundland fishing trade and the renewed growth of the cloth trade at Ashburton. The buildings were seriously damaged by wartime bombing in 1943. They were repaired using traditional materials in 1954.**

of their historical urban counterparts, and probably their chief contribution to the highway scene is the creation of traffic problems in unsatisfactory places! Fairs for cattle and merchandise, on the other hand, have largely died out. Barnstaple, Bampton, Tavistock and Widecombe Fairs are among the few which still survive. The Great Fair at Barnstaple is held on the Wednesday, Thursday, Friday and Saturday preceding 20 September and has always been important for both business and pleasure. As long ago as the mid nineteenth century the money spent on the purchase of cattle alone amounted to £20 000, a considerable sum in those days.

One of the largest sheep fairs in the west of England – as many as 14 000 sheep often being on sale – was held at Bampton before the decline of the woollen trade in the eighteenth century. It is still famous, however, and is held on the last Thursday in October, the principal attraction in recent years being the sale not of sheep but of Exmoor ponies.

A sure sign of the coming of Christmas is the traditional

Tavistock Goosey Fair held on the second Wednesday in October. It is said to have been established by a charter granted by Henry I in the twelfth century.

Widecombe-in-the-Moor, celebrated in song, is probably the best known of all the Dartmoor villages and still draws the crowds for the annual fair in September. The visitor will probably catch a glimpse of 'Old Uncle Tom Cobley' (but not the rest of his celebrated company), mounted on a grey mare, in white smock, black top hat and complete with cider keg. Effigies of the whole company are preserved for posterity on the stone sign standing on the grass verge near the church.

# Public Rights of Way

## The network in Devon

The 3000 miles of public footpaths, bridleways and byways in Devon give access to some of the most outstanding and varied scenery in the country. From high moorlands to coastal cliffs, the rights-of-way network is the single most important means by which people can enjoy the countryside. Public interest in the network has grown rapidly in recent years and the opportunities afforded by rights of way have become increasingly valued as a means of quietly enjoying the peace of the countryside and the beauty of its wildlife.

Devon's paths, which were originally established for business purposes or the general movement of people or animals, now perform almost entirely a recreational role, falling within one of three categories: local village paths; recreation paths adjacent to urban areas; or long-distance paths such as the South West Peninsula Coast Path and the Two Moors Way. The legal basis for public paths is well founded in various Acts of Parliament.

It was established as long ago as 1771 that at common law, parish councils, as representatives of the inhabitants at large, were responsible for footpaths, but there was controversy about the liability for the extent and standard of repairs required. It was not surprising, therefore, that ever since the passing of the Rights of Way Act, 1932, local authorities and parish councils have been under increasing pressure to make proper surveys and records of their public rights of way.

The introduction of the National Parks and Access to the Countryside Act 1949 placed responsibility for the repair of public paths on the highway authority, though still leaving an important role for parish councils to play. The Act required the preparation of the first complete survey of public rights of way. Under the Act every County Council had to compile maps in three stages – 'draft', 'provisional' and 'definitive' – the last of these being conclusive proof that every way marked on it is a footpath, a bridleway or a road used as a public path, i.e. a public right of way.

Very detailed advice was given by the Commons, Open Spaces and Footpath Preservation Society as to how this objective might be achieved. For instance, it stated that 'stiles and gates should be described in more detail where

necessary, e.g. with or without steps, squeezer stile, bachelor gate, etc.' The Society also suggested that an annual perambulation should take place and that Rogation Sunday might be a suitable day as it was already associated with the ancient custom of beating the bounds.

The definitive map for the old county authority was started in 1953 and was completed early in 1970 when the last outstanding objection to the provisional map for Tavistock Rural District was resolved at Quarter Sessions. Work on the review of the survey then commenced so that amendments could be made to the map as a result of changes caused by such events as development, diversions and closing orders. Progress of the review of the definitive maps was slowed down by the Minister's decision that a limited special review should be undertaken as a separate operation and completed during 1971. This review required that the term 'road used as a public path' should cease and such paths be reclassified as byways, footpaths or bridleways. There were approximately 150 paths in this category in Devon and the task was not completed until 1974.

The Countryside Act, which became law in July 1968, conferred new powers on local authorities. The Act imposed a duty on the highway authority to provide a signpost at every point where a right of way leaves a metalled road, unless after discussions with the parish council it was considered to be unnecessary. Commencing in 1969, the necessary timber signs were manufactured at one of the County Council's Health Department workshops.

Fairs, as well as being the original labour exchanges, provided the only opportunity for country dwellers to purchase the luxury goods of the day. Spices, fine materials, jewellery and other 'fancy' goods were the cause of great excitement among largely isolated rural communities. Goosey Fair in Tavistock was typical of many street fairs held throughout the county. Today, although the goods and services on offer bear little resemblance to those of earlier times, the excitement and the economic purpose of the fair is still the same.

The Wildlife and Countryside Act 1981, which came into operation in February 1983, includes reference to definitive maps and reviews. Instead of five-yearly reviews, the Act requires definitive maps to be brought up to date as soon as reasonably practicable after the occurrence of any changes, such as stoppings-up, diversions, widenings or extensions, changes of category and the creation of new rights of way. The Act sets out the procedure for an individual to apply to the County Council for an order to make changes to a path and lays down time limits for the County Council to make the decision.

A long-standing problem worthy of particular mention is that of bulls in fields crossed by public footpaths. Bye-laws made by the County Council under the Local Government Act 1933 prohibited the occupier of any field or enclosure through which there is a public path to permit a bull to be at large. The 1981 Act reiterated that prohibition. However, the section is qualified by the statement that no offence is committed if the bull does not exceed the age of ten months or is not a recognized dairy breed and there are cows or heifers at large in the same field or enclosure.

## Coastal footpaths

Of major importance in Devon are the coastal footpaths which form part of the 870-km-long South West Peninsula Coast Path, running from Minehead in Somerset to Poole in Dorset. The south Devon section was approved in 1959 and officially opened in September 1974. The north Devon section was approved in 1961 and officially opened in May 1978.

Over the years the previously existing lengths of coast path have been linked by new sections and indeed in some cases by ferries, with the last major gap being closed in April 1987 by the completion of the Bideford to Barnstaple coast path/cycleway along the route of the former railway line.

The Devon sections of the coastal path total about 300 km in length. Public use continues to increase, particularly since approximately 85 per cent of Devon's holidaymakers stay within 5 km of the coast. The walks along these paths provide panoramic views and breathtaking scenery, at the same time unfolding a constantly changing landscape. They afford access to fishing villages, lighthouses, estuaries, headlands, moorland and all the natural history of a maritime county.

The number of river estuaries in Devon necessitate several passenger ferries as links in the coastal footpath system. Some of these ferries have a long history. Amongst the oldest still operating is that between Exmouth and Starcross, which was established in 1122. The ferry between Kingswear and Dartmouth was first recorded in 1365, and a passenger-only ferry still operates between Kingswear station, at the end of the Paignton–Kingswear railway line, and Dartmouth (once the only station in the United Kingdom with no railway lines). Another long-established passenger ferry joins Stonehouse in Plymouth to Cremyll in Cornwall, now the landing stage for the Mount Edgcumbe Country Park. This was established in the twelfth or thirteenth century, but was transferred to its present route in 1730. Two much more recently established ferry services cross the River Avon between Bantham and Cockleridge (opened in 1973) and the River Yealm (opened in 1982). Both of these are subsidised by the Countryside Commission, since the tolls alone are insufficient to make them economic.

## Two Moors Way

The preliminary survey for a proposed long-distance footpath and bridleway was carried out in 1969 and the Two Moors Way was eventually opened in 1976. Over 164 km in length, it links Ivybridge in south Devon to Lynmouth on the north coast. The route was chosen to allow people to discover the variety of scenery in the county, from the open moorland of Exmoor and Dartmoor to the secluded woods and valleys of the intervening landscape. Whilst the coastline is still the most popular destination for holidaymakers, inland Devon contains peaceful countryside and many unspoilt villages which are well worth exploring.

South of Teigncombe on Dartmoor the route coincides with a short section of the Mariners' Way, a route which is reputed to have been used in former times by seamen passing between Dartmouth and Bideford.

In June 1987 the County Council considered possible improvements involving the creation of additional foot-paths in place of minor roads. It also agreed to ask the Countryside Commission to give official recognition to the Two Moors Way as a long-distance footpath, thus making it eligible for financial support. This would fund the work needed for creating new sections, including waymarking, publicity and maintenance. The route has increased in popularity since first established owing mainly to the efforts of the Ramblers' Association and this has done much to promote recreation and tourism in parts of the county where such opportunities are limited.

## Repair and maintenance of public rights of way

With the coming into force of the National Parks and Access to the Countryside Act in 1949, the responsibilities for the repair of public rights of way were clarified and put on a proper basis. Despite this, in 1964 concern was expressed that some public paths might be lost through lack of use. Fortunately, there was an upsurge of interest, particularly during the following ten years, by local amenity societies and user groups in the preservation of all public rights of way; indeed, some prepared special booklets giving details of their local footpaths and bridleways.

The County's first Footpath Warden was appointed early in 1972 to co-ordinate the programme of signposting public footpaths and bridleways and to investigate queries concerning public rights of way. The effect of this appointment was soon apparent as many problems were quickly resolved at a local level.

Interest in the network is now stronger than ever and public expectation has also increased. Accordingly, a systematic approach to maintenance is now adopted and procedures have been established for dealing with the common problems of obstruction, ploughing, missing or misleading signs, and overgrown hedges, not to mention the occasional bull which may be at large.

Repair and maintenance are obviously fundamental to the public path system, which otherwise could rapidly become impassable if not lost for ever. Changes in legislation and public need also require that these factors are kept under continuous review. A booklet entitled *A Parish Guide to the Repair and Maintenance of Public Rights of Way* has been published by Devon County Council to assist parish councils in undertaking routine maintenance and repair work themselves. The County Council will normally pay for these works provided the parish contributes one quarter of the cost. However, it still undertakes major works, such as repair of footbridges and retaining walls, as well as more unusual items, such as maintaining the stepping stones where a footpath in the parish of Ashprington can be used to cross Bow Creek (River Harbourne) at low tide.

In 1984 the County Council sponsored a Manpower Services Commission Community Programme to enhance and restore many of the public rights of way which had become overgrown and fallen into disuse with the passage of time. The scheme received much praise from the parish councils, landowners and the many activity groups that make use of the path network and it has since been repeated on an annual basis. As well as improving paths the scheme also gave long-term unemployed people the opportunity for practising rural skills in a working environment and has led many into full-time employment.

As an indication of the growing importance which the County Council accords to footpaths and bridleways, a post of Parish Liaison Officer was created in 1986 to promote the 'Adopt-a-Path' scheme. This encourages volunteers to take an active interest in the proper use, conservation and maintenance of the path network. The volunteers inspect the paths three or more times a year, report on their condition and help keep them in good repair. Response to the scheme was overwhelming and many parishes now produce leaflets about their path networks which highlight areas of local interest. This has helped to foster the growth in public awareness of the countryside.

## Footways

The great increase in the number of motor vehicles in the early part of this century demanded greater safety and convenience for pedestrians. This requirement eventually led to pedestrian-priority schemes which partly or completely segregate vehicles from pedestrians, and which are now a feature in many urban areas. The raised footways in many Devon towns and villages, such as Tiverton, Honiton, Bow and Bishopsteignton, were the forerunners of this idea.

Raised pavements often combined two functions – to protect the feet of pedestrians from the mud and water of the pre-tarmac road, and to cope with the effect of sloping ground. This example is in Bow.

Another example of pedestrian segregation – this time to protect people from the elements – is at Hemyock, where there is a wooden footbridge 14 in. wide and nearly 280 ft long immediately adjoining the road. It has wooden handrails and is carried 2 or 3 ft above road level on piers 9 ft apart. Its purpose is to enable pedestrians to cross when the River Culm is in flood. A similar structure exists on the road from Broadclyst to the A30.

Before pre-cast concrete products were manufactured, natural stone was used for the construction and maintenance of footways. Stone flags, about 3 in. thick and of random area, were used. The footway was usually separated from the road by a stone kerb about 4 in. wide and 12 in. deep, laid on edge so as to provide an upstand of 4–6 in. It was often accompanied by a similar channel block laid flat to prevent erosion of the gutter. One of the best examples of beautifully figured limestone paving and kerbing can still be seen in Seymour Place, Bridgetown, Totnes. An example of granite paving exists around part of Bedford Square, Tavistock, adjoining the parish church. Granite kerbs and channels have been preserved in many other Devon towns. Of the cobbled footpaths in Devon those in the village of Thorverton in east Devon must be among the oldest and best preserved. Cobbles are now sometimes laid to discourage pedestrians from using certain areas at junctions and for enhancement in conservation schemes.

Yorkstone flags can also be found in Devon; they were

In conservation areas the Council's current policy is to continue, as far as possible, the use of traditional materials and skills in maintaining the environment. The original cobbles for the pavement in Thorverton were collected from the bed of the nearby river. The restoration of the footway, undertaken as part of a highway-enhancement scheme, required the complete resetting of the old cobbles.

Before the advent of pre-cast concrete slabs, footways were paved with local stone. The photograph shows a fine example of paving in Totnes, using a colourful local limestone.

imported principally for their 'non-slip' qualities. They are, of course, well known nationally and have an attractively warm appearance. They are pleasant to walk on but tend to wear unevenly. These flags were laid on sand or ashes and jointed with lime mortar.

Pre-cast concrete paving slabs first became available soon after the turn of the twentieth century and they were subsequently used as the standard paving for footways, particularly in urban areas. They were laid in their millions and their widespread use continued until recently.

Now, however, in the interests of economy, the use of flagging for footways is restricted to busy town centres, conservation areas and other approved sites. In these locations pre-cast concrete slabs in a variety of shapes and colours give a very pleasing effect. Smaller slabs are now being used so as to reduce damage caused by vehicles mounting the footway. This is a problem which occurs particularly in narrow streets, where there are commercial premises lacking rear-servicing facilities. Damage is done not only to the footways but sometimes to buildings also. In order to counteract damage to pavements it may be necessary to use types of paving which can withstand the weight of vehicles or, where buildings are at risk, to use bollards and other street furniture as a deterrent.

In recently built residential streets and housing estates the use of materials such as fine cold asphalt or slurry seal provides satisfactory surfaces for footways and makes them easy to maintain. In rural areas surface dressing with natural stone chippings gives a more appropriate finish.

# Roadside Features and Street Furniture

The appearance of the urban street is enhanced by its street furniture; the design and siting of furniture are therefore particularly important. The signs, bollards, traffic signals, road markings, street lighting and all the other paraphernalia are essential for the convenience and guidance of motorists and pedestrians alike. However, some of the early designs may have been functional but were far from attractive and there is now an increasing awareness of the visual impact of street furniture. Street signs and lighting are now more sensitively designed and located, road markings, particularly double yellow lines, are being applied in a less intrusive fashion, whilst bollards and litter bins, for instance, have been improved in design and appearance.

All the obtrusive overhead electricity wires and the tram lines associated with the tramcar era have of course long since been removed, but there is still much Victoriana in Devon's towns and villages which is carefully preserved. This includes street lamps, pillar boxes, telephone boxes, signs, fountains, pumps, stones, crosses and seats, and all reveal something of the county's history. (Signposts are discussed in Chapter 5.)

## Roadside stones

The roadside stones in the county take many different forms. Wayside crosses, milestones, boundary stones, gravestones, memorial stones, commemorative stones, 'take off' stones, parole stones, bound stones and kicking stones are all to be found, sometimes in the most unlikely places. These, apart from bound stones (see Chapter 1), are described below.

## Crosses

There are 318 recorded ancient stone crosses in Devon, of which eighty-eight are situated at the roadside. Many of these crosses are on Dartmoor, primarily for the purpose of waymarking ancient tracks and cross-country paths such as the Abbot's Way believed to link the abbeys of Tavistock and Buckfast. Of particular note is Marchants Cross, set in the bank on the west side of the Cadover Bridge to Meavy

Copplestone Cross is a fine tenth-century granite cross ornately carved with panels of strapwork and illustrations – one of the best examples of its kind in southern Britain. It was moved to its present location to allow a road-improvement scheme to be carried out, despite a legend that bad times – or worse – would befall anyone moving it.

road. Having originally measured over 8 ft above ground, it has crosses incised on both faces.

Crosses can also be found 'in country', as Dartmoor people would say (meaning any land not on the moor). Luscombe Cross on the minor road between Totnes and Harbertonford used to be a favourite haunt for children, who have found coins secreted in its hollow mouldings. Another important example, already referred to in Chapter 1, is Brick Cross at Bicton which stands at the crossroads where the Yettington to Otterton minor road crosses the A376 Newton Poppleford to Budleigh Salterton road. Its square brick column is surmounted by a conventional stone cross. The age of Winson (or Hudscott) Cross in the parish of Chittlehampton in north Devon is not known: it may be medieval or even earlier. The cross is supported by a substantial plinth which was provided by Denys Rolle, of the well-known Devon family, sometime during the last quarter of the eighteenth century; he also planted trees to frame the whole structure.

## Milestones

There are many milestones and boundary stones through-out the county, some dating back several hundred years. It was a statutory obligation for turnpike trusts to provide milestones along their roads not only to indicate directions but also to inform travellers of the distances involved. They were also required to provide stones where the roads crossed parish boundaries. Although the inscriptions on some milestones were obliterated in the early part of the Second World War, many remain, some in simple, some in elaborate form, and are carefully preserved. Some have incised letters and figures while others have cast-iron plates to carry the lettering. There are also a number of direction pillars. At one time tramps were referred to as 'milestone inspectors' and there is no doubt that they knew where to find most of these stones.

There is an interesting milestone built into the fabric of the Traveller's Rest public house on the old A30, some 'IV miles' west of 'Exon'. Its interest lies in the fact that it is constructed of wood, which is unusual if not unique.

Devon's milestones have recently received a facelift so as to reveal the destination and mileage details. Where resiting is necessary, double-sided milestones are being set at right angles to the road, whilst, for obvious reasons, the single-sided stones are being set parallel to the road. Where milestones are missing, detective work in the vicinity often reveals their whereabouts.

'Beating the bounds' has always been a favourite pastime in Devon. Many people will have had the experience of being 'bumped' on the boundary stones to help them memorize the position of the boundary.

## Memorial Stones

There are war memorials in most of Devon's towns and villages where, on a sombre November day each year, the dead of two world wars are remembered. The number of names recorded, particularly from the 1914-18 war, bears witness to the scale of the slaughter of men especially when related to the size of the communities of the time. A memorial of a different kind, however, stands near the Strete Gate–Torcross road at Slapton Sands, close to the freshwater lake of Slapton Ley. It is a tribute also to the living. The granite obelisk bears the inscription: 'This memorial was presented by the United States Army Authorities to the people of the South Hams who generously left their homes and their lands to provide a battle practice area for the successful assault on Normandy in June 1944. Their action resulted in the saving of many hundreds of lives and contributed in no small measure to the success of the operation. The area included the villages of Blackawton, Chillington, East Allington, Slapton, Stokenham, Strete and Torcross together with many outlying farms and houses.'

Recently a resident of Torcross was instrumental in recovering a 'Sherman' tank from Start Bay. This now stands with a commemorative stone between the village of Torcross and Slapton Ley as a further memorial,

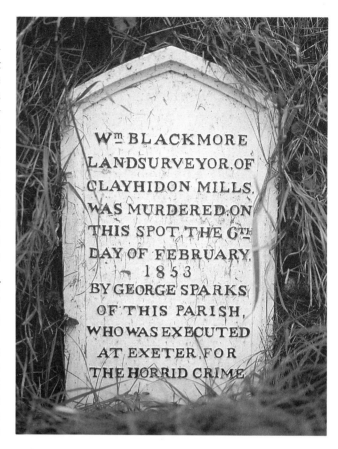

Highways have always attracted publicity seekers. The roads of Britain are strewn with diverse messages on sundry topics from every period of history. Devon has its share of roadside curios too: this well-preserved stone near Hemyock in east Devon commemorates a crime which must have shocked and disturbed the local people.

particularly to servicemen who lost their lives during exercises in preparation for the D-Day landings. The dedication ceremony took place forty-four years later, in November 1987.

## Commemorative stones and statues

Numerous stones and structures commemorate royal personages and events. A number of these, of contrasting sizes and styles, are worthy of mention. One, a simple granite boulder on Leusdon Common, Dartmoor, adjoins the road from Parkland Head to Ponsworthy. It bears the royal crown and incised lettering in honour of the Silver Jubilee of Elizabeth II. A well-known landmark at Exeter is the elaborate clock tower at the end of Queen Street, commemorating the Jubilee of Queen Victoria. In Brixham stands the statue of William, Prince of Orange (afterwards William III) on the quay adjoining The Strand where he landed on 5 November 1688. On the Longcombe Cross to Stoke Gabriel road, near the bottom of Parliament Hill is a thatched cottage with a stone in its garden, recording that 'William of Orange is said to have held his first Parliament here in November 1688'. This is easily visible from the road.

Many of Devon's famous men are honoured by statues,

often in roadside settings. A statue of Sir Francis Drake, that most famous son of Tavistock, stands on the Plymouth approach to the town, while a statue of Sir Redvers Buller V.C., reliever of Ladysmith in the Boer War, mounted on his charger, stands at the junction of Hele Road and New North Road in Exeter. Among the county's literary figures is Charles Kingsley, author of *Westward Ho!* His statue stands, pen in hand, beside the River Torridge at Bideford where he wrote the novel in 1855.

The wife of a famous scholar is remembered at Barclays Bank in Totnes High Street. A plaque on the front of this elegant building reads: 'Here lived Ann Ball who on 19th July 1586 was married to Sir Thomas Bodley founder of the Bodleian Library in Oxford'. The house itself belonged to her father, Nicholas Ball, a rich merchant. The plaque is beautifully embellished and bears his initials.

In 1864 the people of Totnes erected a large granite obelisk in the middle of the Plains to honour a native of the town. He was William John Wills who, with Burke, was the first to cross the Australian continent and who perished of starvation on the return journey in June 1861. The obelisk is well preserved and is protected by granite-sett paving and flower beds. It also serves as a refuge island and is furnished with roadside seats.

William Crossing, whose *Guide to Dartmoor* has become a classic, has two memorials. One is a plaque fixed to a boulder at Duck's Pool and the other is on a house visible from the road at Mary Tavy. The inscription on the plain slate stone reads: 'In this house William Crossing (1847-1928) lived for many years and wrote his "Guide to Dartmoor" and other works. The Dartmoor Preservation Association 1952.'

Anyone passing through the village of Stoke Fleming on the Dartmouth to Torcross road might chance to see an oval plaque fixed to a stone wall. It reads: 'A tribute to the genius of George Parker Bidder recorded in history as the Calculating Boy, with George Stephenson a pioneer of railways, born at Moretonhampstead. A son of Devon 1806 – 1878.' Bidder, a great authority on railway construction, was president of the Institution of Civil Engineers from 1860-61.

On the churchyard wall facing Silver Street in Ottery St Mary in East Devon is a plaque to one of England's great poets, Samuel Taylor Coleridge. He was born at the old Kings School, Ottery St Mary, in 1772, the youngest son of the vicar of that parish, and spent his childhood there. 'The Rime of the Ancient Mariner' is probably the best known of his poems and on the plaque his bust is surmounted by an albatross. Underneath are the lines: 'He prayeth best who loveth best. All things both great and small. For the dear God who loveth us. He made and loveth all.'

## Take off stones

In the days of horse-drawn vehicles the turnpike trustees would allow an extra horse to be hitched to a wagon free of charge to pull the load up some of the steep hills. Some people can still remember when the coach taking passengers from Wrangaton to Salcombe would take on an extra horse at New Bridge, Loddiswell to help pull it up the mile-long hill to Sorley Green. There were strict rules, however, regarding the 'take off' point and, as mentioned in Chapter 1, a granite stone at Beardon with the words 'Take Off' clearly cut into its surface marks the point on the road from Lydford to Tavistock where this adjustment of horse power had to take place.

## Parole stones

During the Napoleonic Wars French prisoners of war housed in verminous and disease-ridden hulks anchored off the naval dockyard at Plymouth were becoming a serious embarrassment. The government decided therefore to build a prison at Princetown to accommodate them: it took 2½ years to build and was completed in 1809. The prison is built of granite quarried at nearby Herne Hole. Some of the French officers, instead of being confined in the prison, were billeted out in other moorland towns and villages, such as Ashburton, Bovey Tracey and Chagford. They were required not to wander more than a mile from their place of billet and stones indicating this distance from the centre of these towns were placed at the roadside. They were called parole stones. A few of these stones still exist; one can be found at Druid's Hill near Ashburton.

## Kicking stones

These stones, found in narrow streets in many of Devon's towns and villages, are usually at the corners of buildings which immediately abut the road and are set at an angle to deflect the wheels of vehicles. They clearly originated in the horse-and-cart days to prevent damage to cob and stone walls by the hubs and iron-bound wheels of carts and wagons. Cob walls, although up to 2 ft in thickness, were particularly vulnerable. They consist of red earth mixed with straw and are usually rough cast to keep them dry. Any damage which would allow water to infiltrate could therefore have serious consequences. The kicking stones are usually of granite, limestone or slate. The granite variety are often dressed to a circular shape; this has the effect not only of more easily deflecting wheels of vehicles away from the wall but also of reducing shock and possibly damage to the vehicles.

The single-storey tollhouse known as Bushouse on the A386 Okehampton to Great Torrington road, has its round end protected by several granite kicking stones. An unusual kicking stone protects the corner of Birdwood Cottage in South Street, Totnes. The deep groove in its surface was probably worn by a ship's hawser, indicating its former use as a mooring bollard. Other materials have also been used to achieve the same objective, including curved iron pipes and bars. The most interesting and unusual in this category is the nose of a naval shell, protecting the corner of a building in a narrow street in Kingsbridge.

Kicking stones can also be found protecting the corners of the parapet walls of some of Devon's narrow bridges.

## Agricultural features

### Milk churn stands

When milk was transported in churns by lorry to the milk factories, mounting blocks (see p.209) were found to be just about the right height from which to lift the churns on to the lorry and so served a dual purpose. Where such a facility was not available all sorts of milk stands appeared and any placed within the limits of the highway required a special permit. Built usually of stone or timber some had quite elaborate thatched roofs where the site was exposed to the sun and where the farm was not on the early round.

### Cattle grids

Before the introduction of cattle grids many of the roads on Devon's moors and commons were gated. The landowners were responsible for their gates and could be prosecuted for allowing them to fall into disrepair.

The use of cattle grids was authorized under the Highways (Provision of Cattle Grids) Act 1950 and three years later the first were installed on Exmoor around Brendon Common. There are now over 160 cattle grids in use on county roads in Devon. Most of the more modern grids incorporate 'hedgehog ramps' to enable small animals to escape from the pit.

Cattle grids enable moors and commons to be more effectively grazed. They reduce the number of accidents

The tollhouse at Bushouse, Okehampton. The angled stones, known as 'kicking stones', were designed to protect the building from damage by cartwheels. They achieved this by deflecting ('kicking') the wheels of passing vehicles back into the road.

involving straying animals and make it easier for the farmer to control his stock. Because of these benefits to the landowner, a financial contribution is required when cattle grids are installed. The responsibility for raising the money is accepted by local commoners' associations and parish councils.

In 1971 an extensive fencing and gridding scheme was carried out at Roborough Down. This length of the busy A386 across moorland between Roborough village and Yelverton had been suffering between forty and fifty animal deaths a year, mainly ponies, and several injuries to motorists. The remedy was to isolate the road from the moor, and hence from the animals, by the construction of seven miles of timber-post and rail fencing together with cattle grids, pony traps (enclosures for the holding of ponies at controlled crossing points), kissing gates and stiles. The scheme cost £35 000 which was recouped in less than three years because of the reduction in accidents involving animals on this length of road.

### Cattle creeps and dry bridges

Where land has been severed by new roads it has been necessary in the interests of safety to provide access for animals over or under the road. These means of access

Water is a fundamental necessity of any human community. Efforts
to manage it, use its power and ensure its supply in sufficient
quantity and quality have littered the landscape with works of every
kind. Ditches, flood-relief schemes, canals, drains, aqueducts, all
bear testimony to the importance of water in cultural development.
A number of Devon towns and villages still have open watercourses
running through the streets. This one is at Otterton in east Devon.

(a)

(b)

(c)

(a) In the days of horses, some of the travelling public needed assistance to mount their animals. Mounting blocks like this can still be seen on many roads.
(b) One of the first things an engineer will look for when beginning a road scheme is a bench mark. This gives him a specific level from which to work.
(c) Decorative vent column.

underneath the road are known as cattle creeps and in the past were usually of masonry-arch construction. Many of these structures still exist in Devon and their whereabouts are often betrayed by short lengths of masonry parapet wall on both sides of the road. The modern structures are in reinforced concrete or corrugated steel known as 'Armco', a sectional pipe arch of American origin. Those over the road, known as 'dry bridges', were formerly also of masonry-arch construction but are now, over the new roads, constructed of reinforced or pre-stressed concrete.

## Water Features

### Water supplies

In earlier times the streams which ran through many of Devon's villages and towns provided the inhabitants with a wholesome supply of water for drinking, cleaning utensils, washing clothes and other purposes. While some still flow in channels up to 6 ft wide and several feet deep, for instance in Otterton and Budleigh Salterton, others are confined to narrow stone channels and gutters, as at Beer and Tiverton.

Reference has already been made to the leat at Tiverton which was the original supply of pure spring water for the town. It runs from its source on Norwood Common, through the cobbled channel in Castle Street and the old market to bubble up at Coggans Well in Fore Street where children still scramble for coins at the annual fair.

At Cullompton, where the town stream once ran in channels on both sides of the old A38 trunk road, 'dipping rights' handed down for generations were very jealously guarded. These rights were granted to the people of Cullompton by the Abbot of Buckland in a charter dated 1264, for the people to take water from the town stream for whatever purpose. (About twenty years ago a road improvement resulted in the stream being culverted and there is now no access for 'dipping rights' to be exercised.)

### Conduits and fountains

Conduits, which are still a feature of the street scene in some parts of Devon, were constructed to provide the inhabitants with 'the pure beverage of nature' at convenient points in a village or town. At Exeter, before the construction of works to extract water from the River Exe in 1834, people obtained their water from fountains or conduits which were erected in the principal streets and connected by lead pipes to springs in the nearby hills. One,

(a) Although this hand pump at Chittlehampton is relatively modern, it stands on the ancient holy well of St Teara and forms a feature in a highway enhancement scheme.
(b) Ornate hand pump at Hemyock, east Devon.

called the Great Conduit or Conduit at Quatre-fois, was rebuilt as long ago as 1461 and stood in the centre of the city at the junction of the four principal streets. It was taken down in 1778 when a new conduit was erected in High Street. Another was built in South Street in 1799 and one in Mary Arches Street in 1839. This is commemorated by a tablet indicating that it was constructed at the expense of James Golsworthy, one time lessee of the waterworks. (A further tablet records that the waterworks were first 'contrived' in 1694 and improved by Golsworthy in 1811, the latter probably by the introduction of iron pipes, for the first time in England.) The conduit in Milk Street, which served the Western Market and the neighbourhood, supplied three cisterns each holding 100 hogsheads of water (about 5000 gallons). The water was then conveyed in pipes to a granite obelisk. Waterbeer Street is said to have derived its name from the trade of carriers drawing water from the conduit at the top of South Street.

Of the conduits or fountains which still exist, some are quite elaborate. The fountain at the south end of the Square at Torrington was the gift of the Honourable Mark Rolle in 1870. Those at Beer and Hemyock also served as gas-lamp standards, as doubtless did many others at the turn of the twentieth century.

A conduit was built in South Ford Road, Dartmouth in 1599 and rebuilt in 1847. Modbury, once described as 'highly salubrious', had numerous springs of pure water and three public conduits, one of which was built by Adrian Swete in 1708.

The drinking fountain at the bus stop in West Charleton, near Kingsbridge, was built in 1896 as a memorial to Lord and Lady Compton. This bears the text 'Thirst for the living water' together with a crown and the monogram 'MFC'. The original horse trough is now used for plants. This memorial, incidentally, was dismantled and rebuilt stone by stone at the back of the footpath when, in 1973, the A379 road was widened.

In Totnes, at the junction of South Street with High Street, is a seventeenth-century conduit. The inscription on a brass plate reads: 'This conduit was erected out of a guifte of twentye pounde geven by Robert Babbett deceased towards ye conductinge of the water in leade and was pformed by Thomas Smythe of this towne Mchant An° 1607.'

Some pumps and fountains have royal connections. At Hemyock square in east Devon a pump in very ornate style carries the inscription 'In commemoration of the Glorious Reign of Victoria, the Coronation of Edward VII and the Restoration of Peace in 1902. Fear God, Honour the King.' A sizeable fountain in granite stood until 1988 at the station approach, Totnes. The metal plate on its face reads '1837 VR 1897. This fountain was erected AD 1904 to commemorate the Diamond Jubilee of the Reign of Her Most Gracious Majesty Queen Victoria. Alfred Michelmore, Mayor, Edward Windeatt, Town Clerk.' It seems certain that this also served as a lampstand, the ironwork and chains suggesting the use of hanging baskets. It has a small stone drinking bowl at a convenient height on one side and a nicely proportioned horse trough in the front at the base. It has now been relocated in the pedestrianized Dartmouth Inn Square.

Before the days of piped water many dwellings were served by roadside or private wells. In high summer the well was a good place in which to cool the cream. The wooden-covered pump with large lead spout was a common sight and 'Pump Cottage' a common name. One or two pumps can still be found, as well as the cast-iron variety that succeeded them. In some cases a large pump would serve a whole community; one of the best examples is in the village of Chittlehampton in north Devon. Another, at Chulmleigh, served the dual purpose of lamp-post and pump. Attractively situated is the pump on the village green of North Bovey, one of Dartmoor's architectural gems.

In many Devon villages the piping of water to individual dwellings was preceded by a piped supply to taps at half a dozen or so points often let into walls at a convenient height. The position of many of these can be traced on old Ordnance Survey maps, marked by the letters 'WT'. As late as 1940 the villagers of Rattery in south Devon were complaining that they were without mains water, and that residents without private wells had to fetch their water in buckets.

## Water-splashes and tidal roads

Before the Second World War, fords – or water-splashes as they are known in Devon – were quite common. Many had a small bridge, usually at the upstream side, just wide enough for pedestrians. Naturally these water-splashes, mostly on minor unclassified roads, were a delightful rural amenity but in times of heavy rainfall they were often completely impassable, particularly during the winter months. Apart from the great inconvenience to local people they were also in some cases the source of flooding of private property and, more seriously, the site of drowning accidents. It is understandable, therefore, that a policy was adopted to bridge or culvert many of them. Between 1949 and 1964 no less than ninety-two were dealt with in this way. The conventional bridging of streams to give sufficient waterway in time of flood is an expensive business, so a form of construction known as an 'Irish bridge' was adopted in many cases. It consists of a pipe or pipes laid on and surrounded with concrete which also formed the carriageway over them. Except for a few weeks

The Clock Tower, Exeter. Originally it also provided water for horses.

each year the pipes are capable of taking the normal flow, and even in times of spate the depth of water over the concrete carriageway can be kept to a few inches instead of several feet.

The 'Irish bridge' at Harbourneford, near South Brent is of particular interest since there is a 'clapper' footbridge built in 1809 just downstream. Water-splashes still exist in their original form at Brooking near Tigley in south Devon, at Ponsworthy on Dartmoor in a delightful setting of thatched granite cottages, at Newton St Cyres, at Hidewood Lane, Clayhidon and on several little-used unclassified roads.

There are a few tidal roads in Devon, i.e. roads which are under water at high tide. At Stakes Road, Aveton Gifford, sections of the old road to Bigbury are completely submerged at most high tides. Another, between South Pool and East Portlemouth, crosses inlets from Southpool Creek in the Kingsbridge estuary.

## Village ponds

Roadside village ponds have largely disappeared but they served an essential purpose in their day. They not only provided a water supply for humans and animals but were the source of water for the replenishment of the thirsty boilers of steam engines or steam rollers and, perhaps more important, for fire-fighting purposes. In the days when many cottages were covered in what was then described as 'that dangerous material straw thatch', a number of Devon towns suffered destructive fires.

An interesting phenomenon occurs in the village of Halberton, a few miles from Tiverton, where the pond is said to be fed with warm springs and for this reason never freezes over.

## Creature comforts

### Horse troughs

With the development of the turnpikes and the establishment of regular coach services with four or six horses 'in hand', a supply of water for horses at regular intervals was necessary. Roadside horse troughs were therefore provided where a good supply of pure spring water could be relied upon – not a difficult requirement in Devon – and many drinking troughs still exist. Most conduits and fountains incorporated a horse trough and troughs also formed part of other roadside features. A substantial horse trough stands in a landscaped area by St Anne's Almshouses at the top of Sidwell Street, Exeter. Its base, which supports a large ornamental shell, is inscribed with the name of its donor, Arthur Kempe. The Clock Tower at the end of Queen Street in Exeter has horse troughs on its western and southern sides, with a fountain for travellers on its eastern side. Besides those of rough-hewn or dressed granite, some troughs simply consisted of a large stone placed across an opening built in masonry. Others were

**Drinking trough in a wall at Dawlish.**

constructed of large slate slabs bolted together, while some were quite elaborate with stone turned arches over the trough itself.

## Roadside seats

Numerous varieties of roadside seat are to be found in Devon. Some seats have survived from the last century; one of wrought iron at Hillmoor, Culmstock is complete with plate which reads '1837 VR 1897' and thus commemorates Queen Victoria's Diamond Jubilee. In the village of Bickleigh, near Tiverton, an attractive wooden seat surrounds a fine horse chestnut tree on the village triangle. The tree was planted in 1937 to commemorate the coronation of King George VI.

## Bus shelters

Whilst numbers of potential users have declined considerably in recent years, bus shelters are still important features of the roadside environment. They range from individual structures found in rural areas, to those of standard design usually found in urban areas. A familiar sight in the large towns are the 'Adshels' which, as the name implies, provide both shelter and advertising space.

## Mounting blocks

Another roadside relic is the mounting block, upping stock, or hooping stone. This consists of a small masonry platform with a few steps on one side. Many can still be found, often adjoining farm buildings or inns; there are two at the rear of the fourteenth-century Cott Inn at Dartington. These were built so that riders could mount their horses more easily, especially country ladies who, of course, rode side-saddle, and farmers' wives who rode pillion behind their husbands when going to market.

## Miscellaneous Roadside Features

### Ventilating columns

At one time, when it was common practice to provide intercepting traps between house connections and public sewers, it was necessary to install a ventilating column at the highest point of the sewer. These were usually of cast iron and often matched lamp columns and other street furniture. To prevent birds nesting in them a copper or galvanized wire-mesh basket was fixed at the top. They could never be considered ornamental and were sited where possible in unobtrusive positions. They were less noticeable where they were able to serve a dual purpose, such as supports for street lamps. A column in Northam Road, Bideford, behind the football ground, doubled as a ventilation shaft and weather vane which, with an elaborate finial, completed the ironwork at the top. No less than fourteen cast-iron vent shafts still exist in Bideford. They were made in Glasgow in 1910 and are of considerable industrial archaeological interest. A similar shaft with serrated top exists next to the railway in Rumsam Road, Barnstaple.

### Telegraph and electricity poles

A once familiar feature of the more important roads of Devon were telegraph poles. Experience has shown, however, that telegraph wires are best placed underground, primarily because they are not exposed to the elements. Thus they have now virtually disappeared from the roadside, except for some survivors in built-up areas. Unfortunately electricity poles, with their attendant wires, still disfigure many villages and towns: an unhappy situation which is likely to persist for some time to come unless more money is made available by the Electricity Board to place them underground.

### Stocks

These devices for confining offenders by their ankles, and sometimes by their wrists as well, in a heavy wooden framework were occasionally to be found at the roadside. Most have now been transferred to guildhalls or museums. However, a well-preserved example can be seen in a roadside setting at The Pound, Chittlehampton in north Devon.

### Fencing

In the inter-war period a feature of road-improvement schemes in rural areas was the use of continuous iron-rail fencing along the road boundaries. This practice was not continued after the war and for several years farmers accepted concrete-post and chain-link fencing by way of accommodation works. No objections from an amenity point of view were raised at first when schemes were few and far between, but by the late 1950s the use of these materials was being severely criticized.

Subsequently, timber impregnated with copper/chrome/arsenic preparations became available, under the proprietary names of Celcured or Tanalized timber, giving the material a very long life. From then on treated timber post-and-rail fencing was more extensively used, usually with low chain link or pig netting to ensure it was stock-proof against lambs, and also with either thorn or beech sets, which in the lifetime of the wooden posts would mature into a live stock-proof hedge. With the advent of mechanical hedge trimming this has proved acceptable to the agricultural community. Boundaries restored on this basis in the 1960s are now to be seen in a near-mature state, for instance, along the A3072 road between Copplestone and Lamerton Cross (Inwardleigh).

Recently there has been a return to the use of metal railings in order to fence some 2230 metres of the Okehampton bypass, on the advice of the Department of Transport's landscape architect.

## Devon hedgebanks

One of Devon's most significant roadside features is the hedgebank (or 'Devon hedge', as it is known locally). These grass-covered banks, often surmounted by a growing hedge, are characteristic of the county's minor-road network. There are those who consider them inconvenient, particularly drivers who find that they add to the difficulties of driving along narrow lanes and also that they hide the view. They have to be maintained and trimmed and farmers would testify to the hundreds if not thousands of acres which they occupy. Moreover, because of the maintenance burden involved, not all farmers are favourably disposed towards their reinstatement when this becomes necessary, except in exposed situations where hedgebanks are an important shelter from the elements for crops and stock.

In their favour is the fact that hedgebanks make a significant contribution to the county's ecology, providing habitats for a variety of flora and fauna. At a time when much land has been reclaimed for agricultural purposes, hedgebank habitats have become particularly important. On balance, it seems fair to say that the advantages of hedgebanks outweigh the disadvantages. Where the removal of 'Devon hedges' has been unavoidable when carrying out road improvements, they have frequently been replaced by post-and-rail fencing, perhaps accompanied by a hedge, both for economy and because it requires less land. What is more, it is not easy to recreate hedgebanks which have become established over centuries. However, the value of replacing them is now recognized, if only to avoid the unsatisfactory appearance of hedgebanks interspersed with short lengths of fencing.

With the increase in the awareness of amenity considerations, the Department of Transport agreed to accept for grant purposes the additional cost of the rebuilding of Devon hedgebanks in the National Parks and other areas where environmental implications are of significance.

Although there are many exceptions, hedgebanks in north Devon are usually stone-faced on both sides, the stones either 'ditched' (on edge) or 'coursed', with through stones tying the two faces together. In south Devon stone-facing is not so usual, the bank structure being entirely of earth with the faces leaning well back. A person standing close to the base of most south Devon banks will seldom be able to touch the face of the bank at shoulder level, even with arm outstretched. To reduce the cost of constructing new hedgebanks, a method was adopted, initially in the South Molton area, of confining the earth filling between steel reinforcement tied to each face. The surfaces are seeded after the intervening space has been filled mechanically. The method, now more widely used, is referred to as the 'Wade bank' after the Divisional Surveyor who developed the system.

Hedgebanks do not, generally speaking, form part of the public highway, which normally extends from the foot of the bank only, so responsibility for keeping hedges cut rests with the owner concerned. Overgrown hedges can cause serious obstruction as well as excluding light and air from the carriageway. The highway authority can serve notice on landowners, requiring them to cut their hedges and, if need be, can do the work itself and recover the cost.

**Many of Devon's minor roads (and even some major roads) are bounded by hedgebanks constructed of earth and sometimes faced with stone. This narrow country lane is a typical example.**

# Buildings

## Tollhouses

Important and lasting memorials to turnpikes and their managing trusts (described in Chapter 1) are tollhouses, or turnpike cottages. 'The name "turnpike" itself is of considerable antiquity, originally referring to the spiked gates which were erected to stop sudden horseborne attacks. Later it came to mean the turnstile erected at the side of the gate to admit foot travellers and hence "turnpike gates" and "turnpike roads" came into common usage both as terms and as features of the landscape.' (John Kanefsky *Devon Tollhouses*). Initially tollhouses were built on the main routes, but as by-roads were improved it became more profitable to build new premises at the junctions, so that tolls could be collected from users of both the major and minor roads. More specifically, tollhouses were located on bridges, at crossroads, at forks or on straight stretches of road. There was great diversity of design, some were single storey, others two storey. The latter were mainly in south Devon, usually post-Napoleonic and located at junctions of new and old roads. They often had a three-sided front with central door and angled windows to give the toll-collector a good view of the road. They were built in local materials and many reflected the architectural style of the area.

Kanefsky identifies over ninety still surviving in Devon. The oldest of these, at Newton Poppleford in east Devon, was built in 1758. Most were built later, between 1815 and 1845. In some cases, especially in towns, a tax-collector's hut served the purpose, and the collector was able to live a short distance away. An example of a toll-hut survives at Yealmbridge and supplements a tollhouse nearby. Kanefsky suggests it must have been erected to combat the avoidance of paying tolls at the tollhouse or 'to correct a bad site'. With the advent of the railways the turnpikes declined and the tollhouses were sold. Many were subsequently demolished, but fortunately this practice has been checked.

The charges were exhibited on a board fixed on the house itself or on a post nearby. The fine for evasion of tolls could be as much as 20s. Nevertheless evasion did occur, as indicated by the name of 'Fishcheaters Lane' which bypassed the Bowden tollhouse on the A381 Totnes–Kingsbridge road about ½ mile south of Totnes. Here fishermen from Brixham would use the lane to reach the villages and hamlets beyond; one was still plying his trade with pony and trap long after the toll system had ceased.

The toll gates and the boards stating the charges were lit at night by large lanterns. The gates were usually wooden, although some were of wrought iron, such as those at Copper Castle, Honiton which are still standing, although set back from the road.

Some tollhouses were built by independent bridge trusts. One at Shaldon was built in 1827 and tolls were collected there until 1948. The bridges of the Stonehouse Trust in Plymouth were taken over by a private company and tolls were levied on Plymouth bridges until 1924. Tolls are still levied on the suspension bridge, opened in 1961, which

Toll house charges board, Kingsteignton. Presumably the water was free!

crosses the River Tamar between Plymouth and Saltash, although they apply only to those travelling from Cornwall into Devon!

## Coaching inns

With the establishment of the turnpike trusts during the first half of the eighteenth century came the development of the coach as a means of travel. This was encouraged by the introduction in 1784 of the first mail coaches. For instance, within the period 1783–5 the journey between London and Exeter was reduced from 48 hours to 24 hours. By 1840 the 'Devonport Mail', known as the 'Quicksilver', was making the journey to Exeter in 16½ hours and to Devonport in just over 21 hours. All the chief towns of Devon were served by regular passenger-coach services by 1820 and, in the 1830s, seventy coaches left Exeter every day.

Just as the tollhouses are virtually the last monuments to the turnpike era, so coaching inns are the last visible signs of the coaching era. For example, in Exeter there remain the Royal Clarence in Cathedral Close, the White Hart in South Street, the Black Horse in Longbrook Street, and the Crown and Sceptre in North Street. At Topsham there is the Salutation, whilst at Honiton the Angel and the Dolphin still survive. The Old Coaching House at Chudleigh and the The Golden Lion at Ashburton served the Exeter to Plymouth road, whilst other notable examples in south Devon were the Castle at Dartmouth and the Seven Stars at Totnes. In north Devon two well-known

examples are Hoops Inn on the present A39 trunk road at Horns Cross and, at Barnstaple, the Exeter Inn, which stands in Litchdon Street, once the main London road.

These are but a few examples of well-known coaching inns in the county; in the market towns particularly there are still numerous examples to remind us of a more leisurely age. Gilbert Sheldon, in his book *From Trackway to Turnpike*, describes the 'Quicksilver' coach as 'in some sort the prototype of the Cornish Express ...'. That train (the Cornish Riviera) now travels between Exeter and London in just over two hours – a far cry from the 48-hour journey in 1783!

Indeed it was the development of the railway age in the 1850s that saw the demise of the long-distance coaches (although apparently a regular coach service between Dartmouth and Kingsbridge survived until 1914). The effect on the function and character of the coaching inns must have been dramatic. Those that survived had to await the arrival of the motor car for their fortunes to be revived.

## Archways

There are no more than a few archways still surviving over Devon's roads. One of the best known is at Totnes in a prominent position spanning the main street at the Eastgate. In medieval times the town was enclosed by walls and protected by four gates, of which Northgate, immediately below the Castle, and Eastgate are the only

**The word 'journey' signifies a day's worth of work or travel. Travellers would be forced to break long journeys at frequent intervals and an entire industry arose to cater for these needs. The Regency period saw the golden age of coaching, with accommodation and refreshment available at frequent intervals along the most popular routes. Much of the north side of Honiton's High Street was once given over to tourism, Regency style. Several of Honiton's former coaching inns remain in use, providing accommodation for the modern tourist.**

two remaining. Eastgate originally had two arches, a large one for carriages and a small one for pedestrians. It now has a single elliptical arch of impressive form with a bow-windowed room surmounted by an illuminated clock, battlemented parapet, bell tower and weather vane. An arch in somewhat similar form can be found at the market approach in Torrington in north Devon.

Cromwell's arch at Bovey Tracey is said to be near the spot where, on 8 January 1646, Cromwell's men surprised the royalists under General Lord Wentworth and took 400 horses, seven colours and a crown with 'C.R.' upon it.

Exeter once had a number of gates, consisting of archways, which have now all been removed. Some of the sites are commemorated by plaques recording location and date of removal. Two such examples are in St Martin's Lane, leading from High Street to the Cathedral Close, and South Gate, near the White Hart Hotel in South Street. Both archways were removed in 1819. Another plaque opposite the well-known Tinley's Tea House commemorates the removal in 1825 of the gate from

Broadgate which leads into the Cathedral Close. The plaque also indicates that Broadgate was one of seven gates for which Royal License (sic) was granted in 1286. Two commemorative stones at pavement level on either side of Broadgate supplement the plaque.

In the north of the county, Barnstaple (reputedly the oldest borough in the country, having received its charter in 930 from King Athelstan) was also a walled settlement. The eighth-century Saxon earth walls were replaced with stone by the Normans in the two years following their successful invasion in 1066. There were four gates into the town: the North and South Gates being at their respective ends of High Street, the East Gate in Joy Street and the West Gate in Cross Street. The South and East Gates were removed 'in the seventeenth century', the North Gate in 1842 and the West Gate in 1852. Plaques mark the positions of all four gates.

## Limekilns

Limestone occurs in many parts of Devon but particularly between Plymouth and Torbay. The process of burning lime in kilns was carried on for several centuries, both for agricultural purposes to reduce the acidity of the soil and for the production of lime mortar for building purposes. Limekilns were therefore very common in Devon, particularly along the coasts and estuaries. Many can also still be seen near the roadside. Some are used for storage or as boat houses. In one case at the bottom of Haldon Hill, near Harcombe, between the two carriageways of the A38 trunk road, two kilns were used as living accommodation until as recently as the late 1950s.

## Telephone boxes

The red public-telephone kiosk is still a familiar feature of the roadside, but the well-known design with its numerous window-panes is under threat. British Telecom is introducing modern vandal-proof designs, and conservationists are now looking to English Heritage to list as buildings of architectural and historic interest at least some of what are known as the K6 kiosks before they become an 'extinct species'. Red kiosks have not always been considered acceptable and on Dartmoor, as in other National Parks, they are painted grey so that they are more easily 'absorbed' into the landscape.

The early AA and RAC lockable telephone boxes (see Chapter 5) regrettably have almost completely disappeared and have been replaced by a post-mounted variety.

## Accommodation works

The term 'accommodation works' refers to works associated with a highway scheme but undertaken on land not within the ownership of the highway authority and for which it does not therefore have the responsibility for future maintenance. The authority is under no statutory

Eastgate Arch in Totnes formed part of the original town wall. It was built some time during the thirteenth century, and until 1835 the gate had a main arch and a postern which restricted passage to one individual at a time. The opening of Charles Fowler's new toll bridge over the Dart in 1826 generated sufficient traffic to require the removal of the postern. A great many medieval arches disappeared in response to the demands of increased traffic, a process which began long before the arrival of the motor car. Exeter's South Gate arch, for example, was removed in 1819 to improve access to South Street.

obligation to carry out accommodation works – for instance, to restore highway boundaries – and could leave it to the owner to carry out whatever work he considers necessary with monies he would receive by way of compensation. However, the County Council considered that such an approach could put the roadside environment at risk, and many years ago it decided that, subject to agreement over details with the owner, it would carry out the work necessary to restore the owner's frontage. These works would on completion become the property and responsibility of the owner concerned. They are considered to be part of the settlement for the land. The Council hoped that by this policy it could ensure that the means of enclosure of the land affected could be replaced in an acceptable way, thereby maintaining the appearance of the area.

# The Natural Environment

## Tree planting and landscaping

In the 1970s many tree-planting schemes on roadside verges were undertaken by the County Council. Others were sponsored by the Devon Trust for Nature Conservation, Men of the Trees, amenity societies and individuals. 'Plant a tree in 73' and 'Plant some more in 74' were popular slogans. Schoolchildren were not only encouraged to participate in the planting schemes but to propagate seedling trees.

Tree planting is now carried out as a matter of course and, although the verges of county roads have limited scope, a substantial number of trees are planted every autumn. Advice concerning choice of species, planting sites, replacement of existing trees and maintenance is given in a County policy booklet.

Extensive landscaping of the motorway and the new trunk roads in Devon has involved the planting of approximately 1½ million young trees, which are now gradually coming into maturity and are being maintained on behalf of the Department of Transport by the Forestry Commission. Over 100 000 trees were planted along the Okehampton bypass alone. Such planting contributes to the integration of the highway into the immediate landscape and enhances the countryside generally. Eyesores and roadside facilities are screened, the effects of cross winds and headlight glare are reduced and a barrier is provided against traffic noise. The verges and banks also provide a haven for various species of mammals, birds and insects.

In the 1970s large numbers of elm trees, including many along roadsides, were killed by Dutch elm disease, with its clearly visible signs of dying foliage and leafless branches. Apart from the visual impact, the dying trees also constituted a danger to those using the highway. However, the County Council was greatly assisted by the owners of land adjoining the road where affected trees were within falling distance of the carriageway. Landowners were cooperative in arranging for the removal of those trees which might otherwise have been a danger to road users.

Every effort is made to retain mature trees when carrying out road improvement works. There are many examples of this practice: for instance, when a footpath was provided on the A384 between Shinners Bridge and Dartington it was so designed as to ensure that several mature oaks were retained. Similarly the dualling of the A380 road across Haldon was designed so as to retain an avenue of valuable beeches, and the design of Bovey Tracey bypass ensured the protection of mature trees which had become established in the former railway line, now the route of the new road.

## Roadside verges

Devon roadmen have always had a natural concern for conservation, indeed the very nature of their employment has made it so. It was largely through their efforts with scythe and shovel that the ground was prepared for the rich and varied flora and fauna of the roadside verges. The diversity of geological formation through which the county's roads pass has also contributed to the variety of plants to be found. In recent years there has been a keener sense of urgency to preserve this roadside environment.

As a result of the great road-building programme of the 1960s and 1970s the road network of Devon underwent dramatic changes. The price was high in environmental terms with the inevitable loss of good agricultural land, the destruction of buildings and the impact on the landscape generally, but the large areas of verge and bank created by the new roads have provided a habitat for plants and wildlife. Indeed, it is probably fair to say that roadside verges have contributed to the survival of many species of plants and wildlife no longer able to exist on farmland because of the considerable changes in agricultural methods and the use of fertilizers and pesticides. Today there are approximately 2000 hectares of roadside verge in Devon. Many people would agree that the wild flowers which grow in profusion on the verges, providing a continuous cycle of scent and colour, are one of the county's particular attractions.

The need to reclothe raw roadside banks and verges was quickly recognized and in 1967-8 considerable effort was put into a voluntary scheme, under the guidance of the late County Alderman H.B. Webber, for the seeding of new banks on road improvement schemes with wild flowers. The seed had been collected by children from over forty schools throughout the county. Germination tests were encouraging and some sixty different species were sown, some broadcast by a number of amenity societies and some by 'hydroseeding', a process whereby the seed was sprayed on to banks by mechanical means in a mixture incorporating straw, fertilizers and trace elements.

Some amenity societies, particularly the South Hams Society, transplanted a large number of primroses from fields due to go under the plough and the B3194 between Stumpy Post and Sorley Green bears witness to their efforts. Similar work was also done by the South Brent and Avon Valley Society on the Abham road at Staverton. The Topsham Society experimented with some success in the sowing of wild-flower seed under glass and used the banks of the Clyst St Mary–Clyst St George dual carriageway as a suitable planting site.

Although interest in nature conservation was stirring on a national scale in the 1960s, the decision of the Council of Europe to declare 1970 'European Conservation Year' brought the amenity and scientific value of roadside-verge ecology into sharper focus. In 1971 the Devon Trust for Nature Conservation began exploring ways of co-operating with the County Council in conserving the species found on verges, especially some of the rarer plants. Its members provided details of ecologically important roadside verges, as also did members of parish councils, amenity societies and other bodies.

In 1972, following a meeting of over thirty amenity and conservation societies, the County Council's Roads Committee appointed a working party to look into the treatment of urban and rural roadside verges. Their unanimous report set out the principles for an overall policy approved by the County Council in 1973. As a result there has been, in subsequent years, a great upsurge in the recognition of the importance of roadside verges to nature conservation, particularly at a time when many species of flora and fauna are at risk. Provision was made in rural areas for cutting verges where necessary for visibility at bends, junctions and intersections and around signs, but elsewhere cutting only a narrow width adjoining the carriageway. In urban areas a reduced frequency of cutting was proposed. Special exceptions were made for the cutting required to eliminate fire risk near woodland or heathland (such as at the top of Haldon where a mutual-aid agreement exists with the Forestry Commission for the cutting of all level areas and slopes to provide a fire break) and for the control of noxious weeds listed in the Weeds Act 1959. The policies are reviewed by the working party from time to time and one result was that the use of chemical sprays on rural verges is limited to selective weedkillers for the spot treatment of noxious weeds, such as ragwort and dock.

Devon's verges provide an ideal environment for some rare or localized species of wild plants, such as certain orchids which are unable to tolerate conditions elsewhere. The County Council identifies known sites as 'Special Verges' and they receive particular protection. This not only ensures that the normal cutting regime is adjusted to suit the particular rare plants, but also that they are not inadvertently damaged by other activities such as road improvements.

The cost of flattening and cutting embankment slopes to a gradient compatible with agriculture is often prohibitive. However, this is not necessarily a bad thing from an environmental point of view because large havens are provided for plants and wildlife.

A summary of the policies adopted by the County Council is contained in a booklet entitled *The Management of Urban and Rural Roadside Verges in Devon*. First published in 1976 there have been three subsequent revisions, the latest being published in April 1987.

## The conservation of wildlife

Apart from conserving roadside habitats, one of the concerns of the County Council is to protect wildlife from the dangers of traffic. To this end, with the help of the Forestry Commission, a number of small red reflectors on wooden posts have been erected on the motorway and on that length of the A380 which passes through Haldon Forest where deer are known to cross. The development by Austrian scientists of this optical warning system for wildlife followed experiments which established that a red light exerts a warning effect on deer. The headlights of approaching vehicles strike the reflectors, causing a red beam to shine into the adjoining forest, thereby acting as a deterrent to animals crossing the road. This device, appropriately nicknamed 'wolves' eyes', has similarly been employed in a particular location in north Devon to protect otters, a number of which had been killed on the road.

A number of animals are vulnerable to passing traffic, particularly hedgehogs, toads and badgers. The needs of the latter were given especial consideration when the M5 was constructed. A tunnel was provided between Maidendown and Sampford Moor on the route of a known badger run. That was in 1975, but it was not until May 1980 that badgers were actually observed using this facility – an event which attracted the attention of the national press! Established badger runs are said to be of prehistoric origin and it is not difficult to understand why they, like all creatures of habit, should continue to use such a long-established run, even if interrupted by the construction of a modern road. In those circumstances too, one can appreciate why the badger felt that it had the right of way and therefore tended to 'face' oncoming cars rather than endeavour to avoid them. The construction of a tunnel duct, such as that under the M5, therefore not only protects the badgers but restores to them an ancient right of way!

The bodies of owls found on the highway are passed to the Ministry of Agriculture, Fisheries and Food for examination since there is national concern at the marked reduction in their numbers.

The conservation of fish life is, of course, a very important aspect of any work in connection with river bridges and other structures. Before work is started on any scheme involving rivers, South West Water is consulted. When bridges are being constructed, contractors are required to comply with the Salmon and Freshwater Fisheries Act 1923-1972 and the Rivers (Prevention of Pollution) Acts 1951-1961. These Acts are intended to ensure that flora and fauna are protected from pollution. They are strictly enforced and carry heavy penalties if contravened.

# Recent Environmental Developments

Many of the features described in this chapter, though now prized for their visual appeal, originated for utilitarian reasons. The accessories of modern highways also have to serve a utilitarian purpose, but after the emphasis on functional cheapness of the post-war years, there is now an awareness of the need to ensure that the roadside environment is enhanced by a sensitive choice of materials and of design, whether in relation to the highway itself or the accompanying street furniture. There is, too, an increasing consideration of the environment for its own sake, with a growing realization that pedestrian needs are of particular importance. The following sections illustrate this changing emphasis in the County Council's management of the roadside environment.

## Enhancement of towns and villages

Devon is fortunate in possessing an inheritance of historically interesting towns and villages. Not surprisingly for some time there has been a determination among individuals and organizations alike to restore the numerous old buildings in the county for future generations to enjoy.

The County Council's policy for the maintenance of roadside verges was developed jointly with such bodies as the Devon Trust for Nature Conservation, the Country Landowners Association and the National Farmers Union. Implementation of this policy over a number of years has ensured that verges have an attractive variety of plant life, particularly in spring and summer.

For its part the County Council has shown equal determination to ensure that the streets, squares, villages, greens and other spaces, which provide the setting for these buildings, offer a fitting environment and make an appropriate contribution to the townscape.

## Conservation Areas

Those parts of the county's towns and villages which are of particular importance in architectural and historical terms have been designated as Conservation Areas. In 1987 there were some 224 such areas in Devon, providing a safeguard for the best of the county's architectural heritage. Within these areas the highest priority is given to the conservation of the environment as a whole, comprising buildings, trees, open spaces, viewpoints and other features which contribute to the character of the area.

Conservation Areas are of many types, from the Georgian terraces and greens of Southernhay, Exeter, the Barbican area of Plymouth, and the small towns of Totnes, Tavistock, Dartmouth and Bideford, to the numerous unspoilt villages throughout the county. These are designated because of the quality and character of the building groups within them. However, it is important to recognize the contribution that the 'floorscape', i.e. the roads, footways and associated open spaces, can make to the character of these Conservation Areas.

In the past townscape qualities have sometimes been eroded, often in the interests of making provision for the growth of motor traffic. There has been a tendency to standardize the treatment of differing areas and the environment has been marred by the removal of traditional paving, the widespread use of bituminous materials, the introduction of unsightly street lighting, discordant furnishings and traffic-sign clutter. In recent years the County Council, in consultation with the appropriate District Councils, has made a concerted effort to restore the character of these areas by the reintroduction of traditional paving materials, the removal of unnecessary signs, the provision of unobtrusive street lighting, landscaping and where necessary curbs on traffic and car parking. The present emphasis is on restoring and accentuating the individual character of places by the use of appropriate materials and furnishings.

In some of the more environmentally sensitive places, cobbles, setts and natural-stone paving slabs are being used to provide the right atmosphere. Tavistock is one town where such an improvement programme has been introduced. In other areas where there is considerable pedestrian movement both traditional brick and concrete-block paving have been adopted as the appropriate materials for entire streets, for example in Foss Street, Dartmouth and High Street, Barnstaple. Enhancement schemes have also been completed in a number of villages in the county, including the refurbishment of the cobbles at Thorverton and improvements to the square at Hartland. Dramatic visual improvements have also been achieved in a number of towns by the removal of concrete lamp columns, and their replacement with suitable wall brackets. Totnes and Exeter High Streets provide examples of such treatment. This work will continue to be important in years to come.

## Highway management in towns of historical interest

In Totnes, Dartmouth, and Tavistock, three towns which display much evidence of their past, a wider view has been taken of the opportunities for improving and enhancing the setting of the towns' numerous well-maintained listed buildings. The centres of these towns have been largely unaffected by modern development and have retained medieval street patterns flanked by continuous facades of old buildings.

It is increasingly felt that these town centres should retain the atmosphere of their past and residents have made painstaking efforts to ensure this in their restoration work. The County Council is complementing these efforts with schemes to provide the right environment for these improved buildings and has made a fundamental change in its treatment of the old streets. The way in which present-day needs can be reconciled with the conservation of the historic environment forms the basis of individual Management Plans for these towns. Much of the footway paving in these town centres was in poor condition and of inappropriate materials which are now being replaced.

The methods employed in earlier times to build roads, walls and pavements created a diversity of pattern and texture still to be seen in many Devon townscapes. Although the materials are modern, this sense of pattern has been retained in recent highway-enhancement schemes by careful selection of small pavers. The example here is of a scheme at Hartland, in north Devon, completed in 1987.

time highlighting architectural features. As the removal of traffic from these town centres has proceeded so has the opportunity been taken to develop more conservation projects.

In Totnes, York stone slabs, which have traditionally been used as a paving material, have been refurbished or reinstated in the most important area of the town. The carriageway in High Street has also been narrowed to prevent damage by vehicles to the Butterwalk. This work has been assisted by grant aid from English Heritage. In Dartmouth, Foss Street and Union Street have been repaved with blue and yellow brick, continuing the traditional use of these materials in the town, and cobbles have been restored at Bayards Cove. In Tavistock the traditional paving is locally quarried granite which is still used in sensitive areas such as Church Path.

The Management Plans have been developed with the co-operation of District and Town Councils, together with local amenity societies. These plans have looked at ways to reduce the visual impact of traffic, as well as including proposals to tidy up parking and to rationalize signs. Yellow lines which define parking restrictions have been replaced in a less discordant form. Street-lighting equipment has been renewed in a less obtrusive manner but at the same

## Pedestrian schemes in town and city centres

The creation of traffic-free town-centre shopping areas is an important environmental aim and those towns which now have an established pedestrian shopping area, such as Exeter, may be compared favourably with others where this has yet to be achieved.

The acceptance of pedestrian shopping areas has been a slow and, at times, a controversial process. The need for pedestrianization has emerged as a result of old town centres being unable to cope with the pressures of the growth in the number of motor cars. This gave rise to a choice of adapting town centres to meet the pressures, possibly by redevelopment, or of introducing measures restricting the motor car, of which pedestrianization is one very effective example. In the 1950s and early 1960s the tendency was to plan the town centres for the needs of the motorist; in Exeter and Plymouth this was possible on a wide scale because of the extensive bomb damage.

However, attitudes have changed: the conservation of town centres and the needs of the pedestrian are becoming more important. Indeed in Devon, where there has been minor redevelopment in town centres outside the main urban areas, pedestrians have generally been given priority, as at Exmouth. Pedestrian proposals nevertheless do give rise to conflicting views. Whilst few would deny that pedestrianization improves the environment for the shopper, there is a genuine anxiety, particularly from traders, that the exclusion of motor vehicles will harm trade and therefore the prosperity of the town centre. This is generally a fear of the unknown, since experience has shown that in general terms trade does not suffer and often, once it has been established, there are requests for pedestrianization to be extended. The traders' fears of pedestrian schemes are similar to those which are often expressed when bypasses are proposed.

Other than traders, there are also those people who regard such schemes as an unjustified threat to well-established shopping habits, particularly where on-street parking has proved, for them, convenient. These attitudes are perhaps more prevalent where schemes are proposed in the smaller towns.

Despite these difficulties, more pedestrianization (or alternatively pedestrian-priority) schemes are gradually being introduced. As motor cars increase in number, so will the realization grow that motor vehicles and shoppers do not readily mix.

Pedestrian schemes are either in the form of purpose-built precincts or are created by the exclusion of vehicles from existing streets.

**Roadside stone commemorating a coaching accident.**

In the first category one of the earliest examples in Devon was Princesshay in Exeter, which formed part of the redeveloped city centre in the aftermath of the blitz in 1942. In fact the foundation stone for the rebuilding of Exeter was laid in Princesshay by Princess Elizabeth in 1949, with the street itself being completed some years later. It runs parallel to, and links with, High Street, affording views of the Cathedral towers. Latterly it has enabled the introduction of a continental feature, the outdoor street café.

Pedestrian schemes in the second category are a more recent development in Devon. The major examples are Exeter and Plymouth. When these two centres were redeveloped following extensive war damage, the plans rightly anticipated the increase in traffic and made provision for a growing volume of vehicles to pass through the city centres. The plans did not, however, foresee the environmental problems which would arise from such large numbers of vehicles. Of late, however, it has been realized that the convenience of the motor vehicle and its passengers has to take second place to the safety and convenience of the pedestrian, particularly the shopper.

The exclusion of traffic, other than buses, from Exeter High Street has allowed a more pleasant and restful environment to be provided, with mature landscaping, floral displays and seats for the comfort of shoppers. This has now become an accepted feature which is slowly being extended, for instance into Gandy Street, the character and appearance of which has improved enormously as a result.

Ambitious plans for the pedestrianization of Plymouth city centre have now been implemented and have transformed Armada Way and New George Street (see p.150). These plans have not been achieved without considerable heart-searching and at times acrimonious debate (mentioned in Chapter 6), usually centring on the smaller traders' concern about the implication, mainly financial, of excluding motor vehicles from a bustling and prosperous city centre. However, protagonists point to the redevelopment proposals which have followed quickly in the wake of pedestrianization, and, once the scheme has matured, future if not present generations of shoppers will no doubt welcome the new and safer environment. Change is often regarded with suspicion, but familiarity usually brings acceptance.

A similar controversy arose in part of Torquay town centre, where pedestrian-priority proposals in conjunction with the redevelopment of Fleet Street/Swan Street gave rise to much opposition, but this was primarily as a result of the loss of some familiar buildings in a sensitive location. Such losses inevitably cause nostalgia as the new urban landscape emerges.

One result of the pedestrianization of shopping areas is the need to provide delivery vehicles with alternative means of access to shops, either at the rear or at a different level from the shopping street. This frequently presents problems in older shopping centres where a variety of uses and multiple ownerships may exist behind the shopping facades, and where streets continue to provide access for delivery vehicles as well as a thoroughfare. However,

Orders can be made to restrict the hours of delivery. In these circumstances environmental improvements can be achieved by paving across the shopping streets with block pavers. These are increasingly used in shopping streets as they provide a suitable surface for pedestrians and will withstand the weight of delivery vehicles. Such schemes have recently been carried out in Barnstaple and elsewhere in the county. In some places such as Gandy Street, Exeter, granite setts have been used to achieve similar objectives.

Pedestrian-priority schemes are not confined to larger centres. A particularly attractive scheme has been successfully carried out in the picturesque resort of Lynmouth, within Exmoor National Park.

## Bypass construction: the environmental benefits

Many towns situated on the main routes through the county prospered from passing trade for many years. Typical examples are Ashburton, Honiton and Cullompton, which provided coaching houses and other amenities for travellers. However, the main shopping street of such towns was also the main thoroughfare, and as traffic increased environmental conditions became intolerable.

Fortunately, many of these settlements, which once suffered the discomforts of heavy traffic, now have the benefit of a bypass which has resulted in dramatic improvements to their environment and safety. The removal of the dust and noise generated by through traffic has encouraged property owners to improve their premises, as can be witnessed at Chudleigh, whilst improvement of environmental conditions has resulted in increased trade from local sources. Honiton is just one such town which is prospering and has benefited greatly from its bypass.

In particular, the completion of the M5 and A38 spine road by the Department of Transport has significantly improved conditions in many towns in the south of the county. The completion of the North Devon Link Road will bring similar benefits to settlements that have suffered from heavy traffic flows in the northern part of the county.

The County Council has contributed significantly to the relief of traffic problems and improvement of the environment generally in various parts of Devon, by constructing bypasses. Inhabitants of towns and villages still waiting for bypasses are continuing to clamour for them to be provided. Many a fierce campaign has been launched to persuade the County Council to meet their wishes, a distinct contrast from the anti-road lobbies of the sixties.

## Integrating the highway into the landscape

A high quality of landscaping and the attainment of good landscaping techniques is now considered essential to achieve the proper integration of new and improved highways into the area through which they are to pass, and for this reason the County Council now ensures that landscaping is developed as an integral part of the design process. Road proposals are examined by a Landscape Advisory Group, which consists of Officers from the County and District Councils, so as to define the environmental requirements which should be included in their design. (This is similar to the role of the Landscape Advisory Committee which deals with trunk roads.) This recent innovation, now firmly established, emphasizes that landscaping is not an afterthought but is thoroughly considered at an early stage when highway schemes are being designed.

The purpose of landscaping is twofold. Firstly, it softens the visual impact of the road on the surrounding area, and secondly it can be used to good effect in screening unsightly views from the road. The process may involve the retention of existing features and trees, which in some cases may require the realignment of a road. This is one of the principal tasks of the Landscape Advisory Group. Where existing features and trees cannot be used to achieve the necessary results, new tree planting has to be introduced. The scale of new planting, already referred to above, is far greater than may generally be realized. Furthermore, planting is not confined to the highway limits. If it is considered that planting is necessary on adjacent land, approaches are made to the landowner so that this can be achieved.

Successful integration of a new road into the landscape needs the right species. Native trees and shrubs are usually the most suitable to plant in rural areas, but more decorative trees can sometimes be successful in urban and suburban areas. Once trees and shrubs have been planted, they have to be nurtured – in their early years they cannot be left untended. This is now well recognized, and in landscaping contracts the County Council requires after-care for a period of years. Where trees and shrubs do not survive they have to be replaced.

To supplement its work on landscaping highways, the County Council provides an advisory service to parish councils, which may plant trees within the limits of the highway, and to individuals or associations wishing to plant trees on land outside but adjoining the highway.

So much for 'soft' landscaping. Great attention is also paid to 'hard' landscaping, the built environment. Facing materials are now used where appropriate to disguise the ubiquitous concrete of retaining structures and bridges. The use of sympathetic materials is also sought for fences, hedges or walls which adjoin the highway. It is particularly important that new work blends with existing structures and this can sometimes be achieved by reusing salvaged materials. Of particular interest was the decision of the County Council to contribute to improving the appearance of buildings affected by, but outside the line of, the Barnstaple urban relief road, the construction of which had resulted, for instance, in the exposure of unattractive gable ends and boundary walls. These with financial assistance from both the County Council and District Council, were treated to improve their appearance.

Modern traffic conditions require the use of prominent traffic signs. However, a surfeit of signs can often be

avoided with forethought and common sense. They may be mounted on existing street furniture, boundary walls, fences and buildings. Their sensitive positioning can further reduce their impact. For instance, it is preferable to set them against a backcloth of trees rather than against the skyline and where necessary trees may be planted to achieve this aim, consistent with safety considerations. Particular attention is paid to the dimensions and siting of signs in areas of historical interest in towns, reducing the size where possible along with proposals to reduce traffic speed and volume.

Particular care is called for in dealing with highways in Dartmoor and Exmoor National Parks. The First Review of the Dartmoor National Park Plan, in dealing with highway improvements, comments that 'road safety requirements must ultimately prevail but liaison arrangements ensure that there is minimum damage to the roadside environment'. Where improvements are necessary particular care is taken to ensure that intrusion into the landscape is reduced by retaining the character of the

**Many bridges were built close to the point where a river was forded and the remains of the old ford may often be seen. In some cases the ford and the bridge are both still in use, as they are at Malmsmead on the county boundary between Devon and Somerset.**

existing boundaries, whether Devon bank, stone wall or hedge, albeit on a new alignment. Also of significance is the unique signposting system which guides different types of traffic along the most suitable routes, so that the need to carry out highway improvements is kept to the absolute minimum.

Roads play an important part in the daily life of the inhabitants of the county and much time is spent travelling along them, whether on foot or by vehicle, so it is important that they not only fit into the landscape but also provide a pleasant outlook for those using them. This chapter has sought to describe the features which in their infinite variety contribute to the roadside environment, and to describe the endeavours of the County Council to enhance that environment.

## Early Surveyors

**O**f all the key appointments in local government the post of County Surveyor is one of the oldest.

It was in 1530, under the Statute of Bridges, that mention was first made of the appointment of 'Surveyors'. The Quarter Sessions had been given powers to appoint surveyors whose duties were the repair, maintenance or rebuilding of those bridges for which the county had responsibility. Roads, on the other hand, were put under the charge of the parishes by the Statute of Highways 1555 and did not become a county responsibility until 1888. Therefore, whilst their duties were initially in a limited field, the earlier surveyors were nevertheless the forebears of the present County Engineers.

In the beginning many of these appointments were part time, the surveyors being building craftsmen. Devon appointed five 'surveyors', four of whom described themselves as 'joyners' and one as a 'gentleman'. However, as the work grew, more counties employed regular Surveyors or Engineers. One such person was Thomas Telford who became the County Surveyor of Shropshire and rose to great eminence in the profession; in fact he became the first President of the Institution of Civil Engineers in 1820.

The work of Telford obviously became known in Devon, as can be seen from the following correspondence between the Clerks of the Peace of Devon and Shropshire in July 1800, concerning the appointment of a County Surveyor for Devon, to be responsible for its bridges.

DEVON CASTLE, *Exeter 6th July 1800*

Sir,

The Magistrates of this County are about to appoint an Engineer to superintend the Bridges of this County, and they have desired me to request the favour of your answering the queries on the other side.

I ask your pardon for thus troubling you, but be assured I shall at all times be happy to render you any service in return either in a public or private capacity in this part of the country.

I am Sir
Your most Obedient Servant
R Eales
Clerk of the Peace.

# THE ROAD BUILDERS

Designers and
Decision Makers

And on the other side of the letter:

It is but this day I have been informed that an Engineer is employed in your County otherwise I would have applied sooner. Pray favour me with an early answer as our Sessions is meeting in 1 week – How many County bridges have you in County? – How are the Bridges inspected or surveyed? by the Magistrates in the different divisions or by the Surveyor appointed for the purpose? –

If by the latter what salary is allowed and does he give up his whole time to it or is he allowed to carry on and conduct other business?

The following reply, dated only four days later, was despatched from Shrewsbury, which certainly speaks well of the postal service of that time.

R Eales Esq. (*Clerk of the Peace, Devon Castle, Exeter*)

Sir,

Mr Thos. Telford is the Surveyor of Bridges for Shropshire and for Shrewsbury – he is appointed under the late act for appointing Surveyors of Bridges. He is also the Surveyor of all other public works in the County and Town under the Statutes for building a Shire Guildhall, 2 gaols, 2 houses of correction here – He is paid sometime by a percentage on the money expended in building and repairing at other times by a bill for plans and estimates, time, trouble, hire and expenses. He follows other briefs and is at present employed on the Caledonian Canal under the Government – the Ellesmere Canal and other public works – he has Clerks under him here and at other places.

When a bridge is in want of repair it is presented by the Grand Jury at Assize or Sessions or the Judge of the Assize or Justices of the Peace under 13 Geo 3rd (17)78. By 12th Geo 3rd @ 20s 13 no sum can be laid out on the repair of bridges until presentment is made....

The present sum of Bridges amount to 30 but they will have increased of late years and will further increase.

Shrewsbury                                          James Loxdale

10th July 1800

The urgency of the correspondence between Exeter and Shrewsbury was not, it seems, matched by any eagerness to appoint a County Surveyor for Devon. The County carried on with its five existing Bridge Surveyors until one of them, William White, the Bridge Surveyor for the Eastern Grand Division, was found guilty of neglect of duty. It was the collapse of the newly reconstructed Fenny Bridges in 1808 that caused the Justices to decide that 'a Civil Engineer of approved talents and ability' be appointed in place of the five Surveyors. Consequently, James Green, who was either a pupil or a junior assistant to the famous canal engineer, John Rennie, was appointed at Michaelmas 1808. Green was invested with responsibility for inspecting and reporting on 237 of the county's bridges and then bringing them up to a good standard. He was an accomplished engineer and left his distinctive mark on many of Devon's

Thomas Telford's first work as an engineer came with his appointment by the Ellesmere Canal Company to design and build a waterway joining the Mersey, the Severn and the Dee. Gradually, with increasing numbers of successful projects behind him, his reputation as an engineer became international. He was also a great road builder, particularly in Scotland and Wales. In 1800 his reputation resulted in enquiries from Devon about his conditions of engagement. Telford's works, still in daily use all over the country, bear eloquent testimony to his energy and engineering genius.

new bridges, perhaps the best example being Cowley Bridge on the outskirts of Exeter. By 1840, his consultancy work had reached a level that forced him to delegate much of Devon's work to his son. This did not satisfy the Justices who gave him twelve months' notice and later it was resolved that 'the unanimous thanks of the court' be presented to him 'for his valuable and efficient services for a period of thirty three years'.

Green was succeeded by Thomas Whitaker in 1842. Whitaker was responsible for such bridges as St Saviour's, Beaford, Rolle and many others, but his most interesting contribution was the preparation, between 1843 and 1856, of a set of drawings of the county bridges, exquisitely drawn and bound into three volumes now safely in the County archives. In 1844 Whitaker applied for an increase in his annual salary of £300, drawing attention to, among other things, the fact that he had to travel an average of 6000 miles and to sleep away from home for thirty nights during the year. He got an increase of £100!

When Whitaker retired in 1865 the Magistrates decided

to divide the county into two – 'a north-east district and a south-west district' – and to appoint two Surveyors, at salaries of £240 and £200 respectively. The jobs were advertised and subsequently George Wickenden Cuming was appointed to the north-east district and Henry Weymouth Farley to the south-west. Cuming died in 1868 and Farley was appointed sole Surveyor at an annual salary of £550. Farley resigned in 1881 and the job was again divided into two, with Edward Hall Harbottle as Surveyor for the Northern District and John Little for the Southern. Harbottle was a Newcastle upon Tyne architect who had come to practise in Devon in 1869. He was responsible for the design of the tower, dedicated in 1890, of the church of St Michael and All Angels in Heavitree. Little, in contrast, was formerly Surveyor to the Torquay Board of Health.

During these years the Quarter Sessions had supervised the activities of its Surveyors and their contractors through Magistrates who lived locally to the bridge sites, since travel throughout the county would have been restricted to horseback. While the Surveyors, who were responsible for bridges and buildings, had wide powers to approve and disapprove the work of contractors, the ultimate financial control lay with the Magistrates who reserved the right to accept tenders and to issue certificates for payment.

## The Creation of Devon County Council

The year 1888 is significant in the history of local government administration in this country as it saw the establishment of the County Councils as elected bodies and provided the framework for the County Councils as they are known today. For the first time the Counties assumed control of the main roads, while the remainder were under the control of borough, urban and rural district councils.

The new Councils set about appointing their County Surveyors. However, Devon, no doubt because of its size, decided to apportion the county into four divisions each with its own Surveyor whose responsibilities now extended to the inspection and financial control of work on main roads. The existing surveyors were retained, with Edward Harbottle taking charge of the Western District and John Little the Eastern District. Two new appointees were made: Henry Masterton, formerly a civil engineer at Devonport, took charge of the Northern District and C.G.S. Acock the Southern District.

In 1897, when both Harbottle and Little retired, the county was divided into two divisions with Masterton taking charge of the North and Acock the South Division. Sadly Masterton died a year later and he was replaced by Samuel Ingram who had previously been District County Surveyor for Bridgwater. It was Ingram who, in 1908, was to introduce reinforced concrete to Devon with a notable design for the bridge over the River Exe at Thorverton. However, Ingram retired after this contract and in 1912 William Percival Robinson, who was formerly Assistant County Surveyor of Somerset, was appointed to the Northern Division.

Proposals to reconsider provisions for the maintenance of main roads were put forward from 1905 onwards, but by 1912 the move towards direct control by the County Council had been deferred again in favour of moves to improve relations between the County Council and the local highway authorities and to increase co-operation on road maintenance activities, a subject that was to recur from time to time. In the spirit of this policy it was decided in December 1912 to appoint an additional County Surveyor and to divide the county into three districts.

This time Acock assumed control of the South and West District, Robinson the East District and Edward Stead from Somerset was appointed for the North District. He brought with him as his deputy Richard Stone, and, when in 1914 Stead returned to Somerset as County Surveyor, Stone succeeded him.

It is Richard Stone about whom the anecdote of the meeting with the County Surveyor of Cornwall is often told. In those days the bridges across the Tamar, which divides Cornwall from Devon, were the joint responsibility of the two Counties. (Today, alternate bridges are the responsibility of each County.) This arrangement apparently called for a discussion between the two County Surveyors which was due to take place at Polson Bridge near Launceston. For reasons not known, the two Surveyors did not hit it off and when they arrived at Polson Bridge each refused to cross to the other side to hold the meeting, instead dispatching their two Assistants to the centre of the bridge to exchange messages while the Surveyors remained firm on their own territory!

Robert Carnegie was appointed County Surveyor in 1946. For his part in co-ordinating relief and reconstruction work after the Lynmouth flood in 1952 he was made a C.B.E.

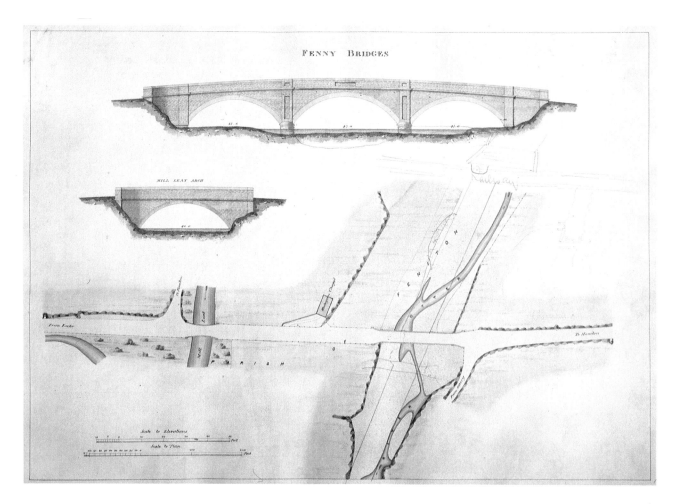

By 1842, James Green's work for the county was beginning to suffer as a result of other commissions he had taken on and he was relieved of his duties as surveyor of bridges and buildings for the county of Devon. He and his son made a somewhat ill-tempered departure, taking their drawings with them. Green's successor, Thomas Whitaker, set about making a complete set of drawings to replace those Green had taken. The drawings, of which this is an example, were made between 1843 and 1856 and are a valuable contribution to the county's heritage.

William Robinson was appointed County Surveyor of Surrey in 1920 and was replaced by F.E. Simpson, who had deputized for him whilst he was away on active service in the 1914–18 war. Meanwhile Acock had died in June 1917. As a result Andrew Warren, Borough Surveyor of Totnes, was engaged temporarily to do work in the Newton Abbot, Totnes, Kingsbridge and Plympton areas. The Tavistock and Broadwoodwidger areas were to be covered temporarily by Stone. In 1928 there was yet another reorganization, this time into a North Western Division and a South Eastern Division.

Today these frequent changes in the division of the county may seem bewildering. However, it must be remembered that Devon is not only large in size but its network of roads is extensive and the upland of Dartmoor towards the centre proved to be a much greater obstacle to communication in those days than now.

Together Stone and Warren provided a period of stability and continuity from the First World War to the end of the Second, a period which saw the first upsurge in the use of the motor car, and later a considerable increase in the road-construction programme which commenced in the late twenties only to be interrupted by the start of the Second World War.

## The First County Surveyor

Whilst Green might be regarded as the first County Surveyor, and indeed he designated himself as such, it must be remembered that he was restricted to bridge work and not all the county bridges at that. After 1888, in practically every other county the responsibility for the main roads and bridges lay with one County Surveyor, yet surprisingly in Devon this did not come about until after the Second World War when, in 1945, it was decided that there should be appointed a single County Surveyor. Accordingly, Robert Carnegie was appointed in June 1946. It was to Carnegie that the responsibility fell of re-establishing the road network of the county following the war years with the inevitable acute shortage of funds. It was he also who had to deal with the aftermath of the Lynmouth flood in 1952 when that small north Devon community was devastated, with considerable loss of life.

When Carnegie died in 1961 he was succeeded by his deputy, Henry Criswell. During Criswell's period of office the task changed from that of merely maintaining the existing road network to that of major road construction arising from growing mobility, increasing car ownership and more leisure time. He will also be remembered for his earlier work, following the Lynmouth disaster, in the design of bridges using pre-stressed concrete, at that time a new technique.

Devon County Council has always encouraged its Chief Officers and staff to contribute professionally to national and international affairs, and also to assist in the development of their professions and to act as advisors to the Association of County Councils. Messrs Carnegie and Criswell were both National Presidents of the then Institution of Highway Engineers, whilst Michael Hawkins has been the National President of the Institution of Municipal Engineers and of the County Surveyors' Society.

## Road Construction Units

The years that followed the Second World War were notable in transportation terms because of the increasing number of motor vehicles and people's desire for greater personal mobility. This led to considerable congestion on a network of highways which was neither designed for nor capable of being improved for the volume of vehicles that resulted from the mobility revolution.

It was not long before the public were demanding an improved national road network, a fact that had been foreseen by the County Surveyors' Society as early as 1938. At the end of 1958 the first length of motorway was opened, in Lancashire. It was soon recognized that, if a national motorway network of the magnitude envisaged

Michael Hawkins took up the new post of County Engineer on the reorganization of local government in 1974. He has overseen an unprecedented period of road construction in the county. The opening of the Okehampton bypass in July 1988 marked the culmination of many years of public debate about the route the road should take.

was to be constructed at the speed which both the scale of traffic growth and public opinion demanded, an engineering organization would have to be established to allow the design and construction to be carried out within the required timescale.

Hitherto, the design of most trunk roads in the country was undertaken on a territorial basis on behalf of the Department of Transport by each County Council acting independently as its agent. When it became apparent that the Department of Transport had it in mind to remove this responsibility and to create a corps of civil servant engineers to undertake the work, the political outcry from the County Councils, who guarded their responsibility jealously, was intense. The result was the traditional British compromise whereby the Department of Transport would establish what were to become known as 'Road Construction Units' based in regions, and certain County Councils (not all) would be asked to form Sub-units comprising mainly staff ostensibly still remaining with the County Council but paid for and closely supervised by the Department of Transport. One such Sub-unit covering Cornwall and Devon was formed in 1968 as part of Devon County Council, with the County Surveyor, Henry Criswell, being the Chief Engineer. Upon local government reorganization in 1974, Michael Hawkins took over the responsibility as Chief Engineer until 1981 when the Department of Transport decided to dissolve the Road Construction Unit system. The majority of the schemes then in hand or projected were transferred to the private sector, but an exception was made in the case of the Devon Sub-unit programme, much of which was handed back to the County Engineer to complete.

When Carnegie died in 1961 he was succeeded by his deputy, Henry Criswell, second from the left in this photograph.

George Creber C.B.E., first leader of the new County Council, formed in 1974.

Many regretted the winding up of the Road Construction Units. Whatever the feelings on this matter, the fact remains that they were excellent examples of co-operation between central and local government, achieving with remarkable skill and speed a revolution in road building in this country that will long be remembered.

## Local Government Reorganization, 1974

In the 1960s it was becoming apparent that the pattern of local government in England, which had served the communities so well for nearly a century, was beginning to show signs of needing an overhaul. The first steps were taken in the late 1960s when a number of urban communities which had grown up in close proximity to one another were merged to form County Boroughs, one of these being the amalgamation of Torquay, Paignton and Brixham to form the County Borough of Torbay in 1968. Elsewhere the divide between the better-off urban areas and the poorer rural communities was becoming very noticeable and the need for change was urgent.

The form that the change would take was debated for a number of years and eventually it was decided by the government at the time to create a new two-tiered system of local government, with the most radical changes occurring at District Council level. One tier was to comprise the County Councils which, as well as taking on other functions, would be the highway authorities for the

whole of the county territory, including the former County Boroughs. The other tier, the District Councils, comprised either the former County Borough Councils or an amalgamation of the former Borough, Urban District and Rural District Councils. Thus in Devon the new Devon County Council assumed control of the highways and transportation for the former area of the county together with the Cities of Plymouth and Exeter and the County Borough of Torbay, to become one of the largest counties in the country, with the greatest road mileage and a population of nearly a million people.

The Local Government Act 1972 which brought this about signalled the greatest change in the administration of local government that this country has ever known and brought with it a good deal of upheaval and disturbance. The new Devon County Council was elected in May 1973 and under the leadership of George Creber C.B.E. and Vivian Lucas, who was appointed Chief Executive to the new Council, preparations began in earnest for the designated changeover day of 1 April 1974. Amongst the new Chief Officers to be appointed was Michael Hawkins, as the County Engineer, who until then had been the Director of Technical Services to the County Borough of Torbay where he had been responsible for establishing the engineering and planning functions for the amalgamated towns which formed the County Borough in 1968.

No road schemes would ever come to fruition without the men who do the actual physical work involved in building them. The history of 'navvies' is a long one, much of it a tale of backbreaking work and low wages. The development of earth-moving and other machinery has taken much of the drudgery out of road building, but it is still no job for those weak in body or spirit. The completion of major road-building schemes is traditionally an excuse for a celebration by the roadmen involved. The open-air party under way here marked the completion of the A380 Fiddler's Elbow improvement in 1963.

James Green's Fenny Bridge carries the A30 trunk road over the River Otter. Until the completion of the M5 motorway, this was the most popular holiday route into the South West.

The new title of County Engineer replaced the title of County Surveyor and the County Engineer's Department succeeded the former Roads Department. This was to recognize the fact that the new department would be responsible not only for the roads and bridges as hitherto, but also for the whole subject of transportation, including vehicle and plant maintenance, and for the first time public transport, road safety, waste disposal, and Exeter airport.

The task of developing the new policies required by these changes was placed in the care of a newly formed Planning and Transportation Committee, with Councillor Arnold Sayers C.B.E. as its first Chairman. Immediately the methods of administering the County Council's engineering operations were totally changed through the creation of four areas, each with its own Area Engineer and Sub Committees, and soon after by a marked reduction in the number of highway divisions. Michael Hawkins also

Arnold Sayers C.B.E., first Chairman of the Planning and Transportation Committee.

assumed control of the Road Construction Unit and later, in 1984, was given the responsibility for the Planning Department of the County Council, thus becoming County Engineer and Planning Officer.

Reorganization in 1974 coincided with the beginning of a virtual revolution in road construction and transportation in the county. This included the completion of the motorway as far as Exeter and of the A38 trunk road to Plymouth and through the city to the Tamar, the rebuilding of the A30, including Okehampton bypass, as well as the construction of the North Devon Link to Barnstaple and Bideford. The congested traffic conditions of towns and cities needed drastic solutions, including pedestrianization and computerized traffic control. On the technical side the changes were as great as the revolution that brought about reorganization, with a major transformation in the way that engineering work was carried out through the introduction of micro-technology and the development of the computer.

When the first Surveyors were appointed it is almost certain that they operated on their own, but as the work expanded, especially after the creation of the County Councils, it became necessary for them to be provided with assistance, albeit limited at first but increasing as the work and professional requirements demanded. Today the County Engineering and Planning Department comprises an organization of men and women, some of them professional engineers and planners, others technicians, with the appropriate support of accountants, clerical assistants and other staff.

As this book goes to press, the great highways of Devon are nearing completion, but there is still much to do. This will be the story told by anyone who decides to write a sequel.

## The Political Leaders

The story of Devon's roads would not be complete without reference to those dedicated men and women who devote their time and energy to the interests of the people of Devon – the elected members.

The Surveyors, whilst being professional Engineers, can operate only within the policies and with the authority of the elected members who decide overall policy and ensure that the appropriate funds are provided. In a history such as this it would be impossible to single out the work of individual Chairmen or members. Moreover, the records of their work in Committee Minutes and Reports do not do justice to the amount of time and expertise that these public-spirited individuals bring to the offices they hold. However, in order to acknowledge the devotion of the various Chairmen both of the County Council and also of the appropriate Committees concerned with roads, a chart listing those who have served Devon over the years is included in Appendix 4.

It should be recognized that their terms of office demanded a high degree of devotion and judgement to the overall benefit of the County of Devon, and it is to them, as well as to the professional road builders over the years, that this book is dedicated.

# Appendix 1(a)

Some of the road-improvement schemes completed in the post-war period, 1946–1964
(Not including those shown elsewhere as having been constructed by the County Council's Direct Labour Construction Section)

| Year of completion | Scheme details | Cost |
|---|---|---|
| **Trunk roads** | | |
| 1953 | A38 Chudleigh Knighton Bridge: approaches to new railway bridge. | £36 201 |
| 1955 | A30 Fowley Bridge to Betty Cottles, Okehampton: rebuilding bridge and improvement of road alignment. | £6 500 |
| | A30 Crawley Bend, Yarcombe, near Honiton: improvement to eliminate bad bend. | £6 230 |
| 1956 | A30 Prospect Corner, Sticklepath: widening and provision of footpath. | £7 122 |
| 1957 | A39 Baxworthy Corner, Hartland: widening and realignment | £29 850 |
| | A30 Lower Northcote Farm, Honiton: widening and realignment. | £21 150 |
| 1959 | A30 Reddicks Hill, Upottery: widening and realignment. | £25 140 |
| 1960 | A38 Dean Prior to Dry Bridge, Buckfastleigh: realignment and widening. | £25 288 |
| | A30 Hayes Farm, Clyst Honiton: widening and realignment. | £10 804 |
| | A30 Pattesons Cross to Ash Farm, west of Honiton: realignment and new bridge. | £56 121 |
| | A30 Nags Head Farm to Iron Bridge, near Honiton: widening, realignment and provision of dual carriageway. | £29 566 |
| 1961 | A30 Coach Bridge, Clyst Honiton: widening and realignment. | £26 635 |
| | A30 South Whimple Farm, Clyst Honiton: widening and realignment. | £18 770 |
| | A30 Bodley Bridge to Bidgood Arms, Rockbeare: widening and realignment. | £25 000 |
| | A38 Marley Bottom, Rattery: widening and realignment. | £36 602 |
| 1962 | A38 Lyneham Inn to Smithaleigh: dual two-lane carriageway. | £49 109 |
| | A38 Lamb Hill, Burlescombe: widening to 33ft three-lane carriageway with crawler lane. | £11 471 |
| | A361 King Street, South Molton: widening and realignment. | £4 250 |
| 1963 | A38 Bittaford to Cross-in-Hand, near Ivybridge: realignment and widening to 33ft three-lane carriageway. | £30 671 |
| | A38 Cross-in-Hand to Ivybridge: widening to 33ft three-lane carriageway and realignment. | £20 442 |
| | A38 Heathfield to Ilsington Junction: realignment and widening to 33ft three-lane carriageway. | £23 900 |
| | A38 Benedicts Bridge to Blackpool Farm, near Chudleigh Knighton: widening to 33ft three-lane carriageway. | £14 300 |
| | A38 Waterloo Cross to Lamb Inn, Burlescombe: widening to 33ft three-lane carriageway. | £27 380 |
| | A38 Lamb Hill to Maidendown, Burlescombe: widening to 33ft three-lane carriageway. | £28 961 |
| | A38 Culmstock Farm to Red Ball, Burlescombe: widening to 33ft three-lane carriageway. | £21 742 |
| 1964 | A38 Peamore Roundabout and Matford Roundabout: construction of roundabouts on Exeter bypass, 200ft diameter. | £73 484 |
| | A30 Ramsley Hill, South Zeal: widening and realignment. | £40 632 |
| | A30 Red Brick Bridge to Youlditch Farm, near Okehampton: widening to 33ft for crawler lane. | £23 800 |
| | A30 Torhill Cottage to Harepath Cross, Drewsteignton: widening to 33ft for three-lane carriageway. | £45 000 |
| | A30 Whiddon Down: junction and visibility improvement. | £65 699 |
| **County roads** | | |
| 1954 | A39 Dean Steep, Barnstaple to Lynton road: elimination of 'S' bend over railway bridge and road widening. | £8 323 |

| 1957 | A377 Saddlers Arms, Lympstone: junction improvement with widening and realignment. | £12 889 |
| | A384 Merrivale Bridge diversion: realignment and new bridge | £37 420 |
| 1958 | A381 completion of Totnes bypass with single two-lane carriageway. | £56 000 |
| | A380 Telegraph Hill to Rushycombe: regrading of gradient from 1 in 7 to 1 in 9, new 33ft carriageway with crawler lane. | £66 250 |
| 1960 | A396 West Exe South, Tiverton: widening and realignment. | £28 069 |
| | A377 Codshead Bridge, near Crediton: widening and realignment for replacement of weak bridge. | £47 469 |
| | A379 The Banjo, Kingswear: construction of turning circle, widening and provision of footpath. | £23 100 |
| 1961 | A377 Newton St Cyres: realignment through village. | £7 614 |
| | A376 Clyst St Mary bypass: construction of new dual two-lane carriageway, one major structure. | £139 563 |
| 1963 | A379 Laira Bridge approach, Plymstock: dual two-lane carriageway. | £71 740 |
| 1964 | A380 Station Road to Penn Inn, Newton Abbot: new two-lane dual carriageway and new structure over railway. | £171 500 |
| | A380 Kingskerswell Arch improvement: realignment and new overbridge. | £126 316 |
| | A386 The Rock, Bideford: realignment and widening, the cut in the rock face having a maximum height of 95ft. | £85 000 |

# Appendix 1(b)

Some of the road-improvement schemes completed in the ten-year period, preceding local government reorganization, 1964–1974
(Not including those shown elsewhere as having been constructed by the County Council's Direct Labour Construction Section)

| Year of completion | Scheme details | Cost |
| --- | --- | --- |
| **Trunk roads** | | |
| 1965 | A30 Roebuck Farm to Nags Head, near Honiton: dual two-lane carriageway. | £120 700 |
| 1966 | A30 Honiton bypass: dual two-lane carriageway, first major bypass in Devon, five substantial structures. 1.88 miles | £880 000 |
| 1967 | A39 Back Road, Instow: widening and footpath construction. | £61 396 |

| | A38 Lower Dean to Dean Prior: dual carriageway using sections of existing road. | £231 306 |
| | A38 White Oxen to Dry Bridge, south of Buckfastleigh: dual two-lane carriageway using sections of existing road. | £52 118 |
| 1968 | A38 Red Cross to Trehill Lodge, Kennford: new dual two-lane carriageway | £330 301 |
| | A38 Lee Mill to Westover, Ivybridge: new dual two-lane carriageway. 1.25 miles. | £252 560 |
| 1969 | A38 Ashburton bypass. | £120 920 |
| | A38 Cutwell Cross to Carew Arms, South Brent: dual two-lane carriageway. | £141 680 |
| | A38 Chudleigh Knighton to Drumbridges: dual two-lane carriageway. 1.08 miles | £446 400 |
| | A30 Lewdown: widening to 33ft three-lane carriageway and regrading. | £95 891 |
| | A38 Beare Village, near Cullompton: construction of 33ft three-lane carriageway and realignment. | £163 750 |
| | A38 Southdown Cross, Burlescombe: construction of new two-lane dual carriageway. | £88 276 |
| | A38 Cullompton bypass: construction of new dual two-lane carriageway with hard shoulder and central reserve widening for future adoption as M5, seven major structures. 4.68 miles | £3.3 million |
| | A38 Tunnel Cottage to White Ball, Burlescombe: widening to 33ft three-lane carriageway. | £102 000 |
| | A38 Great Covert Corner, Burlescombe: widening to 33ft three-lane carriageway. | £78 907 |
| | A38 Red Ball to Tunnel Cottages, Burlescombe: widening to 33ft three-lane carriageway. | £87 828 |
| | A38 Beare Village to Kensham Lodge, Hele: widening to 33ft three-lane carriageway. | £179 814 |
| 1971 | A38 Plympton bypass: dual three-lane carriageway, seven major structures (Devon sub-unit of SWRCU). 4.31 miles | £3.5 million |
| 1972 | A30 Red Brick Bridge, near Okehampton: widening to 33ft for crawler lane. | £60 000 |
| | A35, Yarty River Bridge, near Axminster: new bridge and road realignment. 0.33 miles. | £119 000 |
| | A38 Haldon Hill Diversion, near Kennford: construction of new dual two-lane carriageway and grade-separated junction with A380 Torquay road, two major structures. 2.22 miles. | £1.74 million |
| | A38 Linhay Hill diversion, Ashburton: construction of new two-lane dual carriageway, one major structure. 0.95 miles. | £431 500 |

| 1973 | A30 Devon Smithy, near Ottery St Mary: widening to 33ft for crawler lane. | £130 000 |
| | A30 Pool Cross, Bridestowe: widening to 33ft for crawler lane. | £133 000 |
| | A38 Chudleigh bypass: two-lane dual carriageway, ten major structures (Devon sub-unit of SWRCU). 4.44 miles. | £3.9 million |
| | A38 Ivybridge bypass: two-lane dual carriageway, ten major structures (Devon sub-unit of SWRCU). 4.63 miles. | £3.6 million |

**County roads**

| 1967 | A396 Bolham Road Link, Tiverton (Kennedy Way): new road and bridges. | £99 100 |
| | A386 Bideford – Northam Stage I: widening and realignment. | £65 000 |
| 1968 | A373 Sampford Peverell railway bridge: realignment and new bridge over railway. | £76 500 |
| | A386 Bideford to Northam Stage II: widening and realignment. | £24 000 |
| 1970 | A379 Dartmouth relief road: new carriageway 33ft wide with crawler lane, and escape road. | £167 000 |
| 1972 | A386 Northam easterly bypass: new route east of town. | £114 012 |

# Appendix 1(c)

Some of the trunk-road improvement schemes completed after 1974 prepared by the Devon Sub-unit of the South Western Road Construction Unit

| Year of completion | Scheme details | Cost |
|---|---|---|
| 1974 | A38 Ashburton to Buckfastleigh Diversion: two-lane dual carriageway, nine major structures. 6.5 km. | £7.4 million |
| | A38 Drumbridges to Caton Cross Diversion: dual two-lane carriageway, seven major structures. 6 km. | £3.5 million |
| | A38 Dry Bridge to Syon Abbey and South Brent: two-lane dual carriageway, nine major structures. 5.4 km. | £3.1 million |
| 1977 | A30 Pearce's Hill (M5) to Pocombe Link: two-lane dual carriageway, thirteen major structures. 6.2 km. | £8.5 million |
| 1978 | A30 Pocombe to Cheriton Bishop: two-lane dual carriageway, thirteen major structures. 12.1 km. | £11.5 million |
| | A30 Cheriton Bishop to Whiddon Down: two-lane dual carriageway, seven major structures. 7.8 km. | £6.67 million |

Road-improvement scheme completed after 1974 prepared by the Somerset Sub-unit of the SWRCU

| 1976 | M5 Chelston to Willand |
|---|---|

# Appendix 1(d)

Some of the motorway and trunk-road improvement schemes completed after 1974, prepared by consultants for the Department of Transport

| Year of completion | Scheme details | Consultant |
|---|---|---|
| 1975 | M5 Willand to Sandy Gate, including widening Cullompton bypass to three lanes and link road to Exeter. | Freeman, Fox & Partners |
| 1977 | M5 Sandy Gate to Pearce's Hill. | Freeman, Fox & Partners |
| 1984 | North Devon Link stage 1. | Gifford, Graham & Partners |
| 1985 | A38 Manadon interchange to Tamar Bridge, two-lane dual carriageway and bridge structures. | Mott, Hay & Anderson |
| 1987 | A39 Bideford bypass. | MRM Partnership |
| 1988 | North Devon Link stage 2A. | Gifford, Graham & Partners |
| 1989 | A39 Barnstaple bypass. | MRM Partnership |
| | North Devon Link stage 2B. | Gifford, Graham & Partners |

# Appendix 1(e)

Some of the road-improvement schemes completed after 1974

| Date of completion | Scheme details | Cost |
|---|---|---|
| **Trunk roads** | | |
| 1974 | A38 Voss Farm to Lee Mill diversion: construction of a new dual two-lane carriageway, three major structures. 2.96 km. | £1.28 million |
| 1975 | A30 Bridestowe bypass: construction of new 7.3 m carriageway, with two major structures. 2 km. | £500 000 |
| | A30 Black Horse Café to Clyst Honiton: realignment and new bridge over River Clyst. | £295 000 |
| | A35 Taunton Cross, Kilmington: widening and realignment. | £271 000 |

| 1976 | A38 Wobbly Wheel to Splatford Cross, Kennford: widening to three-lane dual carriageway. 1.2 km. | £90 000 |
| | A303 Marsh Diversion: construction of new two-lane dual carriageway, one major structure. | £2.05 million |
| 1978 | A30, Ottervale, Upottery: junction improvement and widening. | £77 800 |
| 1979 | A30, Hand and Pen, Whimple: junction improvement and widening. | £93 538 |
| | A30 Pattesons Cross, Feniton: junction improvement. | £39 500 |
| | A35 King Edward Road, Axminster: mini roundabout. | £89 000 |
| 1980 | A35 Black Sand Bridge, near Wilmington: new 7.3 m carriageway with new bridge crossing railway. 0.56 km. | £1.1 million |
| | A30 Jack-in-the Green, Rockbeare: visibility improvement. | £26 932 |
| 1982 | A30 Waterslade Lane, Clyst Honiton: visibility improvement. | £25 000 |
| 1983 | A39 Woolsery Cross, near Clovelly: widening and realignment. 0.58 km. | £165 000 |
| | A303 Crinhayes, near Upottery: visibility improvement. | £115 000 |
| | A361 Stuckeridge Bridge, near Bampton: widening and realignment. | £120 000 |
| | A30 bends west of Monkton: realignment and widening. | £92 000 |
| 1984 | A361 Black Cat Junction, near Bampton: new junction improvement. | £104 000 |
| 1985 | A30 west of Ford Cross, near Monkton: realignment and widening. | £106 000 |
| | A38 Marsh Mills to Manadon (The Parkway): construction of new dual two-lane carriageway, 39 major structures, with a three-level interchange at Manadon. 4.58 km. | £32 million |
| 1986 | A30 Country House Inn, Whimple: realignment with dual carriageway. | £303 000 |
| | A30 Monkton Barton, near Honiton: realignment and widening. | £80 000 |
| | A30 Lifton to Tinhay, east of Launceston: provision of new footway and bridge. | £105 000 |
| 1987 | A38 Belvedere Cross, Haldon Hill: construction of underbridge for grade-separated junction. | £970 000 |
| | A30 Whiddon Down to Okehampton diversion: new dual two-lane carriageway in concrete pavement construction, eleven major structures. 8 km. | £14.7 million |
| 1988 | A30 Okehampton bypass: construction of new dual two-lane carriageway to the south of the town, nineteen major structures. 8.88 km. | £22.11 million |

**County roads**

| 1975 | A3022 Torbay Ring Road Stage I: new route with sections of dual and single carriageway. 2.75 km. | £2.75 million |
| 1976 | A380 Newton Abbot–Kingsteignton bypass: new two-lane dual carriageway, thirteen major structures with a viaduct 1444ft in length. 5.73 km. | £10.58 million |
| 1980 | A361 Rolle Street Bridge, Barnstaple: replacement of narrow, weak bridge. | £285 000 |
| | A379 Churston Bridge, near Brixham: realignment and new bridge. | £594 654 |
| | Exmouth urban relief road: new 7.3 m carriageway, adopting the line of abandoned railway. 1.49 km. | £802 469 |
| 1981 | Embankment Road relief road, Stage I Plymouth: new carriageway, using abandoned railway line. 1.2 km. | £2.29 million |
| | A361 Chivenor Cross, east of Braunton: construction of new roundabout. | £379 982 |
| | A3052 Axe Bridge, Colyford: realignment and widening with new bridge structure. | £790 994 |
| | Highweek Street, Newton Abbot: junction improvement, realignment and widening. 0.19 km. | £125 817 |
| 1982 | A386 Roborough bypass: new 7.3 m carriageway and subway. 0.5 km | £446 539 |
| | Exeter Street/Sutton Road improvement, Plymouth: widening of existing road and formation of dual two-lane carriageway. 0.19 km. | £420 854 |
| | Matford link road, Exeter: new 10 metre wide carriageway connection to industrial estate. 1.49 km | £923 619 |
| | Barnstaple urban relief road, Stage I. 0.99 km. | £1.43 million |
| | A385 Totnes inner relief road, Stage I: new crossing of River Dart and road realignment. 0.7 km. | £1.98 million |
| 1983 | A3052 Turks Head, Newton Poppleford: widening and new bridge. | £245 742 |
| 1984 | A385 Totnes inner relief road, Stage II: extension of improvement. | £320 768 |
| | A379 Exminster bypass: new carriageway around the village, one major structure. 2.29 km | £2.52 million |
| | Newfoundland Way Link, Newton Abbot: new 7.3 m carriageway. | £420 396 |
| | Northam westerly bypass. | £533 542 |
| 1985 | Whiddon Down to Winkleigh: improvement of existing roads for lorry traffic. | £1.17 million |
| 1986 | Kingsbridge Relief Road: new 7.3 m carriageway, relieving town centre. 0.7 km. | £1.74 million |

|  |  |  |
|---|---|---|
|  | Tiverton eastern distributor road: new 7.3m carriageway connection to North Devon Link Road. 1.39 km. | £2.90 million |
|  | A380 Ideford Straight to Olchard Lane: dualling and extension of existing improvement. 2.69 km. | £2.50 million |
|  | A376 George and Dragon improvement: extension of dual carriageway to bypass Clyst St George. 1.2 km. | £692 000 |
| 1987 | Plymouth Road dualling Plympton: construction of second carriageway for relief of traffic at Marsh Mills Roundabout, six major structures. 1.4 km. | £4.57 million |
|  | Bovey Tracey bypass: new 7.3 m carriageway, partly along line of disused railway, two major structures. | £3.65 million |
| 1988 | A380 Ideford Straight to Fiddlers Elbow: new 7.3 m carriageway to form dual two-lane carriageway. 1 km. | £1.47 million |
|  | St Budeaux bypass, Plymouth: new carriageway linking A38 trunk road with main A388 distributor to Plymouth city centre. 1.79 km. | £7.82 million |

| 1966 | A382 Slade Cross to Kelly Cross, Lustleigh: widening and realignment following subsidence. | £10 000 |
|---|---|---|
| 1967 | A3072 Holsworthy to Bude Road, Tamarstone: diversion and new bridge over River Tamar. | £30 950 |
| 1968 | A377 Barnstaple to Exeter Road: Bishopstawton to New Bridge, Sections I and II: widening and realignment. | £72 200 |
|  | A388 Woodford Bridge to Westridge Farm, near Holsworthy: widening, realignment and provision of flood culverts. | £21 200 |
| 1969 | A379 Paignton to Dartmouth Road: Goodrington Quarry Diversion. | £142 873 |
| 1972 | A388 Launceston to Landcross road, Landcross to Beaconside: widening and realignment. | £38 710 |
| 1973 | A361 Ilfracombe to Barnstaple Road, Ilfracombe to Mullacott Cross, Section I: widening and realignment with crawler lane. | £69 300 |
|  | A386 Plymouth to Northam Road, 'Brooklands Bend', approach to Tavistock from Plymouth. | £35 894 |

# Appendix 1(f)

Some of the road schemes undertaken from unemployment relief, development and intermediate areas and other supplementary funds (Not including those shown elsewhere as having been constructed by the Direct Labour Construction Section)

| Year of completion | Scheme details | Cost |
|---|---|---|
| 1959 | A39 Dean Steep, Lynton: realignment of right-angled bend, and slackening of gradient from 1 in 4 to 1 in 12. | £35 533 |
|  | A361 Barnstaple to Braunton: construction of dual two-lane carriageway. | £60 096 |
|  | B3358 Challacombe to Simonsbath: widening and elimination of hairpin bend. | £20 321 |
|  | C1. III Middle Street, Brixham, widening. | £45 000 |
| 1962 | A373 Post Hill, Tiverton: realignment of existing road and widening to 24ft carriageway. | £22 500 |
| 1964 | A379 Billacombe Roundabout: provision of roundabout at end of dual carriageway at Laira Bridge, Plymouth. | £35 750 |
| 1965 | A379 Plymouth to Kingsbridge Road: widening and realignment of Aveton Gifford Hill, in three phases of construction. | £39 000 |
|  | B3216 Jacobstowe Bridge: new bridge and realignment. | £35 012 |
|  | C1. III Dawlish Warren to Cockwood Road: widening and realignment. | £20 930 |

# Appendix 1(g)

Some of the road schemes undertaken by the Direct Labour Construction Section of the County Surveyors Department.

| Year of completion | Scheme details | Cost |
|---|---|---|
| 1961 | A38 Red Cross Hill-Wobbly Wheel: construction of dual carriageway. 0.53 miles | £93 667 |
| 1962 | A380 Fiddlers Elbow: diversion to eliminate dangerous hair-pin bend for southbound traffic. 1 mile. | £97 377 |
| 1963 | A38 Haldon Racecourse to Harcombe Quarry, Chudleigh: new carriageway to form dual with existing carriageway. 1.66 miles. | £98 000 |
| 1965 | A380 Ideford Straight: single 33ft carriageway with bridge and agricultural underpass, earthworks for future dualling. 1 mile. | £153 000 |
|  | A38 Harcombe Cross to Holmans Wood: extension of dual carriageway towards Chudleigh. | £50 910 |
| 1966 | A38 Linhay Hill–Caton Cross, north-east of Ashburton: dual carriageway with agricultural underpass. 1.07 miles. | £217 916 |
| 1967 | A376 Clyst St Mary to George and Dragon, Stage I: second carriageway to form dual carriageway, including new bridge. | £65 500 |
| 1968 | A380 Telegraph Hill to Thorns Cross: dual carriageway, with new and existing carriageways (financed by Supplementary Funds). 2.5 miles. | £335 000 |

| Year | Project | Cost |
|---|---|---|
| 1970 | A379 Teignmouth redevelopment, Stage I: dual carriageway and diversion of Exeter Road B3182. | £256 000 |
| 1970 | A376 Clyst St Mary–George and Dragon, Stage II: extension of dual carriageway. | £70 000 |
| 1972 | A379 Teignmouth redevelopment, Stage II. | £124 000 |
| | A379 Oaklands Park Diversion, Dawlish: new route to eliminate 'S' bend. | £73 900 |
| | A376 Clyst St Mary–George and Dragon, Stage III: extension of dual carriageway. | £48 000 |
| | A3052 Bowd Inn improvement, Sidmouth. | £93 500 |
| 1973 | A383 Newton Abbot–Bickington road: Seale Hayne College Section: widening and realignment. | £65 300 |
| 1974 | A382/A383 Exeter Road/Wain Lane, Newton Abbot: new road layout | £225 235 |

# Appendix 2

Railway level crossing installations

| Location | Crossing type |
|---|---|
| Axe Gate | Automatic half barrier |
| Axminster Gate | Full barrier (CCTV remotely operated) |
| Colyford | Automatic open crossing |
| Crannaford | Automatic half barrier |
| Crediton | Full barrier |
| Eggesford | Full barrier |
| Exeter, Red Cow | Full barrier |
| Feniton | Full barrier |
| Hele and Bradninch | Full barrier |
| Kingswear, Higher Ferry approach | Gated |
| Paignton South (Sands Road) | Full barrier |
| Paignton, Torbay Road | Full barrier (CCTV remotely operated) |
| Pinhoe | Full barrier (CCTV remotely operated) |
| Plymouth, Cattedown Road | Open level crossing |
| Plymouth, Marsh Mills 1 | Open level crossing |
| Plymouth, Marsh Mills 2 | Open level crossing |
| Plymouth, Maxwell Road | Gated |
| Salmon Pool, Crediton | Automatic open crossing (locally monitored) |
| Staverton, Dart Valley | Gated |
| Old Mill, Staverton, Dart Valley | Open level crossing |
| Stoke Canon | Full barrier (CCTV remotely operated) |
| Topsham | Full barrier (CCTV remotely operated) |
| Umberleigh | Open level crossing |

NOTE CCTV is closed circuit television

# Appendix 3

Road bridges rebuilt after Lynmouth flood

| Bridge | Class of road | Clear span | Cost £ | Type of construction |
|---|---|---|---|---|
| Smallcombe (Scoresdown) | U/C | 27'0" | 3 952 | Steel beams and concrete slab. |
| Martinhoe (Hunter's Inn) | III | 42'0" | 8 998 | Pre-stressed concrete slab. |
| Newtown | U/C | 38'0" | 3 200 | Steel beams and concrete slab. |
| Leehamford | III | 13'3"×2 | 5 601 | Pre-cast pre-stressed beams. |
| Bridge Ball | U/C | 21'0" | 6 224 | Reinforced concrete slab. |
| High Street, Lynmouth | U/C | 83'5" | 30 659 | Pre-stressed pre-cast beams. |
| Lyndale (Countisbury) | A39 | 80'0" | 39 758 | Reinforced-concrete arch. |
| Hillsford | B3223/ A39 | 57'0" | 26 354 | Pre-stressed pre-cast beams. |
| Barbrook | A39 | 83'0" | 37 000 | Pre-stressed pre-cast beams. |
| Cherry Bridge | U/C | 30'0" | 5 324 | Pre-stressed in situ concrete slab. |
| Parracombe | III | 16'6" | 1 824 | Reinforced concrete slab. |
| West Lyn (Prospect Corner) | B3224 | 51'3" | 33 000 | Steel beams and concrete slab. |

*Note:* Costs are relevant to date of construction, not present-day equivalents.

# Appendix 4

| CHAIRMAN OF THE COUNTY COUNCIL | CHAIRMAN OF COMMITTEE: BRIDGES, MAIN ROADS AND COUNTY BUILDINGS (1889-1930) ROADS (1930-74) PLANNING AND TRANSPORTATION (1974 ONWARDS) | DATE | CLERK OF PEACE (1889-1972) COUNTY CLERK (1972-73) CHIEF EXECUTIVE (1973 ONWARDS) | COUNTY SURVEYOR (1888-1974)† COUNTY ENGINEER (1974-84) COUNTY ENGINEER AND PLANNING OFFICER (1984 ONWARDS) |
|---|---|---|---|---|
| Charles, 20th Baron Clinton | W. R. Coleridge | 1888 " 1889 | H. Michelmore | FORMATION OF COUNTY COUNCILS E.H. Harbottle (Northern District)   J. Little (Southern District) |
| | | 1890 | | H. Masterton (Northern District)   E.H. Harbottle (Western District)   C.G.S. Acock (Southern District)   J. Little (Eastern District) |
| | | 1897 1898 | | H. Masterton (Northern Division)   C.G.S. Acock (Southern Division) S. Ingram (Northern Division) |
| Albert, 3rd Earl of Morley | | 1900 1901 | | |
| Hugh, 4th Earl Fortesque KCB | J.S. Hurrell | 1904 | | |
| | | 1910 | | |
| | | 1912 1913 1914 1915 1916 1917 1918 1919 1920 | F. Bailey B. Stothert Miller | W.P. Robinson (Northern Division) E.J. Stead (North District)   W.P. Robinson   C.G.S. Acock Mr Gray (acting Apr-Jun 1914)(East District)   (South and West District) (North District) R.M. Stone (1914) (North District)   F.E. Simpson (acting)   A. Warren   (East District)   (South and West District) W.P. Robinson (East District) F.E. Simpson (1920) (East District) |
| Sir Henry Hepburn Sir Henry Yarde Buller Lopes Bt. | W. Vicary | | | |
| | Rt. Hon. The Earl of Portsmouth | 1922 | | |
| | W.E. Coulton | 1925 | | |
| | | 1928 | | R.M. Stone (North Western Division)   A. Warren (South Eastern Division) |
| | | 1930 | | |
| | Major G.S.S. Strode | 1933 | | |
| | H.H.G. New | 1936 1937 1938 | A.J. Witheycombe | |
| Sir John Edward Daw | Sir John F. Shelley, Bt | | | |
| | | 1940 | | |
| Sir John F. Shelley, Bt. | Lt. Col. T. Gracey | 1946 1947 | H.A. Davis | R.B. Carnegie CBE |
| | | 1950 | | |
| | | 1952 | H.G. Godsall | |
| Sir George C. Hayter-Hames CBE | | 1955 | | |
| | | 1960 1961 1962 | | H. Criswell |
| | L.E. Currey | | | |
| | A.C. Shobbrook | 1964 1965 1966 | | |
| J.A. Day G. Whitmarsh CBE DL | | | | |
| | E.R. Lawrence | 1970 | | |
| J.E. Palmer CBE DL (1971-74) C.A. Ansell OBE JP DL (1973-77) | A.L. Sayers CBE | 1971 1972 1973 1974 " | C.V. Lucas | LOCAL GOVERNMENT REORGANIZATION M.R. Hawkins OBE |
| H.S. Sargent A.L. Goodrich OBE | | 1977 1978 1979 | D.D. Macklin | |
| | | 1980 | | |
| G.E.H. Creber CBE DL | J.P. Wigmore | 1981 | | |
| D.G. Potter W.E. Evans Mrs E.M. Stacey MBE JP A.L. Sayers CBE | H.M. Luscombe Mrs B.K. Clarke | 1985 1986 1987 1988 1989 | R.D. Clark | |

† Until 1946 the county had more than one County Surveyor, each responsible for a part of the county.

# GLOSSARY

**Abutment**
That part of a bridge which supports the structure (be it arch, beams or slab) and retains the approach embankment.

**Accommodation works**
The fences, walls and other minor works provided for an owner whose property or land is directly affected by an improvement scheme.

**Aggregate**
Sand, gravel, broken stone or other similar inert material.

**Arch ribs**
A series of widely spaced narrow stone arches which form the main structure of many medieval bridges. The spaces between the ribs are covered by masonry to support the roadway. The same term is applied to any series of narrow arches forming a wider bridge regardless of the material of construction.

**Bitumen**
A mixture of hydrocarbons, obtained from either natural deposits or the distillation of crude oil and used to bind aggregates together.

**Bitumen-coated material**
A graded aggregate that has been coated with bitumen, a major part of its strength being derived from the interlocking of the aggregate.

**Bitumen emulsion**
Bitumen which is 'mixed' with water to make it flow easily, even when cold, thus enabling it to be sprayed on to the road surface. Once spread, the water evaporates and the bitumen 'sets'.

**Blacktop**
All-embracing term used to describe all types of black road surfacing.

**Blading**
The levelling of soil by an earth-moving machine fitted with a suitable blade.

**Blinding**
The process of spreading fine material (sand, stone dust or fine gravel) over a surface in order to fill small holes prior to rolling.

**Caisson**
A cylindrical or rectangular structure for keeping water and mud from flowing into foundation excavations. It sinks under its own weight as excavation proceeds and is eventually incorporated into the foundation.

**Camber**
The curved shape of the road surface when seen in cross section.

**Cantilever**
A beam which is firmly fixed at one end and free at the other; an overhanging beam.

**Carpet coat**
A top layer of road-surfacing material.

**Cast iron**
An alloy of iron with about 3 per cent carbon content which has a low melting point and which can be poured when molten into intricate moulds. It is brittle and weak in tension.

**Chamfered voussoirs**
The wedge-shaped stones used to construct a masonry arch are called voussoirs. As a decorative feature the exposed edge can be trimmed off at an angle, or chamfered.

**Channel**
The edge of the carriageway, adjacent to a verge or kerb, which collects surface water and carries it to gullies or ditches.

**Cost-benefit analysis**
A technique for comparing the cost of a road scheme with the benefits it provides for road users, in order to ascertain whether the scheme provides value for money.

**Cut and fill**
The preparation of a road foundation by excavation (known as cut) and the building of embankments (known as fill).

**Cut-back bitumen**
Bitumen to which a lighter solvent fluid is added to make it thinner so that it can be sprayed on to the road surface.

**Cutwater**
The sharp or rounded end of a bridge pier designed to reduce turbulence in flowing water.

**Cyclic maintenance**
Routine highway-maintenance operations to ensure that roads are safe and drainage operates satisfactorily. Includes grass cutting, gully emptying, sweeping, sign cleaning, and clearing of channels and ditches.

**Deck**
That part of a bridge which carries the road surface and traffic.

**Design speed**
The curvature of a new road alignment is designed to enable vehicles to travel safely at a certain anticipated speed. This is known as the design speed and varies with different types of road, e.g. a motorway is designed for 120 k.p.h. (73 m.p.h.).

**Direct Labour Organization (DLO)**
The term used to describe a local authority's work organization, including the manual labour, its equipment, management and administration. In 1988 Devon's DLO became known as Devon Direct Services.

**Fine-cold asphalt**
A finely graded surfacing material that comprises aggregates of less than 6mm bound together with cut-back bitumen.

**Flagging**
The surfacing of a pedestrian area with square or rectangular slabs, usually of pre-cast concrete, but sometimes of natural stone.

**Flail mower**
A grass-cutting attachment fitted to a tractor (side or rear); it works by means of a number of cutters secured by lengths of chain to a spindle that rotates at high speed.

**Flexible composite pavement**
Road construction in which a bituminous wearing course is laid over a cement-bound roadbase.

**Flexible pavement**
Road construction in which a bituminous wearing course is laid over a non-cement-bound roadbase.

**Geotechnics**
The scientific study of the properties and behaviour of materials in the ground when they are subjected to loads from buildings and structures.

**Grade separated junction**
A road junction where at least one road is bridged over another.

**Grouting**
The filling of empty spaces in rock, loose stones or concrete with a material which sets hard.

**Gunite**
Also known as sprayed concrete. A mixture of cement, coarse sand and water which is sprayed against existing rock or concrete to build up the surface.

**Hand pitching**
The placing by hand, and compaction by rolling, of large stones on edge which are wedged by small stones to form a stable base for a road.

**High-performance bitumen**
A bitumen to which various chemicals are added to make it better able to withstand heavy traffic.

**Highway superintendent**
An officer who is responsible to a Divisional Surveyor for inspection of highways, identification of work needed and supervision of work in progress in a defined area.

**Hot-rolled Asphalt**
A high-quality, long-lasting, road-surfacing material produced from a mixture of bitumen and aggregate, used mainly on heavily trafficked roads.

**Infrastructure**
The system of public services – roads, drainage, water supplies, telecommunications – which serve a community.

**Knapping hammer**
The type of hammer that was used to break up roadstone by the roadside.

**Lean-mix concrete**
Concrete containing a small amount of cement and therefore limited in strength.

**Macadam**
A mixture of graded stones and fine sand or stone dust which when rolled forms a strong road-making material. Originally developed by Robert Macadam (1756–1836) from whom it takes its name. Modern macadams are normally coated with bitumen to form bituminous macadam.

**Multiple arch orders**
Two or more different shapes of masonry arch which occur on the same bridge.

**Overlay surfacing**
A layer of bituminous macadam placed on top of an existing road surface to increase its strength and at the same time remove any surface irregularities.

**Pavement**
The whole road construction made up of layers of different materials.

**PCU**
Passenger Car Unit. A unit of road traffic equivalent for capacity purposes to one normal private car. The private car is the unit and other vehicles are measured in relation to that unit, e.g. 1 lorry = 3 PCUs.

**Polymers**
Synthetic materials including rubber that are added to bitumen to increase its strength for use in roads that carry large volumes of traffic.

**Pore water pressure**
The pressure of water in the pores of a saturated soil.

**Pre-stressed concrete**
Concrete in which potential tensile forces have been eliminated by the application of a compressive force. This is often achieved by passing high-tensile steel cables through holes in the concrete and stretching them with a hydraulic jack. The ends of the cables, in tension, are fixed by means of wedges as the jack is removed and this compresses the concrete.

**Racked up**
The process of using small-sized chippings to fill the spaces between larger chippings on a road surface in order to knit them together.

**Regulating**
Forming a surface to the required shape or contour. A regulating course is a layer of material of variable thickness applied to a road surface to adjust the shape in preparation for an overlaying course of uniform thickness.

**Rigid composite pavement**
Pavement in which the main structural element is a high-strength concrete slab, over which a bituminous wearing course is applied.

**Rigid pavement**
Pavement in which the main structural element is a high-strength concrete slab that is also the wearing course.

**Road base**
One or more layers of material, placed above the sub-base and below the surfacing, that constitutes the main structural element of the pavement.

**Scalpings**
Small-sized poor-quality material removed from quarried rock before crushing and screening.

**Setts**
Small rectangular blocks of hard stone, such as granite, that are laid tightly together and grouted to form a very hard-wearing, but somewhat uneven, road surface.

**Shear**
The effect across a beam or arch resulting from the opposing forces of loads acting downwards and the reactions at the supports acting upwards.

**Side drainage**
A drainage system comprising open ditches or pipes that run parallel to the carriageway, in the verge, often following the foot of the hedgebank.

**Slurry seal**
A mixture of fine aggregate and bitumen emulsion which is spread on to a road in thin layers by means of special machinery or hand tools to seal it and provide a new surface.

**Soffit**
The under-surface of a beam or arch.

**Spandrel**
The side wall built on an arch to retain the filling material which carries the roadway.

**Sterling**
Also **Starling**. Piles, usually timber, driven into the river bed to protect bridge piers from the effect of the current and floating debris. In medieval times baskets filled with stones were used to achieve the same effect.

**Sub-base**
A layer of material on the natural ground and under the road base to strengthen it and/or improve the drainage.

**Surface dressing**
A method of sealing a road surface and at the same time restoring its texture and skid resistance by spraying on a film of bitumen and covering with stone chippings.

**Transport and Road Research Laboratory (TRRL)**
The government's central laboratory at Crowthorne in Berkshire which undertakes research and development and provides advice on the management and maintenance of highways.

**Waterbound macadam**
Form of road construction that consists of broken stone, slag or gravel, compacted with the help of water and a binding agent such as sand or stone dust.

**Watertabling**
A local term used to describe the composite operation of cleaning the surface and channels of a rural road, together with associated ditches, grips and easements, in order to ensure that water flows off the road surface as quickly as possible.

**Wearing course**
The top, visible, layer of a road upon which traffic runs.

**Wet mix**
A material consisting of graded stone spread and compacted at a specified moisture content.

**Windrow**
A ridge formed by the overspill of soil off the sides of the blades of earthmoving equipment.

**Wrought iron**
Pure iron with a very low carbon content. It is soft and cannot be used to make castings.

**Yardage**
A traditional expression, no longer used, which described a volume measured in cubic yards.

# INDEX

Page numbers in italic refer to illustrations or to information in the captions.